Audrey

344 Pla

Webster Gro

Washington N. — St Louis, Mo.

1⁵⁰

APES, MEN, AND MORONS

Apes, Men, and Morons

By *Earnest Albert Hooton*

PROFESSOR OF ANTHROPOLOGY, HARVARD UNIVERSITY,
CURATOR OF SOMATOLOGY, PEABODY MUSEUM OF
HARVARD UNIVERSITY

NEW YORK
G. P. PUTNAM'S SONS

1937

PRINTED IN THE UNITED STATES OF AMERICA
AT THE VAN REES PRESS

Acknowledgments and Recriminations

THIS VOLUME CONSISTS, for the most part, of reluctant addresses publicly delivered at the instigation of persons or organizations whose requests I dared not refuse. I will not pillory here the guilty individuals; no doubt my sufferings and those of my audiences weigh heavily enough upon their consciences. A few of the chapters were essays produced for some worthy cause. None of them is a spontaneous creative effort; but nothing of that sort emanates from me. I have brushed off and refurbished those which were written more than a year ago and have added some transitional and integrating bits.

Mr. K. L. Rawson of the publishing firm of G. P. Putnam's Sons is to blame for the present reincarnation. I have been flattered by his interest and helped by his suggestions. Mr. Earle H. Balch has contributed sundry penetrating criticisms, for which I am grateful. The horrid labor of proofreading has been endured by my research assistants, Charity Mason and Elizabeth Parker. The majority of the writings herein contained were originally edited by Pearl B. Hurwitz, upon whom I have long relied for the correction of my errors in taste, style and grammar, but who has recently immolated my literary career upon the altar of her own domesticity by retiring to her family life.

For permission to republish sundry of the contents of this volume, I am indebted to Dr. McKeen Cattell, publisher of SCIENCE and the SCIENTIFIC MONTHLY, Dr. Diamond Jenness, editor of THE AMERICAN ABORIGINES; Dr. Aleš Hrdlička and the Wistar Institute of Anatomy, editor and publishers of THE AMERICAN JOURNAL OF PHYSICAL ANTHROPOLOGY; Dr. Henry Goddard Leach, editor of THE FORUM; Dean L. M. S. Miner of the Harvard

Dental School and the editors of the HARVARD DENTAL RECORD; Dr. L. H. D. Buxton, editor of the Marett Anniversary volume, CUSTOM IS KING, and Hutchinson's Scientific and Technical Publications, its publisher.

   I am also indebted to many of my friends and students for suggesting a considerable number of titles for this book, all unacceptable.

                                                        E. A. HOOTON

Cambridge, Mass.,
June 29, 1937

CONTENTS

APES, MEN AND MORONS

INTRODUCTION

I.

BRIGHT PAST AND DIM PROSPECT
OF A TOTTERING BIPED

A BRILLIANT former pupil of mine (who, of course, has outgrown me) remarked tolerantly the other day: "I see by the papers that you have been out in the Middle West doing your Cassandra act." If I have to be identified with female literary characters, I prefer the evil-foreboding rôle of the Greek prophetess to that of a fatuous Pollyanna, dispensing shallow cheer. The occasionally thinking and persistently well-intentioned members of the educated public are in greater danger of being led to ruin by emollient, soothing-syrupy adjusters of social institutions than by brutal dictators or fanatical proletarians. The most alarming symptom of our sick civilization is that the one searing human question which needs immediate answer is virtually never asked. What is the matter with man? All the social doctors are fussing with the irrelevant secondary symptoms of an undiagnosed human degeneracy—the break-down of free institutions, the disruption of decent human relations, the inadequacy of economic systems. To me it seems clear that the religionists are closest to the heart of the matter because they alone are seriously concerned with human ethics, even as a consideration secondary to the foggy question of the fate of man's soul. They, at any rate, recognize the fact that the human animal emanates something which has potentialities for good and for evil and is organic— not an artificial compound capable of transformation by chemical formula, if one can only analyze it.

Now I am reluctant to abandon the zoölogical detachment of the natural scientist who pursues the study of man through mere disinterested curiosity. Anthropology has had a lengthy and happy childhood of serene and irresponsible play. The desiccated bones of fossil man, the quaint customs of savages, the amusing antics of apes—all of these may suitably engage the attention of impractical professors, who, in the estimation even of the fairly intelligent public, are more than a little mad. People are really very kind and polite to such as I; they try to conceal their conviction that I am a stupendous ass to study man, doubtless reflecting that, after all, there are even more incredible simpletons who pay me to do it. I feel that there is something to be said for this point of view. When I was a boy there was but one clear call for me, and that was negative. My sole vocational ambition was to avoid the ministry (my father's profession). So I gravitated toward a much more ineffectual occupation—the study and teaching of the Classics. My unconscious quest for the ultimate in uselessness carried me quickly from the study of dead languages to the study of dead civilizations and dead men. So I became an anthropologist—unproductive and unashamed, devoid of evangelical fervor, with no ambition to serve my fellow man, curious only to study him and enormously amused thereby. It did not occur to me to pretend to myself that I was doing anything at all useful.

I do not know quite when the serpent of utilitarianism sneaked into my Garden of Eden. Somehow there gradually developed in me a notion that the stuff which anthropologists were grubbing up might be of some use to man. The delicious fruit of futility had turned to ashes in my mouth. My ideal of uselessness had evaporated. I was bitten by the bug of reform, infected with the microorganism of service. Now I really do not think that there is any peculiar virtue in the attempt to save man by science, nor do I yearn to be a saviour. But it does seem that an animal which has hoisted himself to human status by his own non-existent bootstraps ought not to be allowed to let himself down again through sheer ignorance of the methods employed in his own original uplift. In other words, it may be worth while to see whether there is anything in the evolutionary history of man which he might use to extricate himself from the biological mess in which he is involved. If there is, it is certainly not a revelation exclusive to me, but is the common property of every anthropologist. All of the foregoing use of the first person is not intended to emphasize the unique wisdom of the author, but only to exonerate other anthropologists from the charge of participation in his possibly debased and anti-humanitarian point of view. Anthropologists, in general, are free of the Messiah complex, although perfectly willing to dispense the means of salvation, if they happen to have it.

It is difficult to reconcile man's incessant concern over his social condition and his spiritual well-being with the complete apathy which he manifests toward his biological status. An enormous amount of human thought and endeavor has been expended upon the development and improvement of social institutions and upon the devising of new means of wringing a subsistence from reluctant nature. Material culture has been elaborated by many generations of ingenious inventors. An almost unimaginable wealth of comforts and luxuries has been made available to a large proportion of the population of civilized countries. Nor has the attention of man been confined to his material well-being. He has striven continuously to improve his mind, to save his soul, and to cure his bodily ailments. In fact it would appear that the results of human effort and cogitation in the creation of culture are almost enough to explain our excess baggage of brain.

Again, the entire record of human endeavor and everyday experiences of the conduct of this animal in society make it apparent to all, save the most embittered and warped misanthropist, that our species includes a very large proportion of individuals who are eager, at any personal sacrifice, to spend themselves in promoting the betterment of their fellow men. Ingenuity, ideals of service, intelligence, a sifted and refined mass of traditional knowledge, techniques of scientific experimentation—all of these are available for man to improve himself, and he has tried to improve everything except himself.

Here you may object to my generalization on the ground that

the improvement of man himself is precisely the job which medicine is trying to do and in which it is experiencing a gratifying success. I categorically deny this contention and will argue in this book that medical science is doing precisely the opposite; that it is, in fact, a principal agency in promoting human degeneration— of course equipped with a complete stock of first quality, hell's paving-stones.

This is, then, the supreme enigma of modern human policy and behavior: why does not man attempt to cure human ills by going to the root of the matter—which is correcting the evolution of a certain articulate ape? "Physician, heal thyself!" As a matter of fact, I think that this mystery is explicable in the light of human ignorance and prejudice concerning the nature of man. It is only seventy-eight years since Darwin published the "Origin of Species" and offered a body of scientific evidence in support of the thesis that man had not been specially created in his present form, but had evolved in the course of some millions of years through a number of lower animal stages. It was not until 1870 that Darwin really brought the matter home to everyone by writing the "Descent of Man." Certainly this hypothesis was accorded very little recognition, except among a few cloistered savants and philosophic liberals, until after the beginning of the present century. Even now it has not permeated the medical profession—at any rate as a dynamic, scientific reality upon which it must necessarily base any technique of procedure which looks beyond the existence of the individual patient. It has not even penetrated to the dusty and probably empty recesses of the political minds which direct our social destinies. To the majority of the professional leaders of Christianity and other established religions, evolution is not merely an unsubstantiated theory, but an atheistic and anti-social philosophy, the promulgation of which is subversive to the welfare of man.

Now I have no sympathy whatsoever with the mischievous propagandists who have attempted to use the evolutionary hypothesis as a weapon wherewith to attack and destroy established systems of religion and ethics. I am convinced that religion, wholly irrespective of the question of the ultimate validity of its tenets, is a most efficacious and probably indispensable instrument for shaping a decent human society. To put it very bluntly, the intelligence of the mass of mankind is of such a quality that a system of supernatural sanctions—of eternal rewards and punishments—is absolutely necessary for the inculcation and enforcement of a code of practical social ethics. Fear of hell fire is more potent than fear of machine guns, and the expectation of heavenly harps is more satisfying than the cold consciousness of virtue and rectitude. As I have said, I am not concerned with the eternal verities of religion, but only with its temporal utility. Hence it has seemed to me in every respect desirable that systems of religious belief and practice be harmonized with the scientific facts and probabilities of the evolutionary theory. And I am not aware that unsurmountable difficulties have been encountered by Christian scholars in such harmonization. I have, however, been inclined to think that, on the whole, the dissemination of evolutionary teaching among the lower grades of human intelligence—in short to the public at large—may be inexpedient. An inept presentation of evolution to persons of limited mentality is likely to destroy their religious beliefs and fears, and to free them of inhibitions which make them socially tolerable. A knowledge of the theory and evidence of evolution ought perhaps to be reserved for those of sufficient intellect to enable them to reconcile it with their religious convictions or to those who, having no religious beliefs, at least possess sufficient character and fastidiousness to maintain and practice a system of ethics without supernatural props.

Let us leave for the present this question of the practicability of teaching organic evolution and revert to our query as to the cause of man's *laissez faire* policy with respect to his biological welfare. The philosophy of human origins which is implicit in man's effort to improve modern civilized society is that of the Garden of Eden. It runs about as follows. At some time in the relatively recent past man came into being as a perfected animal organism—or rather as a super-animal endowed with the unique possession of a soul and a creative intelligence. He represents the master product of an infinitely versatile artificer who outdid himself by pouring the residue of his creative ability into this culminating *chef d'œuvre* and then quit. Under these circumstances, in so far as man falls short of biological perfection nothing can be done about it, except to recognize and perhaps to deplore some defects in the original design. On the other hand, in this immutable, super-animalistic organism there was placed a willful and not altogether dependable soul and a free intelligence of variable amount and quality. Hence man's departure from ideal social behavior is due to sheer spiritual cussedness which must be corrected, or to defective intelligence. So we have the soul doctor to deal with the former, and the educationalist to supplement the latter by stuffing into all accessible, immature individuals the knowledge accumulated from a few thousands of years of recorded human experience. In order to produce the perfect society it is necessary for the spiritual specialist to restore individual souls to their primordial purity by a supernatural catharsis known as "conversion," and for social theorists to cogitate and experiment until they have hit upon the correct formulæ for ideal institutions, which must then be taught to a receptive world. Now, on the whole, these traditional working hypotheses for the guidance of human behavior have stood up fairly well. At any rate, no satisfactory substitute for them has been devised. Indeed, in individual cases and at certain times they have been applied with quite phenomenal success. It ought to be quite apparent, however, from contemporary experience, that these methods, however sedulously pursued by a considerable body of socially-minded and intelligent men, are completely inadequate to cope with the present situation. Religion is losing ground and is less than ever able to hold the rabble to its standards of ethics. The ingenuity of social technicians has been expended upon the fabrication of really very clever and complicated institutions, which mechanically and theoretically are wellnigh perfect, but which do not work. In my opinion this breakdown of the principal agencies of human improvement is not attributable to lack of zeal, intelligence, or self-sacrificing effort. It is due to the fact that the responsible elements in society are ignorant of the biological basis of human activity as the fundamental element in the social situation. Man is a tottering biped, and we must look to his organic underpinning.

I suppose that no one will deny that human conduct is an indirect function of man's organism, manifested through intelligently controlled action. The mind, whatever its exact nature, is a part of the organism which we know principally through the gross anatomy and the simpler physiological functions of the latter. The achievement of human mental status, of which we are justly proud, has been concomitant with the attainment of man's present bodily form. The two are interdependent. While the correlation may break down in individual cases, so that a brilliant mind may inhabit an enfeebled and degenerate body and a defective intellect may occur in a structurally sound and physiologically capable organism, these disharmonies are wholly exceptional. Mind and body improve in general, or deteriorate, *pari passu*. Under these circumstances, we must examine the record of man's slow and painful emergence from an inferior animal status, to a position of zoölogical supremacy, which latter we, at least, have never seriously questioned. Although that record is full of many gaps and queries, it should nevertheless teach us the fundamental principles of biological progress as exemplified in the evolution of our own species. Nor is this knowledge of mere academic interest. If we know anything at all of life from the study of plants and animals through the ages, it is that higher organisms are never stationary in an evolutionary sense, but are in a continual state of flux. Either progress or retrogression is in evidence when a sufficiently close and accurate survey of the organic facts has been made. Of course, many primitive and generalized forms of life apparently reach a stable evolutionary equilibrium and remain more or less fixed and unchanged for vast stretches of time. Certainly the known data do not indicate that such is the case with man, although society proceeds on the tacit assumption that *Homo sapiens* is the same, yesterday, today, and forever (unless, indeed, he is getting better and better).

The thesis, then, of this volume of occasional lectures and essays is that knowledge of the organic experiences of our animal past is quite as necessary a part of our present equipment, if we are to face the future with any hope of success, as are the traditional records of human accomplishment in the realms of material culture, social institutions, and thought, which we cherish so dearly and utilize so rarely. Let us pull our heads out of the sociological sand, brush the grains out of our eyes, and look at our animal selves.

I find it rather difficult to understand why human beings are so inordinately sensitive about themselves as animal organisms, as contrasted with their comparative callousness in regard to their conduct, their institutions, and all of their extra-organic manifestations. For, indeed, the latter are their own products, for which they may be held more or less accountable, whereas they are not individually responsible for the misshapen mass of body and mind which has resulted from the fortuitous combination of their parental genes and chromosomes. I suppose that the reason for the quick resentment which follows any reflection whatsoever upon the heredity of the individual or even of the species is that there is a general feeling that man's bodily status is no one's fault (except God's) and that nothing can be done about it. Nevertheless it is something peculiarly personal and intimate. Actually we cannot evade responsibility for the physical and mental inheritance of the *offspring* we produce, and something can and must be done about it if we are procreating bad animals. We may not be blamed for our parents' germinal deficiency only as long as we refrain from passing them on to our children.

It would be foolish on my part not to admit at the very outset that we know far less about making men than, for instance, making automobiles, and that we act far more intelligently in raising crops than in raising children. As a matter of fact a good deal more of human thought and effort has gone into devising and perfecting the motor engine than the human engine. We are really more interested in the quality of our automobiles than in that of our progeny. If marriages were made in the Ford factory instead of in heaven, they would probably last longer and turn out more efficient products. In our government we have a Department of Agriculture which is concerned with the quality of seed, with planting and with selective breeding, as well as with the mere tending of growing plants.[1] But bureaus of child welfare leave the question of the quality of seed entirely alone and merely fuss about the growth and harvesting of the crop, which may be a very sad business when the larger part of it is not wheat at all, but tares.

Now, as I have said, we know very little about human heredity, because almost no one has taken the trouble to study it. We certainly are in no position to write a manual on the technique of breeding for genius. But something of this sort is by no means impossible for the future, if society can only be awakened to the fact

---

[1] I am not sure that this agricultural illustration is altogether felicitous. It would be difficult to conceive a human breeding policy as fantastic as that of our present government in relation to agriculture.

that the production of men ought to be given at least a fraction of the attention that is devoted to the production of domestic animals, foods, and gadgets. In other words, that part of the younger generation which is lucky enough to possess a modicum of mental endowment will have to be taught the importance of tackling this problem, before their skulls and their brains become completely ossified by advancing years and the stultifying effect of miseducation. If they can be stimulated or alarmed into studying their own biology, they will discover the measures which will save the species *Homo sapiens* from a horrid process of decay, and they will, incidentally to that process, solve most of the social problems which we have gripped by the tail and which are whisking us about as if we were mere accessory caudal appendages.

Of course nothing can be done with the mass of the middle-aged and elderly in the population whose mental and social petrifaction is complete. Here and there in isolated individuals the brain cells still function ably in a corporeal environment of hardened arteries and senile decay, but, on the whole, progress is with youth. We may indeed expect constructive research, portentous discovery, and possibly the theoretical solution of certain problems in human evolution from those who are already veterans. But even if the aged practitioners of science are still able to draw from their accumulated experience rules and precepts for the biological improvement of the race, the burden and heat of the day will have to be borne by those with fresh ideas and unimpaired mental vigor, who begin where their elders leave off. Even more important is youth in the execution of progressive social and biological measures, by whomsoever devised or advocated. We who have attained or passed middle age are already dead from an evolutionary point of view, unless we are prodigies of virility, like the recently deceased nonogenarian who is alleged to have fathered two children at that indecent age. Further, our ideas have crystallized and we have lost the power of social adaptation and initiative—both indispensable prerequisites of evolutionary progress. Here again there are undoubted exceptions, but, on the whole, I do not believe that the forward march of humanity is led by knee-sprung gray-beards, nor that the clarion call of progress is ordinarily piped from the withered throat of old age.

In the matter of the rising generation of young men and women, I am completely devoid of the pessimism which is supposed to characterize my anthropological utterances and writings. This is undoubtedly because I have had the privilege for twenty-four years of constant association with groups of young college men and women who pass on out of my intimate acquaintanceship before they lose their hair, their figures, and their ability to evolve and assimilate new ideas. I must admit that these young people represent a highly selected and mentally superior class, perhaps even in the assemblage of university student populations. Nevertheless, even discounting the probably unusually fine quality of this sample, I am convinced that with all of our incredible stupidity in the matter of breeding, we have been lucky enough to produce from year to year (in addition to millions of morons), a sufficient quota of intellectually keen and biologically sound youngsters to leaven the lumps. In fact, I should go so far as to say that it seems to me that the mental caliber of Harvard College students, at least, has steadily grown throughout my experience. The intellectually adequate and the brilliant have increased proportionately and there is a gratifying diminution of the dullards and the shiftless. Of course it may be that I have grown more mellow and tolerant, and less critical with the waning of my youthful ideals. However, I am not aware of any waxing geniality or relaxation of standards of mental ability and scientific proficiency. Certainly no one has accused me of the former.

However that may be, I fully anticipate a biological revolution of a most beneficial nature, which will prod our species out of its arrest of development, if only our scanty array of pertinent facts is put before these chosen thousands in such a way as to stimulate them to see the danger signs and go out after the trouble, with which we in our limitations are powerless to cope. So we come back to our single substantial hope which is that we may provide a sufficient smattering of education in human biology to induce these more promising juveniles to educate themselves to a point where they may know how to save the species and may proceed to do it. This of course brings me around to the subject of education, the supposed bulwark of civilization and the perennially regurgitated cud of fusty pedagogues such as I.

I am inclined to agree with the savage criticisms which are

hurled at our academic heads by merciless undergraduate journalists, and with the less articulate but sufficiently explicit objections to the modern systems which are voiced by our children in the secondary and primary schools. Elementary education seems to have ceased to be mental discipline and the acquisition of fundamental, usable branches of learning. It has apparently become a mere avenue of escape from the realities of life, masquerading under the pitiful sophistry of inducing the pupil to "express himself" or to "develop his personality." Dr. Johnson anticipated nearly all that can be said about modern "progressive" education when Boswell asked him what he thought was best to teach children first.

JOHNSON: "Sir, it is no matter what you teach them first, any more than what leg you should put into your breeches first. Sir, you may stand disputing which is best to put in first, but in the meantime your breech is bare. Sir, while you are considering which of two things you should teach your child first, another boy has learnt them both."

I take it that the immortal sage would have had scant sympathy for an educational theory that children should learn by playing at learning rather than by working at it. The elaborate efforts of modern educationalists to make learning easy and interesting for children seem to prevent the latter from learning much of anything. Although an anthropologist, I cannot reconcile myself to a primary education which equips a child with the Eskimo technique of making a snow-house, but does not teach him how to spell. It does not seem to me that an elementary knowledge of the nebular hypothesis is a satisfactory substitute for a thorough grounding in the multiplication tables. In short, I am old-fashioned enough to think that the prime desideratum is that the young be required really to work their minds hard so that they develop the ability to use whatever mental powers they possess and to focus them upon tasks which are useful, even if they are not interesting. Man has to earn his intellectual bread by the sweat of his brow. Why should primary education attempt to convert our children into little lotus-eaters? If ever they can be taught to think, it is during the period when the mind is growing with the body. If they then acquire a little mental endurance, some power of the memory, and a thorough facility in the use of the basic tools—reading, writing, and mathematical reasoning —they are in a position to utilize their primate inheritance of complex nervous organization.

Higher education can build only upon the basic knowledge and mental capacities developed in childhood and adolescence. The university curriculum justifiably presupposes the ability of the student to think and is concerned primarily with rendering accessible stores of knowledge upon which he can exercise his mental powers. Nevertheless there can be no doubt that we are prone to present masses of factual data to the student as if these possessed an inherent value, quite irrespective of their application or utilization as working materials for the mind. I think that this tendency is due to our failure to realize or to remember that our particular primate has advanced only through constant utilization of a cerebral endowment which expands by active functioning and atrophies when idle. This detachment of knowledge from application is least in subjects which deal with man's culture and is at a maximum in biology which tends to divorce itself wholly from the human animal. But if the whole of human culture is dependent upon the organism, it is clear that more educational effort should be concentrated upon the application of biological knowledge to the preservation of our status in the animal world and to its improvement.

I have ample experience for knowing that any aspersions cast upon our godlike species are taken very personally. They constitute the most literal and offensive employment of the *argumentum ad hominem*. The mental and social sclerosis of middle and advanced age does not seem to diminish sensitivity to criticism of the human kind. The only members of our animal group who can take it and profit by it are the comparatively young—presumably in part because they discount the maunderings of their elders, but more, I believe, because they have not yet reached the age of organic retrogression and can still envisage self-improvement for themselves and consequently for others. Of course the young are not usually wise, except again in an organic sense. But they possess a certain fine animal ruthlessness, which, if they are intelligent, makes them cut through the false front of institutions sanctified by custom and examine their real values. The elderly wish only to be reassured. I state what is the veriest commonplace among youthful but not ignorant persons who are being subjected to education, or have recently endured it, when I say that we are not doing a good job in this paramount form of human endeavor. We are trying to improve minds and to impart to them useful knowledge, and are apparently not succeeding very well in either effort.

The quality of any individual mind is probably inherent and immutable. Training, discipline, and use make it more efficient, give scope for its exertions, and co-ordinate its powers. Mental improvement by education or by any other means is possible, in the life of the individual, only in this sense. One can merely develop to its full potentiality the hereditary endowment. Under these circumstances it is clear that the amount and kind of education needed for different classes of individuals depend largely upon their varying mentalities or intelligences. In a very rough way education provides for this mental range in individuals by proceeding theoretically from the simple forms of learning to the more complex. All of the youngest pupils commence equally with the elementary branches of knowledge. Through succeeding years instruction deals with more and more complex subjects, and the various stages of increasing difficulty mark the elimination of those who have reached the point of educational saturation. But this sifting process does not necessarily leave us at the end with the most constructive and brilliant minds, but only with those which happen to be capable of assimilating the largest quantities of the sort of knowledge we pour into them. All of the educational steps are strewn with the frustrated, including the topmost. In the course of the twelve or sixteen years of schooling of the individual, we have probably not succeeded in improving his mind but only in testing his survival ability under educational selection.

For the most part what we do is to feed all of the young into the same educational mill, on the tacit and palpably false assumption that they all have approximately similar mental endowments and consequently that the same educational system will fit them all. We pretend that our children discontinue their education at varying periods because they reach the point of comfortable satiety at different ages. It seems probable, however, that the majority stop because they are defeated and unhappy and are not only incapable of further profit, but have derived very little from the whole process, and perhaps even a good deal of loss. Their failure in education is due not solely to their mental limitations, but perhaps often to ours in not realizing the diversity of educational needs required by different types and qualities of mind.

The democratic fallacy of higher education is a mere carrying over of this same idea that human mentalities are more or less equal and consequently that knowledge is power for everyone— it does not matter at all how useless that knowledge may be. The acquisition of knowledge to any amount does not change an inferior mind into one that is superior. As Mark Twain said, a cauliflower is only a cabbage with a college education. They stink about equally in preparation and boil down to about the same thing. And what all of this clumsy argument boils down to, is that we must improve man before we can perfect his institutions and make him behave. The human improvement required is primarily biological and we do not yet know how to effect it. But there are enough clever youngsters to find out, if only they can be shown the necessity of tackling the problem. They at any rate will know the truth, and perhaps it will make them free. Free from what? From imbeciles and morons who are allowed to reproduce their kind, and to subsist upon the labors of others, from psychopaths who lead the mentally inferior mass of civilized populations into purposeless wars and social revolutions, from the ever increasing numbers of biological and mental inferiors who are anti-social and criminalistic. If the generations to come can be emancipated from these worthless and deleterious elements, it will be a comparatively simple matter to perfect social and political institutions and to adjust human relations to a reasonable harmony.

PART I

Primate's Progress—
Monkey to Man to Moron

2.

APOLOGY FOR MAN

Introduction

LEST any one of my readers has forgotten his Greek, I remind you that *anthropos* in that language means "man" and that anthropology is, therefore, the science of man. However, after nearly a quarter of a century of study of that science, I have decided that the proper function of the anthropologist is to apologize for man. In its primary meaning an "apology" signifies a "defense or vindication from charge or aspersion." Accepting this meaning, I rise to defend our species. However, in commoner usage an apology is understood as "a frank acknowledgment, by way of reparation, of offense given" (Oxford Dictionary). In this sense, I think, the need of an apologist for man is even more urgent. Brashly, perhaps, I venture to volunteer.

To some of you, indeed, it may never have occurred that an apology in behalf of man is required; to others of you, more thoughtful, it may seem that for man no apology is possible. In point of fact, man usually either considers himself a self-made

[1] An address delivered before the Harvard Club of St. Louis, February 17, 1936. Published in an abbreviated form in the FORUM, June 1936.

animal and consequently adores his maker, or assumes himself to
be the creation of a supreme intelligence, for which the latter is
alternately congratulated and blamed. An attitude of humility,
abasement, contrition, and apology for its shortcomings is thoroughly uncharacteristic of the species *Homo sapiens*, except as a
manifestation of religion. I am convinced that this most salutary
of religious attitudes should be carried over into science. Man
should confess his evolutionary deficiencies, and resolve that, in
future, he will try to be a better animal.

The defensive apology which I propose to offer in behalf of
man, pertains to his appearance, physique, and biological habits.
But an apology ought not to be broadcast aimlessly into the cir-
cumambient ether. It ought to be offered to someone to whom
it is due. I suggest that the only proper recipients of an apology
for man's appearance would be the anthropoid apes, whom man
sometimes claims as his nearest relatives. In the absence of such
suitable auditors, I venture, without any insolent implication, to
submit this defense to a probably more sympathetic assemblage
—and to one which is, at any rate, more intelligent.

The second and penitential apology is offered for man's behavior—for his use of the gift of articulate speech, for his attempts to control nature, for his social habits and his systems of
ethics. Such an apology cannot be a complete defense or vindication, but only an acknowledgment of wrong with the plea of
certain extenuating circumstances. It is owed to man himself, to
Nature, to God, and to the universe. The apology for man's physical appearance I undertake with a certain confidence; that for his
behavior with full realization that it is the espousal of a lost
cause.

APOLOGY FOR MAN'S PHYSIQUE

His Nakedness

If you were respectable anthropoid apes catching your first
glimpse of a specimen of man, your modesty would be shocked
by the spectacle of his obscene nakedness. Indeed, even to man
himself it is a well-nigh insupportable sight, unless he be a savage
devoid of culture, or a nudist devoid of sensibility. For here is a
mammalian anomaly which lacks the customary covering of fur

or hair and displays only clumps and tufts disgustingly sprouting from inappropriate areas. What strange capillary blight has afflicted this animal so as to denude his body of the hairy coat which protects the tender skin from bruises and abrasions, insulates the vital organs, and prevents too rapid loss of heat or scorching of the tissues by the actinic rays of the sun? Why has man retained abundant hair only in places where it is relatively useless—such as the brain case which is already adequately protected by a thick shell of bone, and the face where whiskers merely interfere with feeding? To cover his bodily nakedness, man has been forced to slay more fortunate animals so that he may array himself in their furs, or to weave fabrics from their shorn hair or from vegetable fibers wherewith to make inconvenient, unhygienic, and generally ridiculous garments. On the other hand, in order to get rid of the superfluous and entangling hair on his face and head, man has been driven to invent many contrivances for eradicating, cutting, and shaving. The adult male White has experimented unhappily through several millennia, trying everything from a flint flake to an electric lawn mower in order to clear his face from hirsute entanglement without flaying himself. Each morning he immolates himself for ten minutes upon the altar of evolutionary inefficiency, until, at the age of threescore-and-ten, he has paid his full tribute of some 3047 hours of suffering—physical torture, if self-inflicted; both physical and mental, if he has patronized a barber. And even this staggering total is exclusive of hair-cuts.

Probably most theories advanced to explain the vagaries of human hair growth have been evolved by scientists during their matutinal shaving periods. We may dismiss summarily the naïve supposition that parts of the body have been denuded of hair by the friction of clothing. The least amount of body hair growth is found, on the one hand, in Negroid stocks which have gone naked, presumably for at least 30,000 years, and, on the other hand, in Mongoloids, who have probably sewed themselves up for the winter during a considerable part of that period. I do not recall the origin of the suggestion that human hairlessness was evolved in the tropics to enable man to rid himself of the external parasites commonly called lice. It need be remarked only that, if such was the case, the evolutionary device has been singularly unsuccessful.

Darwin applied his vigorous mind to the task of explaining man's irregular and disharmonious hair growth by his theory of sexual selection. He supposed that nakedness of the skin could not be a direct advantage to man and therefore that his body could not have been divested of hair through natural selection. He observed that in several species of monkeys the posterior end of the body has been denuded of hair, and that these naked surfaces are brilliantly colored. It appeared to him that the hair had been removed in order more effectively to display the bright skin color and thus to attract the opposite sex. Darwin noted further that the female in man, and even, to some extent, among the anthropoid apes, is less hairy than the male, and suggested that denudation began earlier in that sex—far back in the prehuman period. He imagined that the process was completed by the incipiently hairless mothers transmitting the new characteristic to their offspring of both sexes, and exercising both for themselves and for their comparatively naked daughters a discriminatory choice of mates. The smooth-skinned suitor would be preferred to the shaggy and hirsute. Thus Darwin, like Adam, blamed it on the woman.

The great evolutionist made a rather feeble attempt to explain the excessive growth of head hair in women and of beards in men. He suggested that long hair is greatly admired, alleged that in North American Indians a chief was selected solely on account of the length of his hair, and finally fell back upon St. Paul's statement, "if a woman have long hair, it is a glory to her." He entirely suppressed the preceding verse of St. Paul's epistle which reads: "Doth not even nature itself teach you, that, if a man have long hair, it is a shame unto him?" [2] Darwin toyed with, but rejected, the theory that the beard of the male serves to protect his throat in fighting, and cogently remarked that the mustache, which presumably had the same origin, could serve no such practical purpose. [3] In the end he had to resort once more to the aesthetic preference of the mating female. His assumption

[2] Darwin, Charles, *The Descent of Man*, Part III, Chapter XX, pp. 915-922, especially p. 921. Cf. St. Paul, I Corinthians, 11, 14-15.
[3] Darwin, *op. cit.*, p. 811.

of the dominating role of the capricious and fastidious female, a sort of prehuman Delilah, is far from convincing. Abundant body hair in the male is traditionally and probably physiologically associated with an excess of strength and virility, and the pre-human female probably liked her man hairy. In any case, zo-ological studies of the habits of contemporary subhuman primates indicate in no indecisive fashion that the female is not asked, but taken; that she is passive, acquiescent, and devoid of aesthetic perception. She does not choose, but only stands and waits. Darwin might have done better with his subject if he himself had formed the habit of shaving. Perhaps he had built up a defense around an inferiority complex with respect to his beard.

Recent students have ascribed more importance to nutrition and glandular functioning in explaining human hair growth than to the romantic theory of sexual selection. Thus Sir Arthur Keith has pointed out that the human baby is not only less hairy than the anthropoid baby, but also considerably more plump. The secretions of the thyroid gland probably affect both the nourishment of the skin and the hair. If man's ancestors at an early time obtained command of an adequate food supply, hairlessness might have been one of the first effects of incipient human culture.[4] As man waxed fat his hairiness waned. The layer of subcutaneous fat would discourage the growth of the hair follicles and take over the insulating function of the hairy coat.

There are other theories to account for this deplorably glabrous condition of man, but none which would satisfy a critical anthropoid ape. Chivalry, as well as common sense, dictates a rejection of the blame-it-on-your-wife theory. I adhere rather to the supposition that we have retained a foetal condition, normal in the third month of pre-natal development, and, on the whole, disadvantageous, but correlated with other persistent foetal features which have a positive survival value. Thus we stand naked, and not unashamed, but claiming that we have done our best to remedy a situation which is not of our making.

His Body Build and Posture

The second aspect of man which would revolt the gazing anthropoid is the monstrous elongation of his legs, his deformed

[4] Keith, Arthur, *The Human Body*, p. 205, London, 1912.

feet with their misshapen and useless toes, his feeble and abbreviated arms, and his extraordinary posture and gait. Beginning with the juncture of the lower limbs and trunk and avoiding indelicate details, a scrutinizing anthropoid would comment unfavorably upon the excessive protrusion of the human buttocks. He would judge the architecture of man's rear elevation to be inept, bizarre, and rococo. The anthropoid gaze, hastily lowered to the thighs, would be further offended by monstrous bulges of muscle, knobby knee-pans, razor-crested shin bones, insufficiently covered in front and unduly padded behind, heels projecting like hammers, humped insteps, terminating in vestigial digits—a gross spatulate great toe, devoid of grasping power; lesser toes, successively smaller and more misshapen until the acme of degeneracy is reached in the little toe, a sort of external vermiform appendix.

Planting these mutilated slabs flat upon the ground, man advances upon his grotesque hind legs, protruding his thorax, his belly, and those organs which in quadrupeds are modestly suspended beneath a concealing body bulk. This coarse and inelegant description could hardly shock the most refined of my readers as painfully as the reality shocks an anthropoid ape. Let us endeavor, for once, to see ourselves as other primates see us.

It now devolves upon me to attempt a defense of these human deviations from the norm of mammalian posture and proportions. The ancestors of man and of the gorilla, chimpanzee, and orang-utan probably started "from scratch" as generalized apes at least as far back as the Upper Miocene Period, perhaps seven million years ago. They were already giant primates, perhaps as large as they are today, and all were mainly tree-dwellers who progressed from bough to bough, principally by a method of arm-swinging which is called brachiation. Their food was largely plant products, mostly plucked in the trees, but partly collected on the ground, to which they frequently ventured. Their arms were somewhat elongated and over-developed by their method of locomotion, but not to the exaggerated extent characteristic of the modern orang-utan. Their legs were comparatively short and weak, equipped with mobile, grasping feet, in which the great toes were separated from the long outer digits by a wide interval, so that the former could be opposed to the latter—a movement essential for encircling a bough. When on the ground, these generalized anthropoids moved on all fours, supporting themselves on the knuckles of the fingers and upon the outer borders of their half-clenched, loose-jointed feet. This quadrupedal progression was awkward and slow. Occasionally they reared up and tottered a few paces on their hind legs. They were more "at home" in the trees.

At this critical juncture of prehuman and anthropoid affairs, man's forebears seem to have abandoned arboreal life and taken to the ground. I diverge from orthodox anthropological opinion in crediting this epochal event to their superior intelligence and initiative rather than to some environmental accident, such as a deforestation of the ancestral abode. Tree-dwelling is advantageous and safe only for small and agile animals. Gravitation and the inadequacy of an arboreal diet joined forces with an innate capacity for grasping environmental opportunities to urge the adventurers to seek a more abundant livelihood on the ground. The bodily adaptations which followed this radical change can be inferred with some certainty.

In the first place, the newly terrestrial proto-humans were confronted with two alternatives of posture and gait: either to go down on all fours like baboons, or to attempt an erect stance and method of progression on the precarious support of their hind limbs. The former was by all odds the easier and the more natural, since it offered greater possibilities of speed and stability. But it sentenced its user to the fate of an earth-bound quadruped, nosing through life with all four extremities devoted to support and locomotion. Bipedal gait and upright posture, on the contrary, provided the inestimable advantages of increased stature, the ability to see wider horizons, and of an emancipated pair of prehensile limbs wherewith to explore, to contrive weapons and tools, to gather food and to convey it to the mouth. Here, forsooth, the ape with human destiny was at the very cross-roads of evolution, and he took the right turning. He chose the difficult path which led upward toward humanity.

Now almost all of man's anomalies of gait and proportion were necessitated by that supremely intelligent choice. The quadruped had to be remade, by dint of all sorts of organic shifts and compromises. The axis of the trunk had to be shifted from the horizontal to the vertical—a result effected by a sharp bending forward of the spine in the lumbar region, between the rib-cage and the bony pelvic girdle. The pelvis itself underwent a process of flattening, increase in width, tilting, and other changes necessary to adapt it for the transmission of the entire weight of the body to the legs and for the extension and shift of the muscular attachments essential for the balanced erect posture. The whole lower limb became enormously hypertrophied and elongated in response to its amplified function; more leverage was necessary for speed and for support; a complete straightening or extension of the legs upon the thighs was indispensable to a standing posture which should bring their vertical axes into line with the axis of the head and trunk.

However, the most profound modifications were effected in the foot, at that time a loose-jointed prehensile member, with a great toe stuck out like a thumb, long recurving outer digits, little development of the heel, and a flat instep. The great toe was brought into line with the long axis of the foot, so that it was directed forward rather than inward; the lesser toes, no longer needed for grasping, began to shrink; the loose, mobile bones of the instep (tarsus) were consolidated into a strong but elastic vault, capable of resisting the shocks and stresses of weight-bearing; the heel was enlarged and extended backward to afford more leverage for the great calf muscles which lift the body weight in walking. Thus a mobile, prehensile foot was transformed into a stable supporting organ, beautifully adapted for its new but restricted function. If it looks awkward and carries a few vestigial and useless parts left over from its inheritance, it is nevertheless much more serviceable than in its unmodified ancestral form. One needs only to look at an anthropoid ape on the ground to realize that the prehensile foot is an inadequate support for an erect biped.

Further, the seemingly grotesque abbreviation of man's arms becomes intelligible if one considers the disadvantages which would attend upon elongated, trailing arms for an animal with upright stance and bipedal gait. The creature would be in continual danger of stepping on his own fingers, and, in order to feed himself or to perform other and more skilled manual movements, would be forced to move the segments of his upper extremity through vast arcs, slowly and awkwardly because of the length of the levers, and with considerable waste of space on account of excessive wing spread. Lifting your hand to scratch your nose would involve a major gymnastic effort. Taking it all in all, man's present posture and bodily proportions are by no means the sorry result of trying to make the best of a bad business, but rather the supremely successful end product of the reconstruction of a thoroughly obsolete mechanism. This series of adaptations may be credited to natural selection's brilliant choice of the fittest variations of an animal which was forever trying to increase his own efficiency.

Of course, if this defense of human posture and proportions seems inadequate, there are other explanations. J. R. de la H. Marett attributes these human anomalies to mineral deficiency in certain early simians. It seems that in the Miocene Period the inland area of the Eurasiatic continent suffered a progressive desiccation. The trees disappeared and the able-bodied, progressive, arboreal anthropoids followed the migrating forests into the well-watered tropics. There remained, crawling in the grass, or shuffling through the sand, the weaker sisters. These inferior apes became adapted and survived by utilizing the surplus of calcium in the arid, alkaline soils. The cartilages at the ends of their long bones grew, thus providing more material to be calcified. Since their arms had already undergone a process of shrinkage, owing to the lack of boughs from which to suspend the body weight, the calcium depposition and growth were concentrated in the lower extremity. Hence the arms lagged and the legs grew enormously, involving the perplexed prehumans in a postural dilemma. They had their choice of progressing in a pyramidal, quadrupedal posture, with the nose barely off the ground and what ought to be the base of the trunk elevated toward the inhospitable skies, or of attempting to balance upon their hypertrophied hind legs and to wabble through life on an unstable and shifting base of support. Owing to certain difficulties with the law of gravity encountered in depressing the intaking end of the digestive tract below the outgoing, these creatures stood up, thereby exposing a vast area of vulnerable front to a hostile world. We need not accept this theory of the evolution of human posture through mineral deficiency, but the revelation of anatomical difficulties encountered cannot fail to evoke the sympathetic understanding of our anthropoid ape critics.

His Face and Teeth, His Brain

Doubtless, to the superior anthropoid ape, man's most unsightly deformity would be his head. Wherefore the swollen brain-case, and the dwarfed face, receding beneath bulging brows, with a fleshy excrescence protruded in the middle, and with degenerative hairy growths pendent from feeble jowls? What of the charnel-house exposed when man opens his mouth—the inadequately whitened sepulchre of a decaying dentition?

Plausible, if somewhat rationalized, explanations of the course of evolution of the primate brain have been offered by the late Sir Grafton Elliot Smith and by Professor F. Wood Jones. The lowliest and most primitive animals of the Primate Order (which includes lemurs, tarsiers, monkeys, apes, and man) possessed potentialities of brain development far in excess of those of other mammals. Primates are inherently "brainy." The impetus toward brain growth in the early and simple forms of primates was furnished by the utilization of their natural organic equipment in the favoring arboreal environment. Tree life put a premium upon the development of the visual sense in preference to the more primitive senses of smell and hearing. It encouraged agility, balance, and muscular co-ordination. However, no great evolutionary advance would have resulted from these stimuli had not the primates been possessed of sensitive, grasping hands and feet—each with five digits terminating in flat nails instead of claws, and with great toes and thumbs capable of rotation so that they could be opposed to the outer digits. This movement of opposition, originating in the encircling grasp of boughs, is the essential prerequisite for every skilled manual act. It enables that ultimate primate, man, to fabricate tools and thus to achieve a material culture which is his unique possession. The early primates were diminutive, long-snouted, small-brained creatures which ran along the boughs on all fours, feeding on every edible which their tree abodes offered. The first step toward higher evolution occurred when some of the more progressive forms, called tarsiers, began to sit up in the trees, thus specializing their hind limbs for support, and what is infinitely more important, releasing from the duty of support and locomotion the upper pair of prehensile limbs. These, equipped with their pentadactyl hands, could be used for plucking food, conveying it to the mouth, bringing objects before the eyes for examination, and for general tactile exploration of the animal's own body and of everything else within reach.

Now, it is a well known biological principle that the greater the demands put upon an organ, the larger it becomes. The movements of the hands are controlled by motor areas in the nervous covering of the forebrain. These areas expand in response to increasing use and complexity of the movements of the members which they direct. Greater use of the brain demands a larger blood supply, which in turn promotes growth. By tactile exploration and visual examination there grow up, adjacent to the respective motor areas in the cortical surface of the brain, areas which picture the movements of the parts concerned, so that the animal is enabled to visualize actions which are to be carried out and to recall those which have been performed. Further elaborations of the neopallium, or new nervous cortex which mantles the brain, probably provide for association areas, in which, according to Wood Jones, the impressions from different receptive centers are blended, and the memories and experiences derived from the several senses are formed, sorted, and stored.[5] In short, this functional theory of the evolution of the primate brain assumes a sort of physiological perpetual motion, in which emancipated hands continually call for more nervous area in the brain to govern their increasing movements and to store up their multiplying impressions, while the expanding and active brain, on its part, devises ever more mischief still for idle hands to do.

But what of our shrunken face, the remnant of a once projecting mammalian snout? Here again the brain functionalists offer a seductive explanation. The elongate muzzle of the lower animals subserves a triple purpose. It provides the structural setting of the apparatus of mastication; by its extreme forward extension it allows the grazing animal to bite off food whilst the eyes, set well back, are still enabled to see what is eaten and to view the landscape o'er for potential enemies. Finally, the snout terminates in the nose, which is not only a sensitive tactile organ in quadrupeds, but also is the principal receptor of the olfactory sense, which, in the selection of food and in the detection of enemies, is the paramount sensory asset—far more important than vision.

[5] Jones, F. Wood, *Arboreal Man*, p. 191. London, 1916.

Now the emancipation of the prehensile forelimbs from the duties of support and locomotion permits them to be used for hand-feeding, thus relieving the snout of its grazing function. Again, the hands not only pluck the food, but begin to use sticks and stones as weapons, and ultimately, as tools. The free use of the hands and fists deprives the jaws of yet another function—that of defense and offense. Generally in primates, great tusk-like canine teeth at the anterior corners of the jaws serve the double duty of fighting appurtenances and blades for shearing through the tough rinds of fruits and through vegetable fibers.

Just as increased function of a bodily part results in its development, so diminished use causes shrinkage. Consequently, the new utilization of the liberated hands results in a recession of the jaws. The dental arches grow smaller; the projecting canine teeth are reduced to the level of their fellows; the outthrust facial skeleton is bent down below the expanding brain-case; the nose, still a respiratory organ and the seat of the sense of smell, is left—a forlorn fleshy promontory overhanging the reduced mouth cavity. To put it concisely, the brain has expanded because greater and greater demands have been made upon it, and the jaws have shrunk because the majority of their functions have been taken over by the hands and the extra-organic objects used as implements.

Of course, an anthropoid ape with an orthodox biological training might reject the foregoing explanation on the ground that it reeks of Lamarckianism—a wish-fulfillment interpretation of evolution which commands little support nowadays. Such doubting Thomases may regard as futile man's attempt to correlate with superior intelligence that vast malignancy which surmounts his spinal cord. For these there remains the endocrine theory of J. R. Marett, who points out that iodine deficiency, arising from life in the arid plains, is often associated with a waterlogging of the body tissues and cranial expansion, due not to increase of gray matter, but to water on the brain or hydrocephaly. It may be interpreted in part as an effort of an overworked and goiterous thyroid gland to counteract bodily acidity—in short, "to alkalize." If indeed remote inland humanoids suffered from hydrocephaly, subsequent increases in actual brain mass may then be due merely to nature's abhorrence of a vacuum—a compensatory growth designed to fill the space left empty by the receding flood of cerebro-spinal fluid, and in no way related to cerebration. However, I am inclined to regard unfavorably this morbid theory of human evolution. I doubt that disease has kicked an inadequate ape upstairs to humanity. Our huge brains, however little utilized at present, are, at least in part, an ancestral achievement, and our flat faces measure our recession from the brute beast.

APOLOGY FOR MAN'S BEHAVIOR

For at least 30,000 years, and quite probably for thrice that period of time, man has existed at his modern anatomical status, erect, accomplished in bipedal stance and gait, with free hands almost unlimited in the variety and precision of their movements, with an enormous and highly organized brain, capable not only of directing, controlling, and co-ordinating bodily activity, but also of storing up and recalling past impressions, of visualizing the future, of deliberating, planning, and formulating abstract concepts. With this superior evolutionary endowment, what has been the achievement of *Homo sapiens?*

An apology for man's behavior should be addressed to some impartial group of superhuman intelligence; anthropoid apes can be invoked only as occasional critics of the broadly zoölogical aspects of man's social activities. I must ask *you* therefore to attempt to dissociate yourselves from the human species and to serve as dispassionate and critical judges, before whom I am to plead in behalf of man.

Man's Gift of Articulate Speech

Man frequently distinguishes himself from other animals by what he proudly calls "the gift of articulate speech." Some years ago, when the late William Jennings Bryan was crusading against evolution, I was inveigled into introducing him to an undergraduate audience. I managed to avoid serving as the target of his wit and satire by suggesting that, if articulate speech be taken as the criterion of distinction between man and ape, Mr. Bryan of all human beings could most justly disclaim a simian ancestry.

To an anthropoid ape the range, quality, and volume of human vocalization would not be remarkable. A gorilla, for example, can both outscream a woman and roar in a deep bass roll like distant thunder, which can be heard for three or four miles. Even the small gibbon has a voice described by a musician as "much more powerful than that of any singer he had ever heard." As a matter of fact, the anthropoid apes have laryngeal sacs which are extensions of the voice-box, capable of inflation and use as resonance chambers. There is also ample evidence that the voice as an organ for the expression of emotion is utilized by the great apes with a variation and efficacy in no whit inferior to that manifested by the human voice, and with far greater power. In fact, one might conclude that an anthropoid ape would regard a Metropolitan opera star as next-door to dumb.

The ape, unimpressed with the range and volume of the human voice, would nevertheless be appalled at its incessant utilization. Lacking, presumably, the ability to fabricate lofty and complicated thoughts, he would not understand man's continuous compulsion to communicate these results of his cerebration to his fellows, whether or not they care to listen. In fact, it would probably not occur to an ape that the ceaseless waves of humanly vocalized sound vibrating against his ear drums are intended to convey thoughts and ideas. Nor would he be altogether wrong. Man's human wants are not radically dissimilar to those of other animals. He wakes and sleeps, eats, digests, and eliminates, makes love and fights, sickens and dies, in a thoroughly mammalian fashion. Why, then, does he eternally discuss his animalistic affairs, preserving a decent silence but once a year, for two minutes, on Armistice Day? "But," I say (in my rôle of apologist), "human culture is based upon the communication of knowledge through the medium of speech." This is, of course, a statement which no anthropoid ape is in a position to contradict. It is probably true. However, it may be pointed out that the record of human culture is far more ancient than that of language, possibly because no material evidence of the existence of the latter is available before the invention of writing. Nevertheless, beginning with the dawn of the Pleistocene, perhaps one million years ago, we possess an almost unbroken sequence of man-made stone tools, which manifest a continuous and ever improving tradition of craftsmanship. These ancient implements doubtless represent only the few elements which have survived because of the durability of the material used. Pleistocene human culture must have included much more than stone axes and scrapers. It is a fact that many competent anatomists who have examined the various fragmentary skulls and brain cases of the earliest known fossil men—undoubtedly the fabricators of some of the more advanced types of implements—have questioned their ability to employ articulate speech. I myself disagree with this view and think that Pithecanthropus, for example, was probably excessively garrulous, though undoubtedly incoherent and nonsensical in most of his linguistic offerings. I should think that man originated from an irrepressibly noisy and babbling type of ape.

However, it seems possible that most of the transmission of culture was effected through watching and through imitation in the early days of human evolution, rather than by linguistic communication. Even today there exist in the Congo forest region of Africa primitive pygmy Negritos, who possess a very simple culture of their own, but apparently no language. They use the speech of their neighbors, which they must have borrowed after the production of their own culture. However, this may be a somewhat trivial and academic discussion.

It is more pertinent to inquire whether man's use of language has not contributed as much to destruction of himself and his civilization as to his preservation and its upbuilding. Although language is the universal possession of all races of *Homo sapiens,* the diversification of speech has been so extensive and so rapid that the world's population from prehistoric times has consisted of many smaller or larger groups whose articulate and written communications are, for the most part, mutually unintelligible. Thus, whereas the common possession of speech might be expected to unite all men, inasmuch as it enables them to understand each other's thoughts, motives, and cultures, the reverse is the case. Language erects more barriers than bridges. There is, apparently, in man an ineradicable tendency to dislike, to distrust, and to judge as inferior the individual or group which speaks a language unintelligible to him. We consider apes to be lower animals because, as far as we know, they have no language. In a lesser degree we rate those men our inferiors who do not use our own language. Since, within the unified linguistic group, culture is now largely transmitted through the instrumentality of speech and language, the differentiation of the latter carries with it to a great extent the diversifying of the former. And, to some extent, the greater the cultural differences between two groups, the more marked their mutual antipathies become, if they are in competition.

It is the common practice of larger and more powerful groups to attempt to impose their own languages upon alien-speaking peoples with whom they come into contact. Such linguistic servitude not only awakens a bitter resentment in the vanquished, but tends to destroy their culture without giving them in exchange an understanding of, and participation in, the culture of their conquerors. In other words, the Indian who is forced to learn English sacrifices his own culture without getting a fair equivalent. It therefore may be argued that, in a broad sense, language has destroyed as much of culture as it has produced. It is also conceivable that imperfect and garbled translations from one language to another have produced more misunderstanding and discord than would have arisen between groups with mutually unintelligible languages, or without any languages at all.

It may be possible today for an inhabitant of Mars to listen to the thousands of humanly made sounds and vocalizations which, in nearly every part of the earth, are amplified and projected into space. What would he hear? He would hear the pseudo-cultured voices of radio announcers murdering the King's English in mendacious statements about the merits of commercial products; he would hear the raucous voices of newspaper reporters broadcasting sordid crimes, the horrors of war, and political misinformation; he would hear the glutinous tones of the female cosmetic tout, the nasal whine of the degenerate crooner, the blaring cacophonies of a hundred "swing" bands, and the platitudinous insincerities of bawling demagogues. He might hear the monarch of the world's greatest empire announcing his ignominious abdication to an audience of two hundred and fifty million mortals (including I know not how many snivelling sympathizers). He might not, unless endowed with superhuman patience, listen long enough to hear anything which would justify man's gift of articulate speech.

His Attempts to Control Nature

Man's attempts to control nature would undoubtedly evoke the awe and admiration of any anthropoid ape and might even command the respect of critical appraisers of human conduct. Certainly it is in the field of material culture that the human species has accomplished its most substantial achievement. Man is pre-eminently an animal good at gadgets. There is, however, grave reason for doubting his judgment in their utilization.

Perhaps the first chemical process which man employed for his own service was combustion. Presumably its earliest utilization was to shed heat upon naked and chilled bodies. It was then discovered to be a most effective means of scaring off nocturnal beasts of prey, as well as an illuminant indispensable in the hours of darkness, a labor-saving means of sharpening wooden implements, and an admirable agent for the preparation and preservation of food. Much later came the discovery that fire could be used in extracting and working metals, and, last of all, that it could be employed to generate power. The destructive power of fire was early experienced by man and was deliberately employed in clearing land for tillage. In comparatively ancient times man began to use fire as a weapon in warfare, beginning with incendiary torches and arrows, proceeding to gunpowder, and thence to explosives, which have been developed principally and most efficiently for the destruction of human beings and their works.

However, man has never been able completely to control fire, largely because he fails to use it with proper caution. It continues to get beyond his check and to destroy him and his property and vast quantities of natural products now as in primitive times. His inadequacy in its handling is evinced by his universal fear of fire.

In the control and utilization of gases, the achievements of our species have not been commendable. One might begin with air, which man breathes in common with other terrestrial vertebrates. He differs from other animals in that he seems incapable of selecting the right kind of air for breathing. Man is forever doing things which foul the air, and thus poisoning himself by his own stupidity. He pens himself up in a limited air space and suffocates; he manufactures noxious gases which accidentally or intentionally displace the air and remove him from the ranks of the living; he has been completely unable to filter the air of the disease germs which he breathes to his detriment; he and all of his works are powerless to prevent a hurricane or to withstand its force. Man has indeed been able to utilize the power of moving air currents to a limited extent by sails and windmills, and to imitate the flight of birds, with the certainty of eventually breaking his neck if he tries it. By dint of much experimentation, man has also succeeded in producing many gases other than the natural air, mostly lethal and useful only for destroying his fellow beings.

Man uses water much in the same way as other animals; he has to drink it constantly, washes in it frequently, and drowns in it occasionally—probably oftener than other terrestrial vertebrates. Without water he dies as miserably as any other beast; and with too much of it, as in floods, he is equally unable to cope. However, he excels other animals in that he has learned to utilize waterpower. He has also been comparatively successful in the physical manipulation of this compound for his own use, and in purifying it, as well as in mixing it in a great variety of more or less harmful concoctions, which he uses as beverages.

Critics of man would be forced to admit that he is clever in his ability to domesticate other animals and plants, so that he may live upon them, their work, and their products. They might, however, comment unfavorably upon the small number of the animal species thus domesticated and the fact that virtually no additions to this useful list have been made since prehistoric times. It might be observed also that man has unintentionally domesticated a considerable number of noxious animals, such as rats, mice, lice, cockroaches, flies, and other undesirable companions which do him inestimable damage. It is of some interest also to reflect that in his attempts to domesticate the members of his own Primate order —monkeys and apes—who are presumably of a higher intelligence than most other mammals, man has failed ignominiously. He has had no luck at all with insects, except bees, and very little with fish. In the domestication of plants he has been, on the whole, more skillful and more successful. Nevertheless, among the cultivated species, commercially produced and distributed, he has included a not inconsiderable number of plants, the use of which has been, and is, a major cause of human deterioration.

Of man's attempts to control micro-organisms, it need be said only that they are incipient, and, as yet, comparatively futile. Surveying the whole situation, however, it might be concluded that man as an animal has shown a good deal of intelligence and ingenuity in attempting to control and to manipulate nature.

It is rather man's lack of judgment in the exercise of control of natural resources which would disgust critics of higher intelligence, although it would not surprise the apes. Man observes that the wood of trees is serviceable for constructing habitations and other buildings. He straightway and recklessly denudes the earth of forests in so far as he is able. He finds that the meat and skins of the bison are valuable and immediately goes to work to exterminate the bison. He allows his grazing animals to strip the turf from the soil so that it is blown away and fertile places become deserts. He clears for cultivation and exhausts the rich land by stupid planting. He goes into wholesale production of food, cereals, fruit, and livestock and allows the fruits of his labors to rot or to starve, because he has not provided any adequate method of distributing them, or because no one can pay for them. He invents machines which do the work of many men, and is perplexed by the many men who are out of work. It would be hard to convince judges of human conduct that man is not an economic fool.

His Attempts to Control Himself

Man's efforts to control himself individually and in society might impel a gorilla to thump his chest and roar with laughter. Let us consider the probable reactions of the chimpanzee to familial functions as performed by modern man. As a matter of fact there is very little in the family life of the most primitive type of modern savage, such as the native Australian, which would appeal to a chimpanzee as in any wise unnatural or extraordinary. But he would find the family conduct of civilized man somewhat eccentric.

Birth is accomplished much the same way in anthropoid and human species, although the ape mother performs for herself the duty of midwife, biting off the cord, cleaning the infant, and seeing that its lungs are cleared. The ape is the more self-reliant. The anthropoid baby is suckled, carried, and cared for by its mother, and by her is assisted in its first efforts to walk. It gets little or no paternal care and attention—which however are only occasional and superfluous features of human infancy. The ape child begins to fend for itself at an early age, gathering its food, consorting with its age mates, and depending upon the adults of the group only for occasional companionship and protection. An anthropoid would not understand the domestic custom whereby the young are maintained as economic parasites by their parents for two decades or more of their lives, long after they have reached sexual maturity and adult size. The ape might doubt whether our practice in this matter, from the general zoölogical point of view, is beneficial to the species. In ape society a young male does not acquire a mate until he is able to take her by beating off his rivals and to make good his possession. The female is, of course, always self-supporting. The situation of the young man who could not marry his girl because they couldn't live with her folks, because her folks were still living with their folks, would not arise in anthropoid society.

While available evidence does not indicate that apes are more restrained in their sexual life than human beings, they appear to manage the number of their progeny with such discretion that no mother produces new offspring while she is still burdened with the care of previous infants. Furthermore, the size of any ape group seems to be restricted by the ability of its members to gain a livelihood in the collecting of food, whereas in human society the less economic capacity, the more numerous the offspring. Again, the weak, sickly, and constitutionally unfit among the anthropoid apes are eliminated, either through neglect or deliberately, doubtless because our cousins are insufficiently intelligent to have developed those humanitarian sentiments which demand the preservation of life, however painful it is to its possessors and however useless to society. No anthropoid ape has ever heard of natural selection, but that ruthless surgeon continually operates to excise from the stock any malignant growth. Finally, the anthropoid ape whose physical powers are waning is no longer able to dominate the group and tends to go off by himself and lead a solitary existence.

Now I am by no means disposed to admit that other primate societies necessarily regulate all of their affairs better than do human groups. I am merely calling attention to certain obvious contrasts between a natural primate social organization and one that is highly artificial.

A critic who had surveyed the great advances which man has made in his material culture—his homes and his buildings, his means of transportation, his utilization of the energy pent up in natural resources, his extraordinary facility in devising methods of communication—might examine with high expectation the extent to which man has applied his intelligence to the improvement of his health and biological status. An animal which aspires to split the atom and to measure the universe, might conceivably extend his own life to a degree commensurate with the extension of his knowledge, might improve his organism as he has improved his tools and weapons.

The ordinary animal tries to protract his individual existence only by eating, fighting, running away, and hiding, and his species' existence by breeding and by some exercise of parental care. Otherwise his organism survives only through its inherent capacities and its luck with environmental hazards. Primitive man has improved markedly all these natural methods of maintaining life and has even attempted to add another preservative—medical care. The medical science of the savage is, however, compounded of magic and superstition and includes few remedies of actual value. It seems probable that, on the whole, the doctor at the primitive stage of culture kills oftener than he cures. He merely adds to the strain upon a long-suffering organism exerted by the pressure of a ruthless natural selection. Actually man's ignorance of his own anatomy and physiology and of the pathological agents which invade his organism has been so crass that medical skill has been a negligible factor in the increase of human populations up to the last century, even in the most civilized societies. Now, however, advance in medical knowledge, together with public hygiene and sanitation, have radically reduced the mortality at the beginning of the life span and literally have taken the graves out from under the feet of the aging. In the United States the death rate of males born alive during the first year has been reduced from 12.7 per cent to 6.2 per cent in 30 years, and the expectation of life from the beginning of the century has increased from 48 to 59 years in males, and from 51 to 63 years in females. Short of homicide, a man has practically no chance of outliving his wife; females, after attaining a certain age, become almost immortal.

Now, it is perfectly obvious to intelligent judges of man's behavior that this preservation and prolongation of life largely increases the proportion among the living population of the constitutionally inferior—the lame, the halt, and the blind. It also makes for a world peopled increasingly with the immature and the senile, of those who have not yet developed their mental powers and their judgment, and of those who are in process of losing both. If medical science were able to make whole the bodies and minds it preserves, one might find little to criticize in the age shift in composition of the population. But it is unfortunately true that we have succeeded all too well in keeping the engine running, but have been quite unable to repair the steering gear. Since the immature are not granted a voice in the government and the decrepit are not denied it, we may expect ever-increasing social ructions as a result of senile decay dominating dementia praecox, in a world of diminishing average intelligence.

One of the human institutions for which apology is required is government. Undoubtedly an anthropoid ape would appreciate and understand government by dictatorship; he might even realize the advantages of a communistic regime. But a superhuman critic of man's affairs would be puzzled by a democracy. He would have to be informed that democracy involves the essential principle that all law-abiding adults have equal rights and privileges and an equal voice in the government. Such a democratic government implies, or should imply, an approximate parity of intelligence in the electorate, or a majority of individuals of superior intelligence, if it is to function capably and successfully. There can be no miracle whereby the group intelligence transcends the possibly moronic mean of its constituent members. Therefore, a democracy becomes a better or worse social instrument as the mean intelligence of its population rises or falls.

Now, on the whole, there is a marked positive association between bodily health and mental health. A ten-year study of American criminals and insane has convinced me that there is an even stronger correlation between mental and social inadequacy and biological inferiority. Since civilized men are preserving the unfit in body, it follows that they are depreciating their intelligence currency. There are plenty of indirect evidences of a decline in the national intelligence of civilized countries, but I am apologizing in behalf of man and not voluntarily contributing evidence which might be used against him.

Judges of human behavior, informed of modern preparations for warfare and of the methods which are employed to destroy human life, might easily leap to an erroneous conclusion with respect to the purpose and function of this highly developed institution. They would probably reason as follows: "Men are too soft-hearted to keep their populations down to the right numbers by birth control or infanticide. They love babies, and like to care for the sick and helpless. Therefore, when the weak, the unfit, and the useless grow to adult years and become a menace to the common good, nations conspire mutually to start patriotic crusades, whereby their superfluous and inferior populations destroy each other in a high atmosphere of heroism and devotion to public duty. 'Dulce et decorum est pro patria mori.' But is this not a very expensive method of population control?"

As the protagonist of the human race, I must admit that in warfare, on the contrary, we select as the victims for sacrifice, not the bodily and mentally unfit, but those adjudged to be, on every scientific test, the flower of each nation. Nor do I know how to answer the inevitable retort that man's right hand certainly does not know what his left hand is doing, when with the one he preserves the worst of his kind, and with the other destroys the best.

I should probably try to divert attention from this issue by discanting upon the grandeur of human conceptions of justice, the wonderful mechanism whereby it is administered, the sanctity of the law, and how we strenuously organize efficient police systems to prevent its infraction; how we are learning to regard the criminal, not as a vicious brute to be exterminated without ruth, but as a wayward and possibly sick child to be rehabilitated and cured by patient and loving care, and ultimately to be returned again to society with the Christly admonition, "Go, and sin no more." I should point out how, at each Christmas season, our wise and noble governors bestow upon their happy states the priceless gift of a goodly parcel of liberated murderers, thieves, and other convicted felons. I should wax eloquent upon our democratic belief that ignorance and social maladjustment is at the root of all crime, that a proper and more extensive education of the young—perhaps extending to middle age—together with a wise reorganization of our social and economic institutions, could eradicate this evil forever.

I fear, however, that all of the ape members of the investigating body, if any remained upon the judicial bench, would resign and take to the nearest trees. For no animal society tolerates the outlaw. The anti-social animal is killed or driven out. Judges of superior intelligence, however, would take a broader-minded viewpoint and put some pertinent questions. "Is it not true that education at the public expense has been extended these many years to nearly every class of person in the United States, and that facilities for more and better learning have increased almost immeasurably during the last quarter of a century?"

To this the protagonist of human behavior, with rejuvenated spirit, proudly answers, "Yes."

"Is it true that in recent times the noble-spirited and socially minded, who in bygone days concerned themselves with the salvation of men's souls, have now, for the most part, turned to the reform of human society and are no longer attempting to prepare men for heaven, but rather to rescue them for a very present and man-made hell?" The answer is again in the affirmative.

"Have not hosts of intelligent and highly educated men and women—penologists, sociologists, psychologists, psychiatrists, jurists, and sheer philanthropists—labored at prison reform and refined the treatment of the delinquent until it may be said that the convicted felon receives more social consideration than the law-abiding working man?" That would be a question which would not justify an unequivocal answer on the part of counsel for the defense.

"Is it not true that, in spite of the advance of education and all the substantial progress in methods of social amelioration, crime is still increasing enormously, and that the discharged convict continues to return to his crime, like a dog to his vomit?" And finally, "Is it not therefore apparent, in the light of the evidence here presented, that modern man is selling his biological birthright for a mess of morons; that the voice may be the voice of democracy, but the hands are the hands of apes?"

3.

PRIDE AND PREJUDICE IN ESTIMATES OF MAN'S ANTIQUITY

LAY readers are often perplexed by the great differences which they note in scientific literature concerning the age of man's culture and of man himself. They may even be forgiven for concluding that a great many of these chronological estimates are little better than capricious guess-work. The skeptic may suspect that pride and prejudice enter into these supposedly impartial dating systems. He would not be altogether wrong. I originally gave the following short address on the age of man at a symposium on time scales, in which the other participants were august astronomers, formidable physicists, and portentous geologists. I had quaking knees, a dry throat, and a moist brow. I felt like a cashier in a ten-cent store addressing the board of governors of the Federal Reserve Banks on the subject of finance. I need not have worried, because on such occasions each speaker is so preoccupied with what he himself is going to say, or with how he has said it, that he never listens to any of the others. Here I shall preface my brief excursus on man's antiquity with some account of various methods chronologists use in obtaining their estimates. Then I shall revert to the residual effects of pride and prejudice, hereinbefore mentioned, upon cold scientific calculations.

Absolute chronologies, of course, carry us back not more than 6000 years, even if we accept a great many shaky correlations and depend upon a considerable amount of dead reckoning and dubious tradition. In order to get so far we have to hitch together a number of Old World systems which are valid only within restricted areas, leaving all of the rest of the world in complete darkness. If we have no point of reference whereby some object or event in a region without recorded history can be tied in with a known date in an established chronology elsewhere, we get into a terrible quandary concerning the absolute age of quite recent events and objects. Thus any date in the New World prior to A.D. 1492 is obtained only by inference and conjecture. There are a couple of methods of making an absolute count by years in areas where no written records exist. One of these is the tree-ring system devised by Dr. A. E. Douglass. Every year a growing tree forms a peripheral ring of variable width according to rainfall and other seasonal conditions. Sections through a log give a series of these concentric rings recording the age of the tree and showing a certain combination of ring patterns. By matching up the ring pattern combinations in different logs taken from prehistoric Indian ruins, Douglass and his students have constructed an absolute chronology for the Southwestern United States going back to A.D. 348. Of course the chronology floats until it is tied in with logs known to have been cut at a given year. But such correlations have been made at various points. There are a number of jokers in this system. Only certain kinds of trees in certain areas can yet be used. There is the possibility that mistakes may be made in the connecting links between series when the tie-in is based on only one or two logs, but Douglass is extremely careful to avoid any but the most firmly substantiated linkages. In any event, the dendrochronology, as it has been called, does not as yet carry us as far back as the recorded human calendric systems and is of present use only in tracing quite recent cultures in benighted areas with belated prehistories.

A roughly analogous system of establishing an absolute count in years was invented by Baron de Geer in determining the time which has elapsed since the end of the glacial period. The ice-sheet, in retreating across the Scandinavian peninsula deposits a layer of sand and silt in the lakes during each summer melting. These superimposed layers are called varves. Series of them of varying widths can be matched up like the combinations of tree-rings. The count has been made across southern Sweden, but the terminal moraine of the last maximum of the ice advance extended across northern Germany. Hence the total of years elapsed since the formation of the Brandenburg moraine (about 25,000) is a partial count of varves filled out by estimates. A closely similar length of time has been estimated and counted by Antevs for the lapse of years since the Wisconsin ice-cap began to melt in eastern North America.

But this 25,000 to 30,000 years does not even get us back to an anatomically primitive type of man. The Late Glacial occupants of the European caves were virtual moderns, from a physical stand-point. The varve count stretched by estimates does not even reach the infancy of human culture, which man achieved long after his body had ceased to be particularly ape-like. Stone implements have been found in the Old World in deposits which indicate that our ancestors were tool-making animals at the beginning of the glacial period, with its four major advances of the ice-sheet and its three more or less genial interglacial periods. It is possible that we, in the last twenty-odd thousand years, have hardly got well-started upon the fourth inter-glacial period.

No one knows how long the Pleistocene or Glacial Period lasted. The depth of deposits or sedimentation, the amount of erosion or weathering, the changing levels of land and water, and other classes of data are used by geologists to enable them to arrive at rough estimates. In general, one has to judge the duration of the Pleistocene in proportion to the thickness of deposits and other evidences of the preceding geological periods. On these bases the Glacial Period is so short that it is hardly worth counting at all. Geologists round off their figures and give it a million years, since they do not use coins of smaller denomination. None of them really cares whether the Glacial Period lasted 500,000 years or 1,500,000 years, because it does not matter at all except in guessing at the age of man. What we did or where we were at a given minute, hour, and day last month becomes important only when we have to furnish an alibi.

Big science, like big business, deals in hundreds and thousands of millions. The high financiers of natural science are the astronomers and physicists who estimate the age of the earth, the age of the solar system, the age of the universe. They scarcely care to bother themselves about the age of life on the earth. The modern method of measuring the age of the earth is based upon the disintegration of radio-active substances through the emanation of rays. Radioactive elements break down at a definite rate which is different for each element. The element thorium breaks down into lead through eleven stages. A given mass of thorium will be reduced to half value in 1800 million years. On the basis of the analysis of radioactive ores, the age of the earth may be reckoned at 3000 million years, if one wishes to be conservative. The beginning of the Tertiary Period which yields fossil remains of the first primitive Primates is about 60 millions of years ago on this radio-active time scale.

It is rather deplorable that many archaeologists and anthropologists seem to have failed to acquaint themselves with recent advances in knowledge of the earth's age resulting from modern physics and geology. While the specialists in the latter sciences have been enlarging enormously their estimates, it has become popular among the students of man to indulge in a perverse reduction of the time allotted to human culture and to man as a human animal. The psychology of this anthropological attitude is interesting and complicated; and I propose to attempt to describe it, although many will disagree with me.

In the first place, the elaboration and advance in material culture during the past century has been so rapid as to give a false impression of the time necessary for cultural changes in antiquity and in primitive times. When we note that iron came into use only 3400 years ago and copper not more than 6000 years ago, it is difficult to conceive of men remaining in the polished stone age with agriculture and domesticated animals but without metals, for more than a few thousands of years. It is even harder to realize that the Old Stone Age endured for hundreds of thousands of years before pottery, domesticated plants and animals, and polished stone shifted the basis of subsistence from hunting and food collecting to arti-

OUTLINE OF GEOLOGICAL PERIODS AND ANIMAL FORMS

	Geological Period	Millions of Years	Climate	Animal Forms	Cultures
QUATERNARY	Holocene or Recent		Transition from cold of glacial retreat to present conditions	Races of *Homo sapiens*, present day fauna	Iron Bronze Copper Neolithic Mesolithic

QUATERNARY	Pleistocene or Glacial		Four major glaciations with three interglacial periods. Repetition of damp cold, dry cold, temperate, damp warm, and damp cool cycles	Fourth glaciation: Various types of *Homo sapiens* including Cro Magnon, Grimaldi, etc., preceded in first maximum of fourth glaciation and in third interglacial and third glaciation by Neanderthal man, also probably in the Middle Pleistocene by Palestine man, Rhodesian man, Solo (Ngandong) man of Java. Heidelberg man, Piltdown man, Peking man, and *Pithecanthropus erectus* of Java are probably still earlier.
				Alternations of warm and cold mammalian fauna, some extant and some extinct. Primates mostly of existing types
					Palaeolithic
					Upper
					  Magdalenian
					  Solutrian
					  Aurignacian
					Middle
					  Mousterian
					Lower
					  Pre-Mousterian and other flake industries, Acheulean and Chellean hand axe industries
					Pre-Chellean

TERTIARY	Pliocene	6	Gradual lowering of temperature from warm to cool, presaging glaciations	Undiscovered human types, generalized ancestors of present great apes, some existing and some extinct mammals	Eolithic
TERTIARY	Miocene	12	Equable and moist subtropical	Generalized great apes—Dryopithecus family, fossil monkeys; herbivores increasing, marsupials disappearing. Probable separation of human and anthropoid stocks	
TERTIARY	Oligocene	16	Tropical or subtropical	First small anthropoid apes, first monkeys; forerunners of living genera of mammals	
TERTIARY	Eocene	25	Temperate or subtropical	Earliest lemuroids and tarsioids, insectivores; generalized placental mammals, abundant marsupials	
SECONDARY	Cretaceous	65	Subtropical	Small mammals, mainly marsupial; greatly specialized reptiles; birds, bony fishes, sharks, rays	
SECONDARY	Jurassic	35	Warm	Diversified reptiles; small insectivorous marsupials; fishes approaching modern forms; first birds	
SECONDARY	Triassic	35	Dry and warm in north; moist and warm in south	First small mammals; greatly developed reptiles; amphibia, fish	
PRIMARY	Permian	25	Arid	Large amphibians, mammal-like reptiles, fishes, molluscs, last Trilobites	
PRIMARY	Carboniferous	85	Moist and generally mild, some glaciation	Upper: earliest amphibians and traces of reptiles, bony fishes, molluscs. Lower: sharks, ganoids, molluscs, corals, foraminifera, etc.	
PRIMARY	Devonian	50	Arid	Fishes, lung-fishes, invertebrates	
PRIMARY	Silurian	40		Fish, first air-breathers (scorpions)	
PRIMARY	Ordovician	85		Armored fish, trilobites	
PRIMARY	Cambrian	70		Trilobites, other invertebrates	
	Total	550			

ficial production. Yet it ought to be clear that cultural progress accelerates enormously, and, conversely, the further back we go the longer become the periods of rudimentary culture in which change is so slow as to be almost imperceptible. We have only to look at contemporary savages to realize that many of them maintain almost the identical manner of life and use the same material culture which characterized our ancestors 8000 years ago. I do not see why it is impossible to believe that palaeolithic man made the same kind of tools for scores of thousands of years when the native Australian has hardly passed the stage of such artifacts today. We get to thinking of man as such a clever, versatile, and progressive animal that we imagine he must have had no slow learning period. Every whit of zoölogical and archaeological evidence indicates the contrary. Our pride in human accomplishment leads us to believe that man is much more of a prodigy than he really is. Thus Sir Arthur Keith, the greatest contemporary student of the physical characteristics of fossil man, has the temerity to cut down the entire range of Tertiary and Quaternary time to 2,100,000 years, whereas the radio-active scale gives us 60,000,000 of years for those periods within which man developed from the lowest primates.[1] All of the evidence indicates that man was an unpromising anthropoid ape for five million years or more, and the lowest kind of an apparently unprogressive and brutish savage for at least another million years. His acquisition of high civilization is very recent and perhaps only temporary. The period of human civilization is as inconsiderable in man's cultural history as is post-glacial time in the age of the earth.

Another reason why anthropologists try to cramp human culture into an impossibly short span of time is that our little minds cannot span the vast reaches of time within which evolution has proceeded. We are still subconsciously hog-tied to something like a Biblical chronology which puts the creation at about the time man was beginning to work metals in Mesopotamia. We do not believe that there can be a billion dollars, because we have never had more than a thousand at a time. A million years of human existence is as inconceivable as the national deficit under the New Deal. Never-

[1] Keith, Sir Arthur, *New Discoveries Relating to the Antiquity of Man*, Frontispiece, N. Y., 1932.

theless we have spent that much time, just as the new dealers have spent that amount of money.

Anthropologists really ought to get their noses out of the dirt and begin to take the spacious views of life and the universe which astronomers and geologists have adopted as a matter of logical deduction from multiple lines of evidence. Evolution is a slow business, and it has taken all of the time that there is. Unfortunately, the effect of this or that clever scientist counting a few thousands of varves or tree rings (which really cover a small stretch of human cultural history) has been to load the minds of many archaeologists to their arithmetic or chronologic saturation point, so that they attribute to human evolution and man's culture their own temporal and spacial limitations.

The various statements in this volume relating to the origin of man's stone tool industry in Pliocene times and the extension of the Lower Palaeolithic industries throughout the whole of the Pleistocene period, from its very beginning, should not be allowed to stand without a reference to another point of view which has lately gained powerful adherents.

Dr. Hellmut de Terra, whose recent study of the geology of the Siwalik formations in Northern India has revealed fundamental correlations of early human industries with Pleistocene deposits, is of the opinion that the older Palaeolithic cultures (Chellean and Acheulean) appear for the first time in Middle Pleistocene deposits. He says:

If we compare the geological setting of early man in the regions (India, China, and Java) we recognize that the Old Paleolithic cultures appeared uniformly during the Middle Pleistocene apparently at the close of the second glaciation and in the second interglacial (or interpluvial). With this perception there become visible two outstanding landmarks in the evolution of Man in Asia: the Pliocene period with its progressive anthropoid evolution, and the Middle Pleistocene stage with its uniform emergence of tool-making races, such as Peking Man. The interval should to all appearance represent the critical phase of protohuman evolution which is the time of both climatic changes and earth revolutions.[2]

[2] de Terra, Hellmut, "Cenozoic Cycles in Asia and Their Bearing on Human Prehistory," *Proceedings of the American Philosophical Society*, Vol. 77, No. 3 (1937), p. 306.

De Terra's opinion, in which I believe Father Teilhard du Chardin concurs, is that *Pithecanthropus erectus* of Java belongs to the Middle Pleistocene horizon which is associated with implements of the old palaeolithic type. He also considers the Peking Men and their industries to be of Middle Pleistocene age. From personal communications of Dr. de Terra, I gather that he is inclined to think that palaeolithic industries and skeletal remains of fossil man hitherto found, including those in Europe, cannot as yet be referred to any earlier geological horizon. This view, of course, does not take into consideration the length of time during which man or his precursors used eoliths—crude and amorphous stone tools not always capable of certain identification as artifacts.

My present view of this new position taken by these excellent authorities is as follows: It is wholly possible that the so-called "fist-axe" industries of the Old Palaeolithic do not begin until the time of the second interglacial period. It seems to me, however, that it is necessary, on the archaeological side, to postulate a very long period of tool-using by early men or proto-men before the stage of typologically well differentiated stone industries was attained. Eoliths must have been used far back in the Pliocene.

From the standpoint of Physical Anthropology I am quite incredulous of such a late dating for man's actual emergence from the ape status as the interval between the end of the Pliocene and the end of the second Pleistocene glaciation. I still believe that man's stock separated from the large anthropoid ape trunk in the Miocene, and that several varieties of archaic types of man developed in the Pleistocene. Further, I see no reason for relinquishing the view that *Homo sapiens*, or modern man, developed early in Pleistocene, although proof of his existence at that time is lacking.

It is quite likely that I am wrong in this view, as I have been and will be in many others. I shall not hesitate to change my mind if the evidence becomes, in my opinion, conclusive. The thrill of new discoveries pointing the way to closer approximations to the truth facilitates a graceful abandonment of ancient, outmoded, and erroneous opinions. Any one working in science ought to be amenable to quick and painless divorces from his cherished theories, rather than to insist upon cleaving to them until death do them part.

The extent to which prejudice enters into over-conservative estimates of the cultural or evolutionary span of man is well illustrated by the present controversy over the antiquity of man in the New World. For many years a limited amount of scientific research failed to reveal convincing evidence of the human occupation of this hemisphere before a very few thousands of years ago. Further, a great deal of legitimate, destructive criticism of ill-founded evidence of glacial antiquity for man in America was necessarily expressed by our best scientific authorities. One of our most brilliant and once progressive archaeologists naïvely expressed to me some years ago his sentiments on this question. He said that it would be a pity to have new evidence come to light which would overthrow all of the admirable scientific work of the past indicating the recent arrival in the New World of the American Indian. This illustrious reactionary has become one of the most indomitable assailants of all of the new evidences of man's early arrival in the New World which have recently come to light, quite irrespective of their value. He has adopted, for better or for worse, a cause which is almost certainly lost.

Anthropologists labor under the difficulty of being men, and therefore of seeing man from his own point of view, although they recognize intellectually the necessity of an unhuman detachment. Also they are mostly afraid of finding out something about man which men will not like, and which, of course, they will not like themselves. But if we are really going to clean house, we shall have to get all of the skeletons out of all of the closets.

4.

THE AGE OF MAN[2]

MAN is a comparatively new animal, a zoölogical upstart. In the parade of terrestrial life he brings up the rear. It is not strange, therefore, that anthropology, the study of man, should be the unkempt urchin of the sciences, tolerated among his elders in hope of latent promise, rather than by virtue of achievement.

A distinguished geologist, in one of his popular and lucid intervals, has summarized the earth's history on the face of a clock, twelve hours representing three thousand million years, by a radioactive scale of time.[2] He allots to man the last $21\frac{3}{5}$ seconds of this twelve-hour period. Because anthropology is a shameless juvenile, pilfering from all the trees of knowledge, I have not hesitated to appropriate Dr. Chester A. Reeds' radio-active clock for anthropometric purposes. I propose to measure the time of man firstly by the duration of his culture, and secondly by the requirements of his physical evolution.

[1] Extract from an address given at a symposium at the Harvard Observatory on the occasion of the dedication of the Astro-photographic Building, March 23, 1932.

[2] Reeds, Chester A., *The Earth, Our Everchanging Planet*, pp. 1-2. "The University Series," The University Society, New York, 1931.

To measure man's antiquity by the age of his culture is to employ a very crude "rule of thumb." Man's culture is quite literally a "rule of thumb," since it is to the use of that mobile and opposable member that he owes most of the paraphernalia of his material civilization.

Let us place the most important cultural achievements of man in some sort of rough chronological order. The smelting of iron ores probably began in southeastern Asia Minor not much later than 1500 B.C., roughly 3,400 years ago. Bronze was cast in the same general area at least as early as the beginning of the third millennium before Christ, more than 4,900 years ago. Copper was reduced from its ores, hammered and cast into tools, weapons, and ornaments for perhaps a thousand years before its alloy, bronze, came into use. Thus six thousand years from today take us back to the Stone Age, even in those areas where human culture progressed with the greatest speed.

For perhaps four millennia before the age of metals, human society in the most favored regions was already well organized upon an artificial basis of existence. Some plants were cultivated for food, and animals had been tamed and bred for the use of man. Sedentary folk were living in village communities, in huts of wattle and daub, timber, mud-brick, or possibly rough stone. The humble earthen pot already was molded and baked by the housewife. The husband and father laboriously chipped and polished his hard stone axes, hewed timber, tended herds and flocks, while his wife stayed at home, minded the baby, and doubtless hoed the garden. The Neolithic period in Mesopotamia may have begun as early as 8000 B.C. Ten thousand years take us back to the savagery of the Old Stone Age, even, probably, in the regions where civilization was most precocious.

Just about this time we overtake the glaciers in their last retreat. According to Professor Hugo Obermaier, the various phases of the epiglacial fluctuations occupied a period of 16,000 or 17,000 years. In the later millennia of this interval, European men were gradually emerging from cave life; Azilians in the Pyrenees were painting pebbles with symbolic signs; their cousins in South Germany were burying the heads of their dead like eggs in nests; the fine stone chipping of earlier ages had given way to a pygmy flint industry. Most of this epiglacial period, going back perhaps as far as

25,000 B.C., was devoted in Europe to the development of a highly diversified industry in small stone implements and bone tools, and to the rise and decline of a realistic art, including representations of men and animals—engraving on stone and bone, and polychrome mural decorations in the caverns of southwestern Europe. The producers of this Magdalenian culture were physically modern types of men, making a living by fishing and hunting.

The Magdalenians were preceded immediately by the Solutrians, fabricators of beautifully chipped laurel leaf-shaped blades, and next by the Aurignacians, of the same fundamental European longheaded type, devoid of archaic simian attributes, skilled workers in flint and stone, gifted sculptors in the round, with a decided preference for fat ladies as artists' models. Here archaeologists reach such a state of quivering timorousness that they can no longer articulate dates. The Later Stone Age or Upper Paleolithic period is thought to have begun in Europe not earlier than 27,000 or 30,000 years ago. Some parsimonious chronologists would pare the estimate to 11,000 years.

During the maximum extensions of the Würmian glaciation and probably throughout the most of the last interglacial phase a beetling-browed, prognathous, shuffling race of Neanderthal men lived in Western and Central Europe. In spite of their apelike features, they made several varieties of flaked flint implements with finely retouched edges; they buried their dead with some ceremony, and they contested successfully with the cave bear the tenancy of caverns with southern exposures. Their sway in Europe is probably to be reckoned in some hundreds of millennia. Yet they were no pioneers. Before them in Western Europe were the Acheuleans, who made symmetrical almond-shaped fist axes, which may be found by the thousands in the glacial gravels of the Somme and other rivers of Western Europe. The men who made the crude precursors of the Acheulean fist axes—pear-shaped implements with coarsely flaked sinuous edges—were the Chelleans. We know none of their skeletons, but they dropped some of their earlier and cruder tools in the Cromer Forest beds, which stand at the base of the Pleistocene. It is probable that the Old Stone Age with its easily recognizable implements made from flint nodules began as early as the inception of the glacial period.

Peering back into the shadowy Pliocene we may discern, sixteen feet down in the Red Crag, the habitation level of the Foxhall men, who used fire and chipped from flint their borers, scrapers, and knives. Anthropology owes this discovery to Mr. J. Reid Moir, of Ipswich, England. Below the Red Crag and in the drift which caps the chalk plateaus of Kent, are found the amorphous, chipped, rolled, and patinated flints, which are called Eoliths—"stones of the dawn." Many of these are undoubtedly of natural origin, but some of them were assuredly utilized by early men who had not yet succeeded in fashioning their tools into recognizable shapes.

Under these considerations I do not think that we can date the beginnings of human culture—the first construction and utilization of tools and implements—much later than the second half of the Pliocene period.

Now if we revert to Dr. Chester Reeds' radio-active chart of geologic time, we find that he assigns one million years to the Pleistocene period and six million years to the Pliocene. The anthropologist is wholly incompetent to judge of the validity of such scales, but the present writer prefers to be a radio-activarian rather than a sedimentalist. Then, if we plagiarize Dr. Reeds' radio-active clock, we find that the twelve-hour dial of man's culture represents no less than four million years. Each second represents 92.59 years. Accordingly, if man's culture was born at mid-Pliocene noon, he began to make Chellean fist axes at 9 P.M.; at 11.54 and 36 seconds he began to draw pictures of animals and to sculp his lady friends; at 11.58 and 12 seconds he was beginning to try to tame animals and plants, to build huts and to live in communities and to polish stone tools; at a little less than 37 seconds before 12 o'clock midnight he discovered the use of iron. Of course this cultural-archaeological clock is hardly accurate enough to justify the splitting of seconds.

A rather larger measure of the age of man employs the stages of human evolution, suggested by the study of recent and fossil types of man. This is a sort of foot-rule, rather than a rule of thumb, for the acquisition of a stable supporting foot seems probably to mark, better than other anatomical features, the transition from the anthropoid to the humanoid type.

The outstanding and most distinctive bodily characters of man are the stabilized supporting foot, the enlarged brain, and reduced jaws with associated chin and nasal prominences. We have to look

far back beyond the stretch of 25,000 years which has elapsed since
the last glacial maximum, for the genesis of any of these features.
As a matter of fact, I am unable to point to any item of man's
anatomy which shows definite progressive evolutionary changes
since the modern types of Aurignacian men succeeded the apelike
Neanderthalers in the caves of Western Europe. Great toes may
have become a little greater; little toes may have become somewhat
more diminutive and degenerate, palates more contracted, and teeth
more liable to rot, but none of these changes are certainly consistent
or cumulative, nor do they obtain in all the existing races of mankind. The wholly modern types of Aurignacian man give way to
the apish Neanderthalers at the maximum of the last or Würmian
Glaciation, but it is necessary to suppose that *Homo sapiens* existed
in the full perfection of his present physical attributes long before
that period, if not in Europe, certainly in Asia and Africa. It seems
probable that the main stems of modern man—Negro, Mongoloid,
and White—were differentiated from the common *Homo sapiens*
stock long before the end of the Pleistocene period. I incline to the
view that essentially modern types of man existed in Europe before
the reign of the Neanderthalers and were responsible for the Chellean and Acheulean cultures, but discreetly withdrew from those
chilly areas during the maximum of the last glaciation, leaving the
archaic Neanderthalers to shiver in caves and contemplate the
glacial moraines.

We have to go back to Neanderthal man to get a human type
which is distinctively anthropoid in jaw protrusion and chinlessness.
Even this ancient race shows considerable snout reduction, together
with rudimentary chin development. The gentleman who owned
the Heidelberg jaw, dug up from a depth of some 80 feet in the
Mauer sands, was probably an early ancestral Neanderthaler. Some
geologists place him in the first interglacial period and others in
the second. The small-brained Sinanthropus skulls, recently dug up
near Peking, China, represent in teeth, jaws, and brow ridges possible precursors of the later Neanderthal types. The actual specimens recovered seem to be of Lower Pleistocene date, but the type
itself must have developed long before. In Neanderthal man the
brain was virtually of modern size and the foot an essentially
human, supporting, non-prehensile organ. Forms probably ancestral
to the Neanderthalers and assigned to Lower Pleistocene strata ex-

hibit only slightly larger jaws, with slightly more rudimentary chins and somewhat less capacious brains.

The lady from Piltdown Common, England, *Eoanthropus Dawsoni,* burst upon us in 1912 with a virtually full-blown human brain and an almost completely chimpanzee jaw. While she may have lasted into the Lower Pleistocene, she is almost certainly the superannuated survival of a Pliocene type. She leads us to the conclusion that the human brain in some progressive stocks had attained its modern size by the beginning of the glacial epoch, although jaw reduction had scarcely begun. We do not know the Piltdown lady's feet, but we may be reasonably certain that they were not prehensile.

Pithecanthropus erectus of Java is anatomically the most archaic humanoid type. He is referred to the Lower Pleistocene of Java, but should represent the survival of an Early Pliocene or Late Miocene type. His brain was halfway down to giant anthropoid size, his jaws and teeth a little more than halfway human, his thigh bone completely that of a man. He must have walked erect on his hind legs, supported by non-prehensile feet. The human type of foot, posture, and gait may well have evolved by the end of Miocene times.

In the Middle and Upper Miocene period, we have encountered no skeletal remains of man or of humanoid types, but only generalized giant anthropoids, especially of the Dryopithecus family. According to the opinion of Professor W. K. Gregory, which I share, man was probably differentiated from a generalized and progressive Dryopithecus-like anthropoid, either in the Middle or Upper Miocene period. It is then, in our opinion, that a giant primate took to the ground, stood upon his hind legs and took the crucial step toward humanity. We must not picture him at this adolescent stage "standing with reluctant feet where the brook and river meet," but wading boldly in, not without splashing.

A little band of willful anthropologists insists upon deriving man from some diminutive ground-dwelling Oligocene primate, apparently desiring to refer to the most remote time possible our ignominious identity with the anthropoid apes. I do not believe in this scuttling homunculus, too slow to escape by fleetness, too weak to win through by combat, and too stupid to survive by wit.

We need at least the full range of the Pleistocene and Pliocene

periods to allow sufficient time for man to develop from a terrestrial
erect anthropoid to his modern human status. There is no evidence
for an unduly rapid evolution of human stocks. The process was
multiple, involving many different lines, developing asymmetri-
cally, at different rates of speed, and to varying degrees of removal
from the anthropoidal status. Many, if not most, of these stocks
became extinct. One or more have survived in modern races of
man.

On the radio-active twelve-hour clock of man's physical evolution we may represent the elapsed time at seven million years, if we
accept Dr. Reeds' estimate of six million years for the duration of
the Pliocene period, and let man start with a supporting non-prehensile foot. Born with this essentially human member at 12 o'clock
noon, he must have acquired his full brain size at about 10.17 P.M.
(end of the Pliocene) and his straight profile and jutting chin at
11.08 and 34 seconds P.M., or thereabouts (mid-Pleistocene times).
It was nearly 11.59 before he began to tame wild animals, to plant,
to hoe the garden, and to become domesticated.

I think that at the end of the Secondary Era, the earth was
becoming tired of reptiles, irritated with their scales, and fed up
with their eggs—especially, perhaps, dinosaur eggs. Then came the
lively lemurs, the pop-eyed, hopping tarsiers, the amusing monkey
tree-dwellers, and the mighty brachiating anthropoids. One of these
last, endowed with a better brain and with a super-primate initiative, sought a richer and more abundant life upon the ground.
From him, in the fullness of time, there developed man, with his
stable foot, his sensitive prehensile hand, and his great receptive
brain. Some men are born to sit aloft in observatories investigating
the fullness of the universe. Others are born to sit on the top of flag-
poles, contemplating the emptiness of their stomachs. None need
be ashamed to have sprung from an ape.

5.

NEW DISCOVERIES AND DISPUTES CONCERNING PRIMATE PROGRESS

STUDENTS of man's zoölogical history no longer discuss the reality of human evolution from lower primate forms. For the last quarter of a century, at least, evolution has been axiomatic. The enormous amount of intensive research which has been devoted to the manifold aspects of this subject has accumulated masses of confirmatory data without uncovering any significant information which weakens the evolutionary hypothesis. There are, it is true, a certain number of ecclesiastical zoölogists who still write books and papers attacking evolution, and, of course, plenty of lay writers with no scientific standing. But these are persons who are influenced by religious beliefs and convictions, who indeed have the right to their own opinions, are to be respected for their conscientious objections, but are unimportant to the professional student of man. I do think, however, that some of these clever anti-evolutionists (for example, Chesterton) are rather useful in that they are always on the lookout for factual errors, false inferences, and defective logic in the work of scientists who take evolution for granted, as clerics take Christianity. Not infrequently they serve the very practical function of "debunking" evolutionary pretensions which have gone beyond the evidence.

For instance, I was highly diverted some years ago when a very eminent prelate, with a mordant tongue and a violent official objection to evolution, attacked the exhibits illustrating human evolution in one of our great public museums. The very reverend and astute critic claimed that the reconstructions of ancient and apelike men based upon fragments of skeletons gathered here and there were imaginative, mendacious, misleading, and wholly without validity. This clerical blast was played up gleefully by the press, and all of the little reportorial buzzards swooped down upon the unfortunate museum director to pick up what they could. The latter, a very famous and learned scientist, in answer to the church critic, deigned merely to emit a somewhat pompous dictum: "The Hall of Man still stands." Thereby he let himself in for the immediate and telling retort of the churchman: "He means that the Hall of Man still lies." Now there is just enough of truth in that statement to make it cut. Some evolutionary exhibits and reconstructions of extinct men and animals have been carried out with an elaboration of detail and an assumption of omniscience which are not justified by the scientific data in hand. It is, for example, absolutely impossible to infer from a human skull the morphological details of the eyes, the ears, the tip of the nose, the lips, the form and distribution of hair, and the color of skin, hair and eyes. So I think that the laugh was on the side of the archbishop, because the scientists had overreached themselves and gone beyond their evidence. A vigorous and caustic opposition is an excellent antiseptic against infections of loose-thinking and slip-shod scientific research.

However, to revert to the status of evolutionary discussion among anthropologists, I think that it may be said with reasonable accuracy that the principal points of dispute on the factual side are at present: (1) Did man evolve from a giant, tree-dwelling anthropoid ape of a chimpanzee-gorilla type in fairly late geological times (Miocene or Pliocene), or from a small ground-ape of a gibbonoid type in the earlier Oligocene? (2) Did the anatomical modern varieties of man (conventionally lumped together in one species, *Homo sapiens*) evolve directly from one or other of the archaic and somewhat apish fossil types of man, or are the ancestors of modern races as yet undiscovered?

From the theoretical and functional point of view (as contrasted with the factual and historical) interest centers upon the causes and mechanisms of evolution—whether in general the organism is a plaything of its environment, or whether it moves toward a specific goal impelled by some sort of internal driving force which also keeps its nose pointing in a predetermined direction. We are really much more perplexed by these old questions of causation and mechanism than by lacunae in our factual knowledge, which we know we can fill sooner or later. In the twenty-seven years which have elapsed since I began to study anthropology, the advance in detailed and accurate methods of observation has been enormous and the accumulation of reliable factual data has been mountainous (not, I hasten to say, on account of any prodigious contributions on my part). In all of this time I cannot see that we have made any very substantial advance on the theoretical side, or that we are much more enlightened on the subject of the causes and methods of evolution. For example, we are still completely at a loss to explain satisfactorily the difficulty about the inheritance of adaptations. We know that the organism in its individual life span has a remarkable power of modifying its various parts, or, in being modified, to fulfill the functions necessary for its survival and that of the species. Yet a great deal of patient experimental work, carried on by extraordinarily ingenious and accurate biologists, has yielded almost no evidence that such individually acquired adaptations can be hereditarily transmitted. The data to the contrary are almost overwhelming. Nevertheless, any survey of a palaeontological series drives one to the conclusion that in some way or other evolution is essentially an adaptational process, in which advantageous modifications get into the germ plasm and are perpetuated. Of course, Darwin's theory of natural selection is intellectually satisfying as an explanation of this phenomenon. But when we attempt to apply it to individual morphological details, we are baffled by lack of evidence. I can point to many anatomical features of man in which the known course of evolution can be explained plausibly by the theory of natural selection, but I do not know of one in which it can be proved.

De Vries' mutation theory, involving the concept of abrupt

evolutionary changes which are hereditary, proves to be very dis-
appointing in the light of experimental evidence, since nearly all
mutations are deleterious and unfavorable. Certainly, I do not
know of a single human feature which can be stated definitely to
be a progressive and dominant mutation.

Mendelian inheritance, which once looked so simple and beautiful, turns out to be such an intricate business, involving such a
multiplicity of factors, that its application to man is as yet confined, for the most part, to the inheritance of a few diseases, malformations, and anomalies. Even in these cases the data are usually
not conclusive, and the positive affirmations of hopeful geneticists
have to be bolstered up with a certain amount of faith. Of course,
there is no real doubt of the validity of Mendelian inheritance,
but we cannot work it out for ordinary human physical features,
or, at least, we have not as yet done so.

Let not the reader interpret these admissions as the wails of a
sour, disillusioned, and frustrated anthropologist. I am really very
optimistic about the possibilities of finding out these things; but I
am also convinced that science pursues a foolish and possibly fatal
policy when it tries to keep up its bluff of omniscience in matters
of which it is still woefully ignorant. Sooner or later the intelligent
public is going to call that bluff, as it has already done in the case
of the religious experts, the economists, the "statesmen," and other
deflated specialists. We can progress in our knowledge of man only
by admitting its woeful inadequacy and by howling for help. We
need a great many more minds to work upon these problems, and,
if I may say so, much better minds.

In the following section I shall deal with some of the factual and
theoretical implications of recent studies of evolutionary development at the subhuman levels—among our lowly primate congeners.
To tell the truth, I am more than a little disturbed at the prevalent
anthropological habit of straining at factual gnats and swallowing
(without a gulp or a wink) theoretical camels. It is even possible
that this eccentricity of functioning on the part of the mental gul-
let may extend to other types of biologists. I insinuate nothing with
regard to social scientists, because I think that social science is like
a Welsh rabbit—not really a rabbit at all.

6.

FRESH VIEWS OF PREHUMAN PROBLEMS[1]

ONE may well begin with some new angles from which recent observers have viewed prehuman problems. These are zoölogical angles rather than mathematical angles. Nevertheless, some of them are acute and others are obtuse. The first problem which may be viewed thus askance is that of the origin of the primates. (I refer to the zoölogical order rather than to the ecclesiastical order.) The research of the last two decades has aroused suspicion that the primates had an origin which was at once lowly and lofty—lowly because they appeared to have sprung from primitive and timorous insectivores, lofty because these insectivores in some previous incarnation had been chased up a tree. There they remained, supposedly, cutting down their litters and their claws, sacrificing philoprogenitiveness for security, and efficiency in scratching for facility in gripping with opposable thumbs and great toes. In the fullness of

[1] Extracts from the thirteenth annual Sigma Xi lecture, given at a joint session of the American Association for the Advancement of Science and the Society of Sigma Xi, Pittsburgh, Pa., December 28, 1934. Reprinted from *Science*, July 12, 1935, Vol. 82, No. 2115, pages 19-31.

time and species gestation, some ambiguous and generalized insectivore was suspected to have given birth to a primate. And believe it or not, this adventure in obstetrics was accomplished by an animal whose static collateral descendant is called a tree shrew (a designation which seems to have been a sort of *ex post facto* prophecy of the articulate gift of that ultimate primate, woman).

However, this simple view has been challenged by the recent ruminations of comparative anatomists. Thus W. E. Le Gros Clark has lately reached the conclusion that the tree shrews must be recognized not as progenitors of the primates, but rather as early secessionists from a primitive primate stock which had already spawned proto-lemuroids.[2] Thereby a mother is degraded to a niece. Some of you may have swallowed our alleged affinity with the anthropoid apes without even a gulp, may have choked down our putative relationship to the regrettably obscene monkey, but may have gagged over the glassy-eyed, frozen-faced lemur, which suggests the product of some unhallowed alliance between a degenerate fox and a libertine marmoset. For these, if such there be, I have a word of cheer. Le Gros Clark and other meticulous primatologists have summarily banished from the assemblage of our ancestors the lemur, the loris and all their ilk. This means that it is no longer "legitimate" to speak of a "lemuroid" phase in the evolutionary history of the Anthropoidea, which include monkeys, apes and man. You may well inquire whose tree it is upon which our simian forbears have perched. The answer is *"Tarsius spectrum."* Who then is this Tarsius who comes knocking for admission to the genealogical order of Daughters of the Human Evolution? The contemporary animal is the size of a small rat, with a furry body terminated by a long tail bare in the middle and hairy at both ends. It has monstrous eyes, seemingly directed forward, very large ears and a pinched and retracted snout. Its ankle bones are enormously elongated (whence the name Tarsius). It hops on its hind legs like a miniature kangaroo. The five digits of its hands and feet are provided with sucker disks; the thumb and the great toe are opposable to the other digits; the second and third toes are clawed. Tarsius is arboreal and nocturnal; it produces one young at a birth and feeds itself with its hands. This otherwise somewhat eccentric animal, found today only in the Indo-Malayan Archipel-

[2] Clark, W. E. Le Gros, *Early Forerunners of Man*, p. 250. London, 1934.

ago, has become the storm center of a zoölogical controversy. It displays a certain number of features suggestive of a real affinity with the higher primates—among them the absence of a moist muzzle, the conformation of the external genitalia, the form of the incisor and premolar teeth, the type of the placenta, the tubular shape of the auditory meatus, *et cetera*. In some other features it is related to the lemurs or merely "apes the apes." [3] Particularly because Tarsius sits erect, feeds itself with its hands, has a short snout, frontally directed eyes and a brain in some respects well-developed, ingenious anatomists have made it the hero of a sort of scientific Just So story of primate evolution. Thus hopping and squatting on the hind limbs encourages an upright body poise and "emancipates" the fore limbs. These pentadactyl extremities, clawless and with opposable thumbs, can investigate the animal's whole corporeal entity and adjacent objects of the external world. They can be used to lift things toward the eyes for visual examination, toward the nose for olfaction and toward the mouth for tasting, chewing and swallowing. In short, these emancipated hands become not only mere conveyors of nourishment, but instruments of research and investigation and the potential creators of tools and all the appurtenances of material culture. However, the mere prehensile function of the hands is of small import in comparison with the secondary effects of this new usage upon other organs. The exploratory digits relieve the snout of its tactile function; the feeding fingers absolve the jaws from grazing duties; the protrusive muzzle recedes, and the laterally directed eyes (apparently in a strabismic effort to ascertain the fate of the vanishing snout) swivel round to the front so that the fields of vision converge. The animal can now look down its nose to examine with stereoscopic clarity and depth the object presented by its prehensile hands. The recession of the overbalancing jaws gives poise to the head and facilitates rotary movements, so that parts of the body previously invisible are presented to the sight, as well as being accessible for palpation. Sound waves are now caught by turning the head instead of cocking the ears; the latter curl up. As the jaws shrink, the temporal muscles relax their constricting grip upon the skull vault, and reluctantly retreat down the parietals. This of course gives the brain its chance. But the modest yet ambitious neopallium has other

[3] Clark, Le Gros, *op. cit.*, p. 265.

incentives for expansion. The investigative digits seek and acquire in the brain cortex not only motor representation but also adjacent areas of pictured movements; now the animal can not only see what it is doing but can also recall to the mind's eye past actions and can even build castles in the air. Naturally association areas then spread like a rash; the neopallium becomes furrowed with thought; the brow bulges with cerebration. All this we owe to Tarsius—a humble primate Prometheus. If you are a functionalist, you may thumb your nose at the specter of Weismann, and accept as your ancestor this spectral tarsier thumbing its way along the ascending road of evolution—hopping toward humanity. A slight difficulty may indeed obtrude itself when one considers certain specializations of this, our ratlike ancestrix. We ought with such a pedigree to have the gait and pedal extremities of a kangaroo, and eyes like teacups, millstones or towers—such as those possessed by the three marvelous dogs in Hans Andersen's story, "The Tinderbox." For it appears that even the earliest fossil tarsioids exhibit evidence of enlarged orbits and elongated ankles. Here, forsooth, we find ourselves impaled upon the horns of a dilemma: either we are descended from a tarsioid which had not yet become specialized for hopping and had refrained from orbital exaggeration, or else our tarsioid or subsequent ancestors have violated the law of the irreversibility of evolution. In the former case we are indeed lost, because if there was no hopping there could have been no handling, no hand feeding, no cortical representation, no Anthropoidea, no *Homo sapiens*. In the latter case we dare not face the palaeontologists.

As a matter of fact, it is comparatively simple to evade both of these difficulties. In the first place we need not accept literally the Lamarckian lucubrations of Professors Elliot Smith and Wood Jones, whereby Tarsius in merely sitting up initiates a train of motor cause and cortical effect which inevitably leads onward to humanity. The only existing primate of certain tarsioid ancestry is the diminutive goggle-eyed beast of Borneo, which is apparently no farther away from man than the most of the twenty fossil species of Eocene tarsioids. The dogfaced baboon is not only an inveterate hand-feeder but also a confirmed quadruped, which has either redeveloped a prodigious snout in utter defiance of the law of irreversibility or, having preserved and enlarged a primitive primate snout, has nevertheless managed to rotate his eyes around to a frontal plane and to achieve stereoscopic vision, with a complete disregard of the views of Professor Frederic Wood Jones.

The so-called law of the irreversibility of evolution is easy to circumvent by a sophistry which enables the palaeontologist or zoölogist to include in man's ancestral line the fossil precursors of almost any primate, however specialized its modern descendants. Thus in the case of tarsioids it is merely necessary to state that man's ancestors have sprung from a generalized proto-tarsioid stock which had not yet developed the evolutionary specializations, which would rule the modern tarsier and most fossil tarsioids out of the human line of descent. In this way the zoölogical genealogist manages both to eat his cake and to have it.

Another convenient device much used in evolutionary dialectics is known as the "law of convergent or parallel evolution." This law affirms that similar or identical variations may be developed independently in unrelated forms "which happen to be subjected to similar environmental forces." [4] Citation of this law enables the fabricator of family trees to dismiss as irrelevant and illusory all morphological similarities in those animals which he wishes to exclude from close relationship to man. Wielding the law of irreversibility of evolution in one hand, and that of convergent evolution in the other, the brain trusters of the zoölogical New Deal can excommunicate from the assemblage of man's ancestors any unfortunate stock of which the contemporary representatives seem undesirable poor relations. Conversely, by a skillful blending of motifs upon the same two instruments, the pied pipers of primatology lead off ratlike tarsiers and godlike men in one genealogical rout. Hence the mere anthropologist remains unimpressed when Professor Wood Jones in a single burst of zoölogical rhetoric reads out of man's party the tree shrews, the lemurs, all the monkeys and even the anthropoid apes. However, even the ardent advocates of parallelism and irreversibility are ill content to leave man out on the end of a limb with no company in his family tree except that of a nebulous, nocturnal tarsier.

Yet, apart from the heresy of Wood Jones, who has seceded in a body from orthodox opinion as to man's descent, other minor dissensions have arisen in the ranks—voiced at times by major dissentients. Thus we have to deal with the growing heresy which

[4] Clark, Le Gros, *op. cit.*, p. 5.

maintains that man is not descended from a giant brachiating ape, but from some small ground-walking anthropoid which had abandoned tree life and cut himself off from relationship with the arboreal ancestors of the great apes as far back as the Oligocene period. This infant Ishmael seems to owe his existence principally to an unhappy afterthought of Professor Dudley J. Morton, added to his otherwise admirable memoir upon the evolution of the human foot.[5] Morton observed that the mid-tarsal pattern of the gibbon resembles that of the monkeys, whereas in the great apes this region of the foot is decidedly shortened. Man appears with the more primitive pattern of a long mid-tarsal region. Morton therefore infers that man could have avoided the mid-tarsal shortening only by separating from the great ape stock before it occurred. He suggests that the shortening of the mid-tarsal region in the great apes has been the effect of the attainment of a great body bulk, the weight of which has crushed the mid-tarsal bones, and that man gained this great increase in size after he had adapted the use of his foot so that the crushing effect of body-weight would not be exerted upon the mid-tarsal area. Dr. Morton further concludes that "the retention of the more primitive mid-tarsal pattern supplies evidence of three phases in man's history; the early attainment of the erect posture, separation from the great ape stock before it had attained its modern large size and early adoption of terrestrial habits." This sweeping conclusion has been greeted with acclaim by the protagonists of the Homunculus theory, *i.e.*, the diminutive dawn man. For my part, I see no reason why "Wolff's law" of atrophy and hypertrophy, which Dr. Morton frequently invokes, should turn a somersault by "crushing" the mid-tarsal region when the bodily weight is transmitted to it, although enlarging the heelbone when the bodily weight rests upon the latter. If one insists upon crying "Wolf! Wolf!" when there probably is none, one may as easily ascribe the supposed shortening of great apes' mid-tarsal region to adaptation for greater mobility in grasping; or to atrophy as a result of these animals' brachiating habits, whereby they suspend the weight from the hands rather than rest it upon the feet.

On the whole it seems to me that it is most unsafe to attempt to determine degrees of phylogenetic relationship solely by the

[5] Morton, Dudley J., *Am. Jour. Phys. Anthrop.*, V: 4, 305-336, 1922; VII: 1, 1-52, 1924. *Cf.* especially p. 36.

examination of resemblances and differences in such a highly adapted organ as the foot. The only safe bases for reckoning affinity are hereditary, non-adaptive variations of organs in which form is not closely dependent upon function. The foot and the pelvis in man are perhaps of all skeletal parts the most rigorously adapted to human bodily habits and to functional needs. By virtue of such stringent adaptation they are the least suitable structures from which to deduce phylogenetic conclusions. Zoölogical classification should never rest upon the evidence of any single anatomical character, however important, but always upon the cumulative testimony of as many non-adaptive hereditary features as can be marshaled for examination. Beware of special pleaders who would chart the course of primate evolution by the use of a compass whose needle points always to the same magnetic pole—whether it be the tarsus, the tympanic ring, the frontal sinus, the placenta or the pattern of molar teeth! Gifted persons may conjure rabbits out of silk hats or *Homo sapiens* from a hopping tarsier, but though the hand may be quicker than the eye, no one need believe that the topper has conceived a bunny.

It is with relief that one turns from the school of prestidigitative or saltatory evolutionists to the tortoisian plodders who escort our postulated progressive primate to the goal of humanity by a slower and less spectacular, but surer route. As the heavyweight champion of the great ape theory of human descent, we may acclaim Dr. William King Gregory, who has suffered the bludgeonings of Wood Jones and the pro-tarsioids and has emerged with head not only unbowed, but not even perceptibly bloody. Dr. Gregory neglects no biological system which may furnish evidence apposite to the solution of the problem. He makes a clean sweep through the whole range of vertebrate evolution. Although he displays an astounding familiarity with all the minutiae of vertebrate anatomy, Professor Gregory is perhaps most intimate with the development of the skull and the teeth. He is indeed such a consummate master of odontology that, were we to start anew with a planned, controlled and supervised organic evolution, we should without doubt entrust to him the destiny of dentition, merely stipulating that he devise this time a less cumbersome and misleading terminology. In his most recent monograph entitled "A Half Century of Trituberculy" (which is not to be mistaken for the autobiography of a trebly afflicted unfortunate), Dr. Gregory convincingly describes eleven stages of molar tooth development leading from primitive fish to modern man, the ninth or anthropoid ape stage giving rise to a five-cusped lower molar with a so-called Dryopithecus pattern of cusps and grooves, which is preserved in the first molars of most primitive and many modern men. Gregory considers the evolution of the locomotor skeleton, the jaws and teeth, the face and the brain-case, carrying the story of each from the early vertebrate forms up to the human culmination, all themes of the various narratives leading to the conclusion that man developed in late Tertiary times from a giant, brachiating, arboreal ape of a generalized Dryopithecus type. Dryopithecus is the name of a family of anthropoid apes represented by numerous fossil jaws and teeth from the Miocene and Pliocene deposits in Europe, Africa and Asia. Unfortunately the remains are usually restricted to jaws and teeth, because these are the most durable parts of the skeleton. But a femur from the Lower Pliocene in Germany, referred to Dryopithecus, apparently represents the anthropoid thigh bone before it was affected by giantism, and is long and slender like that of a gibbon. Schlosser could discover in it nothing that would forbid its giving rise to the more specialized and shortened femora of the great apes or to the hypertrophied thigh-bone of an upright bipedal man. Moreover, the humerus supposed to belong to this same early anthropoid ape is shorter than the femur, contrary to the condition in the modern specialized great apes.

An important discovery of the past decade is that of the skull of a juvenile anthropoid ape at Taungs, Bechuanaland, South Africa. This specimen consists of most of the face and forehead and a cast of a portion of the brain. Professor Raymond Dart, the describer, gave it a place between the highest anthropoid apes and the lowest grades of humanity. Sir Arthur Keith has concluded that this fossil, Australopithecus, was an ape with a closer resemblance to the chimpanzee than to the gorilla, but a cousin form to both.[6] Nevertheless, in the volume of the brain, in the reduced size of the milk canine and in the persistence of certain infantile traits, Keith thinks that this ape approaches nearer to the human prototype than any form heretofore discovered.

[6] Keith, Sir Arthur, *New Discoveries Relating to the Antiquity of Man*, pp. 37-116, New York, 1932.

In the summer of 1936 Dr. Robert Broom, a distinguished South African palaeontologist and anthropologist, found the larger part of the skull of an adult fossil anthropoid ape probably belonging to the same genus as the Taungs ape. The specimens were blasted out of ancient cave debris in the lime works at Sterkfontein, near Krugersdorp in the Transvaal. A brain-cast, skull base, part of the face and upper jaw with three teeth were recovered. The brain of this ape, probably an adult female, may have had a capacity of 600 c.c., which is larger than that of the average adult gorilla. The teeth (three in number) are beautifully preserved and of the greatest interest. The socket for the canine (which is missing) shows that this tooth was relatively small. The first molar is fairly large and displays characteristics reminiscent both of the Pliocene anthropoid *Dryopithecus rhenanus* and of Neanderthal man. The second and third molars are much larger than those of man or of any living ape except the gorilla.

Dr. Broom thinks that the Sterkfontein ape was more closely allied to the Dryopithecus family of the Miocene and Pliocene than to the existing chimpanzees and gorillas, but that it also displays a number of human characters. The other fossil mammals in the deposit indicate that the age is probably Upper Pleistocene, as contrasted with that of the earlier Taungs discovery, which is probably Lower or Middle Pleistocene. Dr. Broom states: "It seems moderately certain that during the greater part of the Pleistocene, and possibly during the Pliocene, large, non-forest-living anthropoids flourished in South Africa, and not improbably it was from one of the Pliocene members of this group that the first man was evolved." [7]

Of no less importance are the specimens of fossil apes recovered by Dr. Hellmut de Terra from the Siwalik deposits of North India. Preliminary reports have been made by G. Edward Lewis,[8] while detailed studies are being conducted by Doctors Gregory and Hellman. These finds include several new genera and species which, in the shape of the dental arch, the reduction of the canines, the absence of diastemata, or gaps, are said to approach so closely to the human type that they may well be near the stem which led

[7] Broom, Robert S. "A New Ancestral Link between Ape and Man," *The Illustrated London News*, p. 476, September 19, 1936.
[8] Lewis, Edward G., *Am. Jour. Sci.*, XXVII: 161-179, March, 1934.

to the Hominidae proper. Such finds raise high hopes that we may yet discover the remains of that miraculous evolutionary deviant among the apes, which eventually foisted upon the faunal world Huxley's erect and featherless biped.

A few years ago Dr. S. Zuckerman published a fascinating work on the functional affinities of man and the other primates.[9] He has assembled the evidence relating to differentiation of the mechanism of reproduction, blood reactions, visual and olfactory processes, behavior patterns, diseases and parasites, affinity and divergence as shown by hybridization, psychological measures of intelligence, implications of cortical physiology. Zuckerman concludes:

Man's immediate phyletic relationship to the ancestors of the anthropoid group of Primates cannot be doubted, unless it be argued that he developed the same blood groups, the same serum proteins, and the same peculiarities in purine metabolism independently of the anthropoids.[10]

Nevertheless, after an impartial review of the physiological evidence, he feels that it is impossible, in our present state of knowledge, to determine whether man's divergence from the common anthropoid-humanoid stock took place in the Oligocene before the present great apes had differentiated or at some subsequent period. For he points out that such physiological peculiarities as the blood groups, which man shares with the anthropoids, seem most probably to have developed independently in the different stocks, and are therefore due to convergent or parallel evolution and orthogenetic evolution within the confines of a natural subgroup.

In the past two decades experimental psychologists have become ape-conscious, and one of our great universities has been a pioneer in the recognition of the academic status of the chimpanzee. There has been accumulated a mass of experimental data tending to show that monkeys and apes differ from other mammals in that the former manifest a characteristic called "insight," which implies a complete solution of an experimental problem as a result of a general survey of the entire layout. This behavior with "insight"

---

[9] Zuckerman, S., *Functional Affinities of Man, Monkeys and Apes*, New York, 1933.
[10] Zuckerman, S., *op. cit.*, p. 169.

is contrasted with the "trial and error" methods generally believed
to be characteristic of lower animals. Gradually an edifice has been
built up which seems to start with the inferior intelligence of rats
in the basement and to progress upward story by story until it
reaches the almost human faculties of the anthropoids on the roof,
man with his supreme endowment hovering over all. Thus Yerkes
and Yerkes in 1929 were able to conclude their colossal work upon
the great apes with a formidable list of psychological contrasts
between primate types:

phylogenetic differences in behavioral expressions of curiosity, interest, attention, emotion, mood, sentiment; confidence in man and
intelligent co-operation with him, rapidity and extent of adaptation to captivity; diversity and complexity of receptivity, sensibility, and perception, functional importance of contact senses,
degree of value and dominance of hearing and vision; analysis and
synthesis of mental objects; vocalization, approach to speech, inter-
communication by visual and auditory signs and symbols; diversity
of actions in problematic situations; frequency and importance of
accidental (trial and error) adaptations; ability to perceive and
react adaptively to relations (structure-function) *versus* familiar
objects; insight, understanding, anticipation, expectation, disap-
pointment, foresight; preadaptation; temporal span and complexity
of memory; creative imagination, versatility, ingenuity, inventive-
ness, constructivity; adaptive modification of environment, modification of other organs by tuition or instruction, use of objects as
instruments, construction or fashioning of implements.

Some of these phenomena are observable in all primates, some in
all except the Prosimiae, others only in ape and man, and a few
in man alone. Usually vast gulfs separate the types, and with a few
exceptions the indicated or definitely demonstrated trend of development and serviceability is from lemur to man.[11, 12]

Unfortunately even this grand and towering structure has been
scarred recently by bullets of revolutionary and communistic
snipers who will have none of this primate hierarchy. Thus Zuckerman points out that the term insight is no explanation of behavior,
but simply an aid to description which leads nowhere if too much

[11] Yerkes, R. M., and Yerkes, A. L., *The Great Apes*, p. 578, New Haven, 1929.
[12] This quotation recalls Huckleberry Finn's comment upon Bunyan's *Pilgrim's Progress:* "The statements was interesting, but tough."

reliance is placed upon it.[13] It is rather disconcerting to discover that behavior with insight, so far from being an exclusive prerogative of higher primates, is also characteristic of cats, dogs and even of rats. It is even more discouraging to learn that an ordinary American monkey tested by Dr. Haan seemed to be no less intelligent than the chimpanzee and much more so than the gorilla, orang, and gibbon. Various other investigators, whose work is summarized by Zuckerman, have apparently found that there is no exact positive correlation between zoölogical status within the primates and so-called measures of "intelligence."

On the whole, then, it would appear that the labors of paleontologists, comparative anatomists and psychologists have not yet led to any precise determination of man's relationship to individual genera and species of the primate order. No primate with a properly developed instinct of self-preservation would be willing to entrust his weight to any of their zoölogical family trees.

For myself, a naïve physical anthropologist, the way still seems comparatively straight and plain. I adhere to the old-fashioned belief that the more numerous and detailed the resemblances between two animals the closer the relationship between them. Effects of similarity or difference of habitus can not obscure man's fundamental likeness to the great anthropoid apes, and especially to the gorilla and the chimpanzee. I therefore persist in the opinion that these two apes are our nearest collateral relatives, and as yet am aware of no convincing evidence which conflicts with the theory that the gibbon was an early deviant from a small and primitive generalized anthropoid ape stock; that the main line of anthropoid-humanoid development continued at least into the Miocene period, when giantism began to affect simultaneously the diversifying strains of these arboreal apes. Then it would appear that the ancestors of the orang-utan first began their course of evolutionary divergence, leading ultimately to a rigid specialization for slow brachiating. For some time thereafter it seems probable that the ancestors of man and the African apes pursued similar evolutionary courses, until accident or initiative (and I favor the latter explanation) led the protohuman stock to take its chance on the ground. This radical change of habitus must have taken place before our ancestors had undergone any of the excessive specializations con-

[13] Zuckerman, S., *op. cit.*

sequent upon brachiation, which have involved the hypertrophy of the upper limbs and comparative atrophy of the lower limbs in contemporaneous great apes. But I see no reason for supposing that the descent to the ground occurred before the latter part of the Miocene period, when man had already stamped upon his molar crowns the indelible sign of his Dryopithecus heritage.

7.

TEETH THROUGH TIME[1]

TEETH tell the tale of human evolution better than any other
bodily structure. No, I have not forgotten brains. But we do not
understand the evolution of the human brain. Our brains are apparently much too big for the use we make of them. Certainly,
neither we nor our immediate or remote ancestors have taken
thought sufficiently to add many cubic centimeters to our cranial
capacities. Yet here we are—all decked out in our $7\frac{1}{4}$ hats—and
no place to go. We have less reason to be proud of our brains than
to be ashamed of our teeth.

Teeth seem to be a distasteful subject for popular consideration.
They are unpleasantly reminiscent of the apprehensive minutes
spent in the dental waiting room with the futile distraction of back
numbers of cheery periodicals—and other far worse experiences.
Yet our teeth have had an illustrious past; they have a serviceable
present, and with due conservation they will continue to perform

[1] Originally published under the title "Apes, Men, and Teeth." Reprinted from *The
Scientific Monthly*, January, 1934, Vol. XXXVIII, pages 24-34.

an indispensable function in the future of man. But if the human dentition breaks down, it will carry with it in its fall the human species.

You must know the history of the teeth in order to appreciate them, and because this history epitomizes human evolution. The control of future human evolution is now in man's own hands—or perhaps rather in his teeth.

Short History of Teeth

Teeth are the most nearly imperishable relics of the vertebrate body. If an animal's teeth last until death, they will continue to defy the destructive action of time and the elements—sometimes for millions of years. After death the soft parts of the animal body decay rapidly. The bones are much tougher. But bones are frequently crushed into dust or dissolved by the action of chemicals in the earth. Furthermore, they are often and perhaps usually devoured by carnivorous animals for which they are a *bonne bouche*. But teeth are singularly unpalatable and indigestible morsels. No animal eats them or, if it does, manages to digest them. They remain as monuments of extinct species. This is peculiarly fortunate for the student of evolution, since the teeth are not only the most durable, but also the most instructive of bodily parts.

Teeth are derived from scales—as are also nails and hair. In the shark—one of the most primitive of existing vertebrates—the skeleton is still cartilaginous rather than bony, and the teeth are rows of modified and sharp-pointed scales which succeed each other in series, a fresh row rising up to take the place of its worn-out predecessor. But in some sharks the teeth form a sort of continuous and blunt pavement. The kind of teeth which grow up in successive rows are laterally compressed cones with cutting edges, at the base of which two or more smaller cones may be developed. But in one existing and several extinct groups the hinder teeth have already developed blunt crowns for crushing the food. Sharks are next to the oldest fishes known, and first appear in the Devonian period—far back in the Primary era (350 million years ago, according to most recent radio-active scales of time).

It is hardly necessary to state that teeth are primarily for the purpose of grasping food and biting it off, and secondarily for the purpose of chopping or crushing it up into pieces small enough

to be swallowed and digested. The mouth of an animal naturally
is situated at the head end, in which the sense organs and nervous
system are concentrated. This end goes first and the intake of food
is conveniently at the prow or snout and the outgo of waste products at the stern or tail. A primitive vertebrate needs some sort of
snout or projection of the facial skeleton to carry the smelling and
biting apparatus well in advance of the visual organs. It is desirable
to get one's teeth and even one's nose into his food, if one is a
grazing animal—but never the eyes. So the snout is an ancient
vertebrate inheritance—rendered obsolete only by hand-feeding in
the primates and man. A long snout generally goes with a shortage
of brains, over-emphasis of the sense of smell in brain area, and a
generally inferior zoölogical position.

In the Devonian period, 350 millions of years ago or more, there
also appear progressive bony fishes with teeth sharply differentiated
in form from scales, covering the margins and inner sides of the
jaws and the roof of the mouth. The marginal teeth are pointed
with complexly infolded bases. These teeth are now often set in
sockets.

The most primitive teeth, such as the shark possesses, are of a
predatory grasping type. In later and more evolved fishes the jaws
become adapted for various purposes—nibbling, grinding, sucking,
and the like.

The first land-living, air-breathing vertebrates seem to have developed from the lungfishes of the Middle Devonian. This group of
lungfishes is represented today by a few degenerate survivors in
Africa, Australia and South America, some of which come up to
the surface to take an occasional gulp of air, while others breathe
exclusively through the lungs during the dry season, being immured in a sort of cocoon in the mud. Thus the first breathing may
have been done in a mud hut. The teeth are the same as before—
with elaborately infolded bases.

Apparently as far back as the middle of the Devonian period
some of these lungfishes got to living permanently on land, breathing continuously by means of lungs instead of gills, and crawling
around some way or other by using their paired pectoral and pelvic
fins as paddles, props, and eventually as limbs. Just how the fins
developed into limbs is still a mystery—but they did. The teeth
changed very little. So the amphibians, the first four-footed, air-

breathing vertebrates, came into being. They still had strong predatory jaws with sharp pointed teeth—capable, however, of deploying into various specializations of types for crushing shelled invertebrates, herbivorous diet, fish-catching, et cetera.

The first reptiles developed from amphibians in the Carboniferous period, principally by getting rid of the tadpole stage characteristic of the latter. For the eggs of amphibians are laid in the water, and the young at first breathe through gills and only in adult stages become air-breathing and land-dwelling. Reptiles, on the contrary, lay their eggs on land, and the young are lung-breathers from birth. Reptiles must have come upon the stage some 200 millions of years ago.

In some of the early but progressive forms the teeth have begun to lose their infolded bases and have tended to become simple peg-like cones, embedded in sockets, and all alike—fore and aft. The primitive reptile forms seem to have been more or less predatory and carnivorous. The process of differentiation of teeth into different forms according to their location in the jaws had already begun. Obviously, the teeth at the front end of the jaws should be shaped for cutting and piercing, because that is the end of the jaws with which bites must be taken. These anterior teeth sweep through a greater arc and with a greater velocity than the back teeth. At the corners of the jaw the primitive reptilian peg-like form tends to be preserved in the canines or tusks—used for piercing and holding—and the front teeth may be modified into chisel forms for cutting—the incisors. The farther back in the jaw the teeth are, the greater the leverage of the jaws and the more force may be brought to bear upon the teeth. These, however, move through a smaller arc than the front teeth. Consequently, they are better adapted for crushing and grinding. If you have lost your back teeth, you realize that chewing with the front teeth is both public and ineffective.

Some of these early reptiles began to be suspiciously like mammals. Instead of going on their bellies, or waddling with their knees and elbows bent and thrust out sideways from the body, they managed to get their fore and hind legs well under their bodies, straightened them a bit, perhaps, and really were progressive. They "got going." They had two sets of teeth—not simultaneously, but successively—even as you and I. One of these was a milk set to carry on with while their jaws were growing, the other a "permanent" set which was supposed to last them the rest of their lives —and probably did, contrary to our common experience. The mammal-like reptiles did not content themselves with monotonous rows of peg teeth, but boasted incisors, canines, premolars and molars—in fact, all the recognized and respectable varieties. If you do not believe this, go to South Africa and dig up a Therapsid from the Triassic beds. No doubt any one there can direct you.

From these advanced and progressive mammal-like reptiles—not slimy, crawling marsh denizens, but dry land-dwellers—the mammals evolved in the Triassic period. Throughout the Age of Reptiles (say from 200,000,000 B.C. to 60,000,000 B.C.—a few millions more or less, if you like) mammals apparently remained wretched and insignificant little creatures, of small importance in the zoölogical world. They were lying low. Probably the earliest of them were insectivorous. They seem to have had four incisors, one canine, five premolars and six molars, on each side above and below. Probably the molar teeth had already begun to take on a three-cusped triangular form—suitable for crushing bugs.

At any rate, in some fashion or other, the molar teeth became broadened for grinding and developed in the upper jaw three cones or cusps and in the lower three cusps and a crushing basin, so that the upper and lower teeth efficiently interlocked for chewing purposes.[2]

Because they were puny and crafty—or modest and self-effacing —these small insectivorous mammals skulked in the underbrush and slunk out of the way of the giant reptiles of the Secondary Era, biding their time until they should develop into the masters of the world. This period of incipient and suppressed mammals seems to have lasted for about 140 million years—until 60 millions of years ago, according to radio-active time scales. During this long interval the tiny mammals developed in various directions in bodily form and tooth adaptations, but the stock which gave rise to the primates (lemurs, tarsiers, monkeys, apes and man) was arboreal. It is represented today by the primitive tree-shrews.

---

[2] This may seem unimportant to you, but just stop to consider. If you are unable to chew your food properly, you must either subsist on soft fodder and "slops" or swallow large gobbets, thereby putting a huge task upon your digestive apparatus. Simultaneous digestion and cerebration are incompatible. If you spend all your time digesting, you will never learn to think.

Here I must descant upon the advantages of arboreal life for a small mammal. The forest nursery offers a comparatively safe existence. Large predatory carnivores find it unprofitable to chase the small animal up trees. The agile climber is secure, providing he does not fall out of the tree. He can eat leaves, shoots, nuts, fruits, birds' eggs and insects and birds, if he can catch them. Nests may be built and the young comfortably reared. But more than this, arboreal life puts a premium on sight. Smell is the most important sense for a small ground animal, both for finding food and for avoiding enemies. The snout is both an olfactory and a tactile organ. The little animal "noses its way" through life. But supposing he climbs a tree! Smelling becomes relatively unimportant, acuity of hearing is not so essential as on the ground. But the arboreal animal must "keep its eyes peeled"!

The insect-eating pre-primates had long snouts with moist muzzles, eyes laterally directed, five digits on the hands and feet, two incisors, one canine, four premolars and three molars on each side, above and below. They were small quadruped climbers, long of tails and short of brains, with dietetic habits which extended to fruits, leaves, shoots and nuts as well as insects.

From these humble little brutes sprang the primates, at the beginning of the Tertiary Epoch, 60 millions of years ago. At first there was nothing higher than lemurs—small arboreal cat-like animals whose descendants may still be seen in the forests of Madagascar, Africa and the Indo-Malayan region (or in the better zoölogical gardens). The lemur, however, represents a considerable advance over the insectivore.

Lemurs are omnivorous. Pause and contemplate the advantages of being able to eat almost anything. (If you live in a boarding-house, you know this already.) In the struggle for existence, it often means survival. Even in human society a good digestion and an ability to eat all kinds of food is better than riches or even intelligence. The modern lemurs have lower incisor teeth which lean forward and are supposed to be used for combing their fur; [3] they have three premolars and three molars. Apparently, when the teeth become differentiated and the diet is generalized, fewer teeth avail

---

[3] Dr. Russell Stein has recently destroyed this hoary tradition of the fur-combing lower incisors of the lemurs. The incisors are so close together that the fur will not go between the teeth of the alleged comb.

the animal. The earliest lemuroids are found in the Eocene in North America—the first of the Tertiary geological deposits. Now we have to look for them in out-of-the-way tropical forests in the Old World.

The tarsioids are little cousins of the lemurs—geologically about as old and in structure almost as primitive, but they were more progressive and upstanding, or rather upsitting. These tarsiers went right on eating everything they could find in the trees and remained unspecialized in teeth, but began to specialize in eyesight, in tactile sense, perhaps even in common sense. At any rate, the habit of hand-feeding, the shorter snout, the better vision and larger brain are all inextricably evolved in the organism of the little omnivorous animal. The tarsier is the infant prodigy of the Primates.

Out of some primitive but progressive tarsioid of the Eocene period (some 55 millions of years ago) there evolved the stocks which have led to the higher Primates (monkeys, apes and man). We may profitably pause to consider very briefly a tiny fossil monkey, named Parapithecus, found in the lower Oligocene of Egypt (dated about 35 million years ago). This little animal, represented only by a lower jaw and teeth, stands, in the opinion of Professor W. K. Gregory, at or very near the line of descent leading to the anthropoid apes and eventually to man. It may be regarded as a generalized super-tarsioid, or pre-monkey of the Old World. It already has the human dental formula: two incisors, one canine, two premolars and three molars, on each side and in both jaws. It has small and unspecialized canine teeth and blunt premolars and molars which would seem to preclude carnivorous or flesh-eating habits. Its incisors, leaning gently forward, and its low-cusped cheek teeth seem to point to a mixed diet—perhaps insects, fruits, birds' eggs and small reptiles. In fact, it ate hors d'oeuvres, omelette, entrée and dessert. From such an early form the Old World monkeys diverged, specializing in different directions, but in general tending to display an elongation of the canines, useful in fighting and in piercing the rinds of tough fruits, and a pairing of the molar cusps, four in each tooth, in groups of two. These molar cusps have now become quadrate, having lost the earlier triangular form.[4]

We need only two more steps in dental evolution to bring us up

[4] But four-course dinners do not necessarily demand four-cusped teeth.

to man, but we have to "step high." The first of these is taken in the most ancient and primitive fossil anthropoid ape—Propliopithecus—again a find of the Lower Oligocene of Egypt. This early anthropoid with the jaw-breaking name may have lived some 35 millions of years ago. Nothing survives of this little ape except a lower jaw with its teeth, but its lower canines were smaller than those of recent gibbons, its snout shorter and its molar teeth less specialized in form. Propliopithecus was no bigger than a human suckling; he was a proto-ape with a small brain and no chin; but that little jaw and those generalized teeth mark out the pattern of development which eventually lead to man. Propliopithecus—not Tut-ankh-Amen—is Egypt's crowning glory.

The final step preceding the arrival at the human plane of dental and general body development may be studied in the remains of the great Dryopithecus family of generalized giant apes, from which it seems most likely that the gorilla, the chimpanzee and man eventually developed as separate modern descendants. This family was flourishing in mid-Miocene times—roughly 14 million years ago. The stems leading to the modern apes of Asia—the gibbon and the orang-utan—had previously diverged from the common anthropoid-human trunk. Jaws of members of the Dryopithecus family clearly show the ancestral pattern of the molar teeth which is found in the chimpanzee, the gorilla and man. These apes had the same number and kinds of teeth as you have, but the lower canines were large and pointed with erect tips. The hinder premolars were bicuspid as yours are. The lower molars were arranged with five main cusps, three on the outside, two on the inside, and sometimes a smaller hinder cusp in the middle. This is Professor Gregory's "Dryopithecus pattern," which is preserved in the molar teeth of most fossil men, of many recent savages and in your first and second lower molars and in mine—if we still have them and are not too degenerate.

We must conceive these generalized precursors of man and the African great apes as large primates with projecting jaws and only moderately large brains, who progressed through the trees by brachiating—swinging by the arms; who had prehensile feet as well as grasping hands. They were probably not specialized in the tremendous elongation of the arms that we observe in the gorilla, the chimpanzee and the orang-utan of today—animals which have displayed the conservatism which limits evolutionary development and which has induced them to remain tree-dwellers, or half-hearted quadrupedal ground-dwellers like the gorilla, long after their size, strength, intelligence and dietary requirements demanded a fuller and richer existence as erect, terrestrial bipeds. Note that man, like Zaccheus, owes his importance to the fact that, having climbed a tree, he straightway came down.

One of these Dryopithecus lines had the supreme gift of super-anthropoid intelligence and initiative. Its members took to the ground and eventually stood up on their hind legs, having developed stable supporting feet from the ancient Primate grasping organs. Their arms and hands were set free for prehension. They began to use weapons and tools—a step which initiated human culture and took the strain off their jaws and teeth, previously employed for offensive and defensive as well as masticatory purposes. Gradually the snout shrank back, and this recession seems to have been accompanied by an overgrowth of the brain. These are associated evolutionary phenomena, but the one did not necessarily cause the other.

Now I am by no means contesting that man developed from a shark purely through shifting the form and function of his teeth —or that he ate himself up to a human status. Nothing that a primate does or does not do with his teeth makes him a man or a gorilla. But I can determine whether you are a man or a gorilla as quickly and correctly by looking at your teeth as by observing any other feature of your anatomy or any item of your behavior. In other words, teeth tell the story of human relationship, but they do not explain why we have this possibly disreputable ancestry. It is there, whether we admit it or not.[5]

The Teeth of Fossil Man

But we must pursue the rise and decline of the human dentition through fossil man and down to modern and degenerate times. The earliest representative of the humanoid stock of which we possess remains is the *Pithecanthropus erectus* of Java—still nearly halfway down to the ape in brain size, but with a thigh bone

[5] Throughout this section I have levied a very heavy toll upon Professor W. K. Gregory's work, "The Origin and Evolution of the Human Dentition," *The Journal of Dental Research*, 1920, 1931.

which indicates that he strode erect through the forests, even as you and I over the pavements. He belongs back in the beginning of the Pleistocene—nearly one million years ago. What kind of teeth had Pithecanthropus? We have only a couple of molars to go by. They are large and with strongly divergent roots and fangs, but they already show some degeneration and cusp reduction which is essentially human and not anthropoid, although one of them recalls to Professor Gregory the fine old Dryopithecus pattern.

Photographs of the Pithecanthropus molars show in at least one a wrinkling of the enamel on the crown highly reminiscent of the teeth of the orang-utan. Recently Dr. Ralph Von Koenigswald has found many teeth of fossil orangs in Java. He considers the Pithecanthropus teeth those of the great Asiatic anthropoid ape.

Somewhat more advanced in brain development than Pithecanthropus are the recently discovered men of the Sinanthropus type, found in deposits of the Lower Pleistocene near Peking, and dating back probably to the early quarter of that period—750,000 years ago. These early Pekinese had jaws with incipient chins—a jump ahead of the chimpanzee, bath-tub shaped jaw. The canines were not projecting as in anthropoid apes. The molar teeth were low-crowned like those of a chimpanzee—the molar cusps in the lower jaw being five in number like the ancient Dryopithecus pattern. Curiously, the front halves of the molar teeth are ultra-human or almost degenerate, and the back halves are ape-like. But the queerest feature of these ancient Chinese teeth is found in the pulp cavities of the molars. The crown of a tooth is the part above the gum; the roots are sunken into the alveolar bony sockets of the jaw. Through the roots run fine canals into a central cavity which is filled with pulp—blood-vessels and nerves. The walls of the pulp cavities are of dentine or cement, and the outer layer of the crown of the tooth is hard enamel. In modern man and the apes the pulp cavities of the molar teeth are small and do not extend down below the crowns. But in Sinanthropus, and in the later Heidelberg and Neanderthaloid races, the pulp cavities are enlarged and the body of the tooth with the pulp cavity is prolonged downward below the alveolar borders of the jaw at the expense of the roots, which are short.

This specialization is called taurodontism, because it occurs in animals which chew the cud. It is exactly the opposite of the cynodont or dog-tooth condition found in the anthropoid apes and in modern man. Must we infer that the ancient precursor in China was a ruminant? I think not. He was probably omnivorous and knew neither rice nor birds' nest soup. But the importance of this specialization is that it seems to remove Sinanthropus, and the other ancient types which show it, from the direct line of descent which leads to modern man. The premature herbivore-like specialization of molar teeth is peculiar to Sinanthropus and the low-browed Heidelbergers and Neanderthaloids.[6]

I do not propose in this chapter to pick over the teeth of every fossil type of man, but merely to jab at a few suspicious and tender spots—marking significant findings—as your dentist does when he is looking for cavities. In general, the successively higher types of fossil man show a decrease and recession of the jaws, a gradual thrusting forth of the chin, and the change of the palate shape from a long, narrow U type found in the apes and associated with snoutiness to a parabolic type in which the dental arches spread from front to back, no doubt in correlation with the increasing breadth of the brain case to which the jaws are hafted. The teeth themselves gradually become smaller, the molars wider and shorter, and the number of cusps tends toward reduction in both upper and lower jaws. The molar teeth also get smaller going from the first back to the third or wisdom tooth, whereas in some fossil types and anthropoid apes they increase in size from front to rear.

Probably the most striking change from the anthropoid ape type to human type has to do with the reduction of the great projecting tusk-like canines, which in apes interlock, stop skidding of the jaws, and effectually prevent the lateral and rotary movements of the jaws which are characteristic of primitive man, but seem to be retained in effete civilization principally among gum-chewing stenographers and tobacco-quid-masticating rustics. It is here that we run upon an unsuspected snag in navigating the little known stream of human dental evolution. For the Piltdown skull, familiarly known as Eoanthropus or the Dawn Lady, unexpectedly turned up in a Lower Pleistocene deposit with a beautifully formed

---

[6] Since this chapter was written, Black, the describer of the Peking skulls, has pointed out that their molar pulp cavities are enlarged at the expense of the crowns rather than the roots. This condition is argued to be primitive and generalized in contrast to the Neanderthal taurodontism.

brain case, complete with high brow and capacious brain, but with a chinless jaw like that of a chimpanzee and a projecting tusk of a canine which belongs in that jaw. The molar teeth of this anomalous and contrary female were low, narrow and long—highly reminiscent of the chimpanzee—and possessing in the mandible the ancestral five-cusped Dryopithecus pattern. But in some important respects they approximate a human type.

Confronted by this highly contradictory combination of ape-like jaw and teeth and wholly human brain case, some anatomical skeptics have attempted to cut the Gordian knot by attributing the advanced brain case to some pre-English Boadicea and the jaw to her pet chimpanzee. However, this view fails to account for the lady's missing mandible and the ape's lost brain case, and is based upon a mistaken idea that the course of human evolution was symmetrical in all parts—that all types advanced harmoniously from the ape to the human form. We know now that human evolution was a multiple and asymmetrical process, involving many different types struggling upward toward humanity, some precocious in one part of the anatomy and laggard in another part, while others displayed reverse combinations in the association of prematurely human and retardedly anthropoidal parts. Thus Pithecanthropus got his human gait and legs before he attained a human size of brain, and Sinanthropus was scarcely human in brain size but prematurely specialized on the human side in certain features of dentition. So we must accept the Piltdown lady as a mysterious compromise who may be in our own ancestral line in spite of her chinless chimpanzee-like jaw and projecting canines. The pulp cavities of her molar teeth, like ours and those of our anthropoid cousins, were not enlarged. Her canines were beginning to shift from the sides of the jaws to the front and she may have been able to chew from the outside in toward the middle, as all good primitive men and women chew. This is a sort of motion which can not be managed by the apes on account of their interlocking canines.

It is sad to relate that fossil men of glacial times already show clear hints of certain dental degeneration. The Ehringsdorf jaw, which may be 500,000 years old or perhaps only 250,000 years, shows definite decrease in size and degeneration of the cusps of the third molar or wisdom tooth. Some of the Neanderthalers have upper third molars with only three cusps instead of the primitive four.

However, the most shocking person in the array of fossil ancestors is the Rhodesian man, dug up in a zinc mine of South Central Africa and equipped with the most gorilla-like beetling bony brow-ridges, the longest face, the largest palate and the worst teeth of antiquity. Not only has this fellow reduced and degenerate wisdom teeth, but nearly all his teeth have been attacked by caries or decay; there were abscesses at the roots of many, and the "danger-line" was riddled with pyorrhea—a septic condition of the gums which leads to eating away of the bony tooth sockets, loosening of the teeth, the entrance of all sorts of poisons into the system through the absorption of pus, to say nothing of "pink toothbrush." This Rhodesian man had an abscessed condition of the mastoid region, which had drained right out through the bone. In fact, he sorely needed a dentist.

The Decline of Human Dentition

Savage or primitive types of modern forms of man have smaller teeth than the fossil men, but their palates are broad and capacious, their incisor teeth meet edge-to-edge in most cases; their molars have four good cusps in the upper jaw and five in the lower, and the third molars are usually not much reduced and not greatly retarded in eruption. The good old Dryopithecus pattern of molar teeth evinces their illustrious ancestry.

Civilized man has smaller teeth and frequently a small contracted palate. Usually the lower incisor teeth bite behind the upper incisors so that the latter overhang, giving rise to an "overbite" and often, when they protrude, a "buck-toothed" effect. But, worse than this, the lower and upper teeth frequently fail to erupt in their proper positions, so that they do not engage efficiently and permit proper mastication of food. This malformation of the jaws is called "malocclusion" and comes in a variety of forms. Its cause is complicated and obscure, but seems to lie in hereditary evolutionary tendencies of a degenerative nature, possibly induced to some extent by lack of proper healthy exercising of the jaws and teeth—a consequence of the excessive use of soft cooked foods.

Malocclusion is principally a phenomenon of modern civilization and it is increasing most alarmingly. It must be combated. The dental specialists who are striving against this retrogressive tendency in human evolution are called orthodontists. Theirs is the difficult task of finding out the cause of this malformation and eradicating its disastrous effects. They are most skilled to warp and move and straighten teeth so as to bring them back into efficiency and symmetry, but as yet they do not know how to keep them there, just where the teeth should be moved, and why they erupt out of position in the first instance.

The other two great manifestations of the decline in the human dentition are caries or decay and pyorrhea. Most savages show few or no cavities in their teeth. They may wear their teeth down by eating gritty food, until the pulp cavities are exposed and the tooth dies and decays, but the primary caries—the eating away of the tooth by bacteriological or other destructive agencies in the mouth—is extremely rare—at least until the savage comes into contact with civilization, missionaries, canned foods, groceries and candy. But nine out of ten school children in the United States have decayed teeth, and civilized adults probably show nearly 100 per cent of mouths which contain one or more carious teeth. This decay of the teeth means the introduction into the system of poisons which cause rheumatism and a host of major ailments which may follow this primary infection. Yet no one today knows the cause of dental caries. It may be partially a matter of diet and particularly caused by diets lacking in one or more of the necessary vitamins. But it is by no means exclusively due to diet, since primitive peoples living under a wide range of dietetic conditions usually manifest few if any ravages of this terrible disease.

Pyorrhea is a septic condition of the gums, which is even more obscure in origin and far more difficult to treat than simple dental caries. The bacteriological agencies present are to some extent known, but the cause is not the lack of use of a toothbrush, nor is the remedy to be found in frequent scrubbings with this or that allegedly antiseptic toothpaste. Of course brushing the teeth is like buttering the baby's heel; it can not do any harm and it may do some good. This is always providing that the toothpaste used is not abrasive nor of such a nature as to attack the enamel. Of course the teeth should be kept clean, just as the feet should be kept clean. And the mouth and teeth which guard the digestive tract are much more vulnerable to germinal incursions than is the skin.

The facts that we must face are, in brief, that human teeth and the human mouth have become, possibly under the influence of civilization, the foci of infections that undermine the entire bodily health of the species and that degenerative tendencies in evolution have manifested themselves in modern man to such an extent that our jaws are too small for the teeth which they are supposed to accommodate, and that, as a consequence, these teeth erupt so irregularly that their functional efficiency is often entirely or nearly destroyed.

How to Stop Dental Degeneration

In my opinion there is one and only one course of action which will check the increase of dental disease and degeneration which may ultimately cause the extinction of the human species. This is to elevate the dental profession to a plane upon which it can command the services of our best research minds to study the causes and seek for the cures of these dental evils. Such an improvement of the quality of the dental profession is an indispensable prerequisite for the attacking of these tremendous pathological and evolutionary problems. No effective measures of public education in care of the teeth can be taken until dental practitioners cease to be tinkers and learn to be scientists. In making such a statement I by no means wish to belittle the tremendous progress in the field of dentistry which has already been made.

As a matter of fact, if I were asked in what occupations the United States indubitably leads the world, I should reply without hesitation "Dentistry and plumbing." American dentists have reached a pitch of mechanical skill which is equal to that of American surgeons. But carpentry is not enough. Stopping teeth does not stop tooth decay. In the dental profession today are many brilliant scientific minds and many practitioners of consummate skill whose aims are humanitarian rather than pecuniary, but there are too few of such men and they have been insufficiently trained.

The dental profession has been for too long a time a neglected and disowned orphan child of medicine and surgery. While millions have been lavished upon medical schools and hospitals, and upon medical and surgical research, almost nothing has been allotted for these purposes to dentistry. Our schools of dentistry have been forced to struggle along without endowments; their teaching staffs have consisted almost entirely of devoted but unpaid men who give part of their time to teaching, but have to make their living in practice.

The prerequisites for admission to dental schols have not been sufficiently high. In the past many schools have admitted high-school graduates and students with only one or two years of college preparation. This low standard of admission implies a supply of inferiorly educated men and a commercialized technical course, rather than the broad background of general education essential to the rigorous training of a professional school of medicine. As a result there has been very little scientific research in the dental school and what has been carried on has been principally commercial in its aim. The faculties of dental schools recognize these short-comings and are striving to raise their standards and to transform dentistry from a trade to a profession, from a craft to a science. But they can not succeed in any large measure until the public and the philanthropic foundations, and especially the medical profession itself, recognize the essential parity of dentistry with other branches of medical science.

I am well acquainted with only one dental school—that connected with an old and famous New England university. Like every other dental school, it has been regarded as a yellow dog trailing at the heels of the medical school. It has been slighted in endowment, in gifts for research, and generally neglected and half starved. Yet this dental school includes in its faculty some of the most enlightened, altruistic and scientifically minded teachers and research workers with whom I have been privileged to come into contact. It was the first university dental school in the world; it was the first to lengthen its academic year to nine months; the first to require written examinations; the first to demand graduation from a high school as an entrance requirement; among the first to increase that requirement to two years of college.

This institution is now seeking an endowment which is absolutely necessary for its proper development. Let us not attempt to evade the issue. Either we must spend the necessary sums to give dental research and dental practice their proper status in the medical profession, or we must spend vastly larger amounts upon dental tinkers, whose unpleasant duty it is to lean over the dental chairs in which we sit, gaze upon the shocking vista of human degeneration which our open mouths present, and attempt the hopeless task of stopping decay and sepsis. I firmly believe that the health of humanity is at stake, and that, unless steps are taken to discover preventives of tooth infection and correctives of dental deformation, the course of human evolution will lead downward to extinction.

8.

THE ENIGMA OF FOSSIL MAN

IN the past two decades the specialists who deal with fossil man have been confronted with an ever-increasing number of geologically ancient skeletal remains, each succeeding one adding to an existing confusion. At the beginning of the century the tale of fossil man was brief and apparently fairly intelligible. A series of finds in Western Europe had revealed the bony remains and the stone implements of a race of men who inhabited caves during the last glacial advance. These Neanderthaloids were short, bull-necked, barrel-chested individuals, with many features of the bones of the trunk and of the extremities suggesting an affinity with the great apes less remote than that of the modern man. The most striking features were, however, those of the skull. The long and narrow brain-cases were of moderate size or even large, but flattened down and low; their orbits were surmounted with huge bony brow-ridges, behind which the forehead retreated in an ignominious fashion. The jaws were protrusive to the verge of snoutiness; the chin receded practically to a vanishing point; the teeth were massive but without canine projection; the pulp cavities of the molars were enlarged, as in animals which chew the cud. These apish men seemed to fulfill the requirements of an early ancestral human type which had not yet sloughed off many of its anthropoid attributes. They were succeeded in the upper strata of the European caves, representing the last glacial retreat, by several morphologically modern types of man. In 1907 a sand pit near the university town of Heidelberg yielded a massive human jaw which looked like a plausible progenitor of the Neanderthaloid race. This mandible was referred to the first or second interglacial period, many scores of thousands of years before the flourishing of the Neanderthalers. Also in 1892 a Dutch scientist had unearthed a most extraordinary humanoid fossil in the island of Java, apparently dating from the beginning of the Pleistocene period or the end of the Pliocene. This specimen consisted of a very apish skull-cap, too large for any existing anthropoid ape and too small for any man except an idiot, a few ambiguous teeth and a thigh bone which certainly belonged to an erect biped. This thing was christened *Pithecanthropus erectus*, "the erect ape-man," and was generally conceded to be nature's finest effort in production of a "missing link." Without unduly stretching phylogenetic possibilities, one might conceive of Pithecanthropus as a late survivor of a stock which had already crossed the threshold of humanity, having achieved erect posture and biped gait, without as yet having attained a full quota of brain. It was further possible to suppose that some Pithecanthropidae with superior genes had produced the higher Heidelberg type, which again, stimulated by the Kultur of the Pleistocene, ultimately evolved the Neanderthalers. These last, in the throes of species parturition, were held by some to have given birth to modern man, apparently themselves expiring with the effort. These were the short and simple annals of the poor Hominidae. It is true that certain recalcitrant Thomases had interposed doubts, calling attention to various skeletal finds which suggest that morphologically modern man existed in Europe even before the advent of the Neanderthalers, and asserting that Pithecanthropus was a palaeontological monster fortuitously assembled from spare parts of men, apes, and microcephalic idiots.

However, about the time that the politicians were stirring up a world war, an inquisitive amateur geologist trespassed upon a small gravel pit in a Sussex lane near Piltdown Common and disinterred some skull fragments which were subsequently named *Eoanthropus Dawsoni,* but might better have been called Pandora. If the associated remains were assigned to one individual, it was necessary to suppose that at the beginning of the Pleistocene period there existed a type of man with a modern brain-case and a projecting, chinless, ape-like jaw. Such a being could not be fitted into the line of descent which includes Pithecanthropus, Heidelberg man, and the Neanderthal race, since all these fossils were probably provided with large brow-ridges and receding foreheads. Almost alone, Sir Arthur Keith committed himself unhesitatingly and definitely to the theory that human evolution has involved the differentiation of a number of distinct genera and species of man, of which Pithecanthropus, Heidelberg and the Neanderthaloid group represent lines which are not directly ancestral to *Homo sapiens.* According to this view, Piltdown man (*Eoanthropus Dawsoni*) represents a survival into the Early Pleistocene of a Pliocene form which had already developed modern brain size, but had not as yet undergone the reduction of the jaws and the refinement of the dentition characteristic of morphologically modern man.

One of the cardinal tenets of Sir Arthur Keith's position was his defense of the Early Pleistocene dating claimed for the Galley Hill man, a skeleton discovered in the 100-foot gravels of the Thames Valley as early as 1888. The bones were those of a short-statured adult male with no especially apelike features. The skull is very long and narrow, without excessive development of brow-ridges or of frontal slope; the jaw has a well-developed chin and the teeth are not extraordinary. This find is merely the most famous of a fair number of morphologically modern human bones for which Middle Pleistocene or earlier age has been claimed. All these finds had been rejected by the majority of anthropologists on the explicit ground that their geological provenience was questionable, but implicitly because of the belief that the occupation of Europe at the end of the glacial epoch by apelike Neanderthalers delimited the extent of human evolution at that period. It was then inconceivable that an anatomically modern type should have ranged Europe one or two glacial cycles previously.

However, in 1933 the young British archaeologist, Dr. L. S. B.

Leakey, announced a discovery which seemed to establish, once and for all, the Early Pleistocene antiquity of our own species, *Homo sapiens*. In previous expeditions to Kenya, East Africa, Leakey, a most energetic worker, had discovered and described an elaborate sequence of cultures of the Old Stone Age, which he had correlated with the pluvial periods in that area. A pluvial period is a rainy climatic phase supposed to occur in unglaciated regions of the earth more or less contemporaneously with a glaciation farther north. Dr. Leakey had also found a number of skeletons of modern-appearing, somewhat Negroidal men, in the archaeological deposits which he ascribed to the closing phases of the Pleistocene. These would be dated roughly to the period when the Cro-Magnon and other types of *sapiens* men replaced the Neanderthalers in the European caves. Although some of the correlations of the archaeological cultures with geological conditions needed further substantiation, Leakey's findings were generally accepted, since he is undoubtedly a well-trained and brilliant archaeologist. Consequently, when he announced in 1933 the discovery at Kanam, again in Kenya, of a human mandible of modern type in a deposit of Lower Pleistocene Age containing an archaic extinct fauna, it seemed probable that the high geological antiquity of *Homo sapiens* had been finally proved. Dr. Leakey formally reported his finds to committees of archaeologists, palaeontologists, geologists, and physical anthropologists, sitting at Cambridge (England), and these bodies issued statements which seemed to indicate that they found his conclusions acceptable. However, it was decided to send another expedition to Kenya in order to secure a final confirmation of the age of the specimens which was alleged to be comparable with the antiquity of the Java, Peking, and Piltdown finds. Unfortunately this investigation revealed serious defects in the evidence. The photographic record was incomplete owing to a faulty camera; the exact locality from which the skull came could not be ascertained; there was some uncertainty as to the undisturbed character of the deposit and its exact geologic age. Thus it became necessary to reject this discovery as proof of the existence of anatomically modern man in the earlier part of the Pleistocene or glacial period. It turned out to be yet another case upon which a Scotch verdict was rendered.

It should be emphasized, however, that the Kanam failure by no

means destroys the probability of the high Pleistocene antiquity of
Homo sapiens. It is merely an insufficiently attested find, prematurely publicized by an able man who made a mistake, possibly
only in his technique of recording the evidence. It is always dangerous to make predictions in anthropology, unless one is prepared
subsequently to swallow them. Nevertheless, I am of the opinion
that Dr. Leakey was probably right and that he did actually find
the ancestor of modern man in an Early Pleistocene deposit, but
that he was unfortunate, or insufficiently careful, in not securing
at the time of the discovery the absolutely irrefragable evidence
which is essential for the proof of such critical cases. Unless a
skeleton is viewed and photographed *in situ,* in an undisturbed
deposit agreed to be of a specified geological age, and associated
with fauna of that age, the unfortunate fossil man is inevitably
doomed to the stigma of bastardy. I am going so far as to say that
I believe and hope that Dr. Leakey will vindicate his opinion by a
future discovery in the same area, which will be iron-bound, im-
pregnable and unassailable. For many years I have adhered to Sir
Arthur Keith's view that *Homo sapiens* is geologically very ancient and did not spring from the Neanderthaloids or from any
other known archaic and apelike form of fossil man. Sir Arthur
has been wavering in that opinion for the past few years, and now
he seems to be in full retreat from his palaeontological Verdun. It
is not for me to raise again the standard and say, "They shall not
pass"; but I think that Keith's former position is still tenable, and
in a humble, unheroic way, I am sitting in it.

In the meantime fresh discoveries have seemed to substantiate
the opinion that modern man must have evolved through a generalized Neanderthaloid stage. In 1921 the Rhodesian man was
exhumed in South Africa—a specimen which in size of face and
upper jaw exceeded any human type previously known, and
which, in the hugeness of its brow-ridges, virtually out-gorillaed
the gorilla. Yet this skull displayed also a mixture of anthropoidal
and modern human features, and the limb bones uncertainly associated with it were those of a recent type of man. Nevertheless,
most authorities elected to classify Rhodesian man as a variant of
the Neanderthal type.

Then came the series of discoveries in Peking, China, beginning
in 1927 and closely associated with the industry and scientific

acumen of the late Professor Davidson Black. The Sinanthropus crania, of Lower Pleistocene date, are of an evolutionary status intermediate between that of *Pithecanthropus erectus* and the well-known Neanderthal race, although possibly neither the descendants of the one nor the progenitors of the other.

As the work of excavation proceeds at Choukoutien, the site which yields Peking men, an extraordinary wealth of fossil human skulls, jaws, and teeth is coming to light. It would be futile to attempt to state here the exact numbers, since new finds would certainly make them incorrect before publication. Three adult skulls were found in November of last year and Professor Franz Weidenreich, the able successor of Dr. Davidson Black, has recently published a splendid monograph upon eleven lower jaws of Sinanthropus, or the fossil man of China.[1]

These Peking skulls are found in a consolidated deposit representing the debris in an old cave of which the roof has collapsed. They are referable to Middle Pleistocene times or possibly to the Lower Pleistocene. None of the skulls are accompanied by other bones and they commonly lack the basal parts. There are rather strong indications of death by violence and the severing of the heads from the bodies. The removal of the skull bases (for extraction of the brains, possibly), is unpleasantly suggestive of cannibalism. The cave yielded plenty of ashes and a considerable number of crude stone implements of an old palaeolithic type presenting some analogies with the Mousterian culture of the European Neanderthaloids.

All of the skulls are small, primitive and apelike, with great ridges of bone above the eyes and low foreheads. They are distinctly inferior in evolutionary status to most of the European Neanderthaloids and are not much, if any, above the level of Pithecanthropus. Some of the high points of their anthropology, as summarized by Weidenreich, are extreme dolichocephaly (narrow skull breadth relative to skull length), small cranial capacity (cubic contents of brain-case), great size difference between the sexes, broad flat noses and low eye-sockets, projecting and puffed out faces (lacking supraorbital fossae), broad high palates, large and chinless lower jaws. Several anatomical details (shovel-shaped

---

[1] Weidenreich, Franz, "The Mandibles of *Sinanthropus Pekinensis*, A Comparative Study." *Palaeontologica Sinica*, Series D, Vol. VII, Fascicle 3, Peiping, 1936.

incisor teeth, "Inca" bone, mandibular torus) incline Weidenreich to the belief that these ancient Pekinese may have been ancestors of the modern Mongoloids—an opinion which I do not at present share. The brow-ridges of the Peking men are more sharply set off from the forehead slope than are those of Pithecanthropus of Java, and the brain casts of the Chinese specimens exhibit a very chimpanzee-like feature in the pointed frontal lobes. Some of the new Sinanthropus skulls in general form and size are not far divergent from the skull of the famous Java specimen. The Peking men, however, have slightly higher arching of the frontal bone (forehead), although the offset of the brow-ridges and the pointing and elongation of the frontal lobes of the brain bring them in these respects closer to the chimpanzee and the gorilla than was *Pithecanthropus erectus.*

The molar teeth of the Sinanthropus specimens have enlarged pulp cavities, but Davidson Black distinguishes this roominess of the pulp cavities from the similar condition in Neanderthaloid teeth, called taurodontism, on the ground that the latter enlargement is at the expense of the roots, whereas in the Sinanthropus type the cavity extends more into the crown. This latter condition is regarded as the more primitive and generalized. I gather that Weidenreich regards the Sinanthropus form of man as a stem human type from which Neanderthal man developed as a primitive specialization, but which also in more progressive forms may have led to *Homo sapiens.* One of the new Sinanthropus skulls presents peculiarities which Weidenreich regards as essentially Neanderthaloid and indicative of a differentiation in that direction. The *Pithecanthropus erectus* of Java is apparently regarded by Weidenreich as very closely allied to Sinanthropus, and rather less primitive and more specialized than the reverse. The actual Pithecanthropus specimen is probably the skull of a small female.

Since 1931 the Dutch scientists in Java have been finding new fossil skulls in the Pleistocene beds laid down by the river Solo, only six miles from the spot which yielded Pithecanthropus. The deposits in which the so-called *Homo Soloensis* occurs are said to be a little later than those in which Dubois found Pithecanthropus. The skulls, of which there are several, have not yet been fully studied. They are of great size with enormous brow-ridges, flattened foreheads, and attachments of the neck muscles which are very large, but of a modern conformation.

The Dutch anthropologists hold that the Solo type of man is closer to the Rhodesian variety than to the Neanderthal type. Sir Arthur Keith considers that *Homo Soloensis* may be a descendant of Pithecanthropus, while Weidenreich thinks that Pithecanthropus may be merely a female form of the new Java type. Most recently the same deposits in Java have yielded an almost complete skull of an infant, as yet undescribed. Certainly all of the new discoveries indicate that the Pleistocene period witnessed the development of a number of coarse-boned types of men with big brow-ridges and low foreheads, but otherwise not particularly closely related.

The best preserved and most complete of these new fossil finds is the group of skeletons discovered in 1931-32 in limestone caves on the western slope of Mt. Carmel by a joint expedition of the American School of Prehistoric Research and the British School of Archaeology under the direction of Miss Dorothy Garrod. Mr. Theodore C. McCown, the young Amercian who was actually in charge of the excavations when most of the finds occurred, has spent several years in London, chiseling these ancient Palestinians out of the matrix of stone in which they were embedded, and studying them under the direction of the great physical anthropologist, Sir Arthur Keith.

While the full report of Sir Arthur Keith and Mr. McCown upon the Palestinian skeletons will not appear for some months, a recent preliminary paper provides many interesting facts and provisional conclusions.[2] The remains come from two caves, Skhūl and et-Tabūn, very close to each other in the same valley on the western slope of Mt. Carmel. The implements from the skeleton-bearing strata are of practically the same types (Levalloiso-Mousterian). The animal remains indicate that the inhabitants of both caves lived in the latter half of the last interglacial period (Riss-Würm), but there are slight faunal indications that the Skhūl people may have been a little more recent than the Tabūn dwellers. In the latter cave the most important human remains

[2] Keith, Sir Arthur, and McCown, Theodore D., "Mount Carmel Man. His Bearing on the Ancestry of Modern Races." *Bulletin* 13 *American School of Prehistoric Research,* pp. 5-15, May, 1937.

are the almost complete skeleton of a small woman, and the very large lower jaw of a male. The Skhūl type is represented by two nearly complete skeletons of very tall men, the skeleton of an infant, and fragmentary remains of several more individuals. The Tabūn woman in most respects closely resembles the well-known western European Neanderthal type, but she had a pelvis much more apelike than any hitherto reported, and a much more modern foot than that of the classic Neanderthal race. On the other extremity, her hand has Neanderthaloid features. The Skhūl skeletons are more modern in their pelves and long bones; they present a mixture of Neanderthaloid features and of those which are neanthropic or characteristic of anatomically modern man. In neither type do the teeth show the enlarged molar pulp-cavities which occur in Neanderthal man and in Sinanthropus. All of the skeletons have big brow-ridges, but none have the protruding bun-shaped occiputs of the European Neanderthaloids. The Tabūn woman has a chinless mandible, but the other specimens have incipient or moderately well developed chins. Some of the skull vaults are high, others low; some long and narrow, others of medium length relative to their breadth. The cubic contents of the skull (or the cranial capacities) vary from small to quite large. The authors consider the Tabūn woman to be a more generalized Eastern variety of the Neanderthaloid family. The Western Neanderthaloids are thought to be too specialized to belong in the direct ancestry of modern man. On the other hand, the Skhūl type, while morphologically intermediate between Neanderthal man and modern man, is considered to be a likely ancestor of primitive forms of neanthropic man—especially the Cro-Magnon cave dwellers of the last glacial episode in Europe. The authors, however, state that "his physical characteristics are too well defined and he is too late in the Pleistocene to provide us with an ancestor for *Homo sapiens* in the widest sense of that term." [3]

It is to be hoped that the final report of these careful and gifted students will examine fully the possibility that the Skhūl type represents the result of a racial intermixture between the more archaic Tabūn type and some early variety of *Homo sapiens*. Neanderthal man may have been a "good mixer."

While the scientists have been steadily adding to the number

[3] *Op. cit.,* p. 14.

of accredited remains of fossil man in the Old World, during the past quarter of a century that formidable and indomitable veteran, Dr. Aleš Hrdlička, has stood like Horatius at the land bridge between Asia and North America, mowing down with deadly precision all would-be geologically ancient invaders of the New World. In fact, the story of alleged fossil man in America is virtually the tale of how well Hrdlička kept the bridge. With penetrating analysis and devastating criticism he has annihilated *seriatim* the claims of each successive fossil pretender. Undoubtedly he has preserved science from a credulous acceptance of many spurious Pleistocene Americans. It is indeed passing strange that, if man really inhabited the New World during the Pleistocene epoch, we have not found his implements and his bones *in situ* in indubitably Pleistocene deposits, and associated with extinct animals which do not incur the suspicion of having survived into recent times.

A reliable authority upon the present status of the problem of man's antiquity in the New World, the palaeontologist, Alfred S. Romer, says:

> The association of man in America with certain fossil forms is unquestioned, and there is a growing body of evidence strongly suggesting his contemporaneity with a considerable number of mammalian types no longer living. Such contemporaneity, however, by no means indicates any remote geological antiquity for man on this continent, and there is at present almost no palaeontological evidence suggesting his presence here at a time earlier than that of the withdrawal of the last Pleistocene ice-sheet.[4]

The canny and conservative archaeologist, N. C. Nelson,[5] is even more pessimistic and positive in reaching a similar conclusion.

Nevertheless, evidences suggesting a considerable antiquity of man in the New World keep cropping up, and each succeeding growth is tougher and harder to trample down. There is, for example, the case of Minnesota Man, who appears to have been a young lady who fell into a lake which preceded the post-glacial Lake Agassiz, and whose remains, sealed under a concrete highway,

[4] Romer, Alfred S., "Pleistocene Vertebrates and their Bearing on the Problem of Human Antiquity in America," in *The American Aborigines*, p. 81, Toronto, 1933.

[5] Nelson, N. C., "The Antiquity of Man in America in the Light of Archaeology," in *The American Aborigines*, pp. 87-129, Toronto, 1933.

were brought to light by the combined efforts of Jack Frost and a roadscraper. This young woman, although of an ordinarily modern appearance in most features, nevertheless possessed teeth and jaws of altogether exceptional size—quite outside of the range of civilized debutantes.

My friend, Dr. A. E. Jenks, Professor of Anthropology in the University of Minnesota, has finished an exemplary piece of scientific research and description in the recovery and recording of the remains of Minnesota Man.[6] The skeleton was found in 1931 beneath a concrete highway which was being repaired. The highway had been built in a cut made through a varved silt deposit and the skeleton lay at a depth of about ten feet in the apparently undisturbed strata below the road. The silts were laid down in the bed of pro-glacial Lake Pelican, which was formed in front of the ice-sheet of the Late Wisconsin glaciation and antedated the pro-glacial Lake Agassiz. The age of the silt deposits is estimated at twenty thousand years. The skeleton is that of a female of about fifteen years, who is supposed to have been drowned in Lake Pelican about one-half mile from the foot of the glacier, having fallen from a water-craft or through the ice. The bones of the skeleton, apart from the skull, exhibit no important features which would differentiate them from recent Indians. The cranium is mainly remarkable because of its alveolar prognathism or jaw protrusion. It presents a number of features which may be characterized as Mongoloid. The teeth are extraordinarily large. The crowns of the lower molars exceed in size the averages of modern races and of the Piltdown, Heidelberg, and Neanderthaloid individuals adduced for comparison. Incisor teeth hollowed posteriorly like a coal-shovel are characteristic of the Minnesota specimen. Such shovel-shaped incisors occur oftenest in Mongoloids, but are found sporadically in other racial groups. Dr. Jenks concludes that this woman represents a primitive *Homo sapiens* of an early evolving Mongoloid type, a precursor of the American Indians, but especially foreshadowing the Eskimo.

The importance of this skeleton does not lie in its morphological characteristics which, with the exception of size of the teeth and a few other features, are not outside the range of present day Indians. Indeed Dr. Hrdlička maintains that the skeleton is that of

6 Jenks, Albert Ernest, *Pleistocene Man in Minnesota.* Minneapolis, 1936.

a recent female Sioux,[7] intrusively buried in the ancient lake silts. The strata immediately above the skeleton were destroyed by the building of the road so that the precise nature of the original ground surface cannot be ascertained. Hrdlička suggests that the posture of the body is not that of a drowned person "as usually seen in medico-legal experience." (What is the ordinary posture of a drowned person?) He argues also that the completeness of the skeleton is incompatible with the presumption of drowning, since a body could scarcely be silted over before it had decayed and the bones had been scattered. Again, with the skeleton were found pieces of cut and drilled conch shells from the Gulf region, such as were brought north in trade by the historic Indians.

Clearly the problem of the Minnesota Lady is one which has to be settled on geological evidence rather than upon anthropological grounds. It has to do with the antiquity of man in America, and in no wise with the antiquity of man in general. My own opinion is that there is nothing about the anthropology of the specimen which is incompatible with the very modest Late Glacial antiquity which is claimed for it. A man of twenty thousands of years ago need not be expected to show any particularly simian characteristics. On the whole, the geological evidence presented is conclusive as to the age of the deposit, and the chances against the skeleton being intrusive are very large, on the basis of the testimony of eye-witnesses of the original find, on the evidence furnished by the redigging of the site carried out by Dr. Jenks, and finally on the consensus of the judgments of competent geologists who have examined the locality. I am therefore of the opinion that this discovery establishes a very strong probability, although not an absolute certainty, of the existence of Homo sapiens in the New World in Late Glacial times.

[7] Hrdlička, Aleš, "The Minnesota 'Man,'" American Journal of Physical Anthropology, Vol. XXII, No. 2, pp. 175-200, 1937.

9.

BIOLOGY AND FOSSIL MAN[1]

INTRODUCTION

FOSSIL man is, paradoxically, a very live issue in anthropological research. Knowledge of our defunct predecessors seems at times to progress more rapidly and more surely than that of the omnipresent species, *Homo sapiens*, rather ineptly so-called. Further, the achievements of fossil man entitle him to more consideration, certainly, than modern savages deserve by virtue of the lack of achievement which commends them to anthropological attention. Fossil man invented the first tools and discovered the use of fire; he was probably the originator of articulate speech. He made himself from an ape and created human culture. If his successors have accomplished anything more substantial, I am not aware of it.

My subject permits an inquiry into the application of biological theory to our knowledge of fossil man, or, alternatively, a discussion of fossil man's biology. The immodesty of ignorance im-

---

[1] Address delivered at the Symposium on Early Man, of the Philadelphia Academy of Natural Sciences, March 19, 1937.

pels me to attempt both. Knowledge of fossil man is confined within the limits of the evidence and by the limitations of the investigators. I shall deal with the latter category first, since it is the more stultifying, and, like the diseases euphemistically called "social," flourishes amid a conspiracy of polite silence.

I. PSYCHOLOGY AS AFFECTING BIOLOGICAL INTERPRETATIONS OF THE STATUS OF FOSSIL MAN

Psychology of Anthropologists

In order to survive, an animal must be born into a favoring or at least tolerant environment. Similarly, in order to achieve preservation and recognition, a specimen of fossil man must be discovered in intelligence, attested by scientific knowledge, and interpreted by evolutionary experience. These rigorous prerequisites have undoubtedly caused many still-births in human palaeontology and are partly responsible for the high infant mortality of discoveries of geologically ancient man.

Fossil Human Miscarriages

In the first place it is clear that innumerable mute, inglorious fossil Miltons must have been exhumed or washed out from their primeval geologic beds with no discerning human eye to pity and no arm to save. About these lost ancestors one can only elegize. Another large class of fossil men has been the victim of its premature rebirth into a benighted world. Even when delivered by a precociously scientific discoverer, as was the Foxhall jaw by the American dentist in London, they have been promptly ushered out, both literally and figuratively, by the Adamitic creationists adhering to the cosmic chronology of an English bishop. The pre-Darwinians looked upon fossil man as the rustic upon the giraffe, and exclaimed with him, "There ain't no sech animal!" Many a foresighted pioneer of human palaeontology cast his pearls before scientists who trampled them underfoot and turned again to rend him.

Even more to be regretted are the numerous fossil men who, possibly legitimately conceived, have been reborn, so to speak, without due documentation of their arrival. Torn from the womb of earth by the impetuous efforts of amateur obstetricians, these palaeontological orphans have been denied scientific baptism and confirmation. The bar sinister can never be expunged from the scutcheon of Galley Hill Man and many other aspirants to geological antiquity.

Premature Discovery of Neanderthal Man

It has long been apparent that the early discovery of Neanderthal man, arrayed in a full panoply of simian morphological reminiscences, has warped and constricted the viewpoints of many students of human evolution. The Western European classic Neanderthaloid type was altogether too complete an answer to Darwinian prayer. It facilitated a transition from Adamitic to evolutionary monogenism which instilled into zealous converts a bigoted omniscience not uncommon in those who have a little knowledge.

Taking the rigidly delineated morphological traits of Neanderthal as the one permissible prototype of Man—a sort of anthropological true cross—these unilinear genealogists were able to postulate a few intermediate precursors bridging the gap between man and ape, each with progressively and symmetrically more simian features—smaller brain cases, larger brow-ridges, snoutier faces, larger teeth, less erect posture, and more prehensile feet. In the other and modern human direction a harmonious reduction and attenuation of apelike characters was anticipated and prescribed as the sole path of orthodox human evolution. Heretical and non-conforming fossil men were banished to the limbo of dark museum cupboards, forgotten or even destroyed. The oversimplification of evolutionary processes implicit in this view is almost certainly wrong.

Nationalistic Attitudes

The psychological climates which condition the biological interpretations of finds of fossil man are to a considerable extent national. Divergent schools of anthropological thought and method develop in different countries. Over and beyond the interpretational slants imparted by the influence of individual scientific leaders, there tends to be added a certain ethnic quality which is almost ludicrously consistent and predictable. I am going to commit the indiscretion of discussing these national attitudes.

Germanic anatomy and physical anthropology proceed under a long and honorable tradition of exhaustive and scrupulous, if somewhat pedestrian, treatment of morphological and metric variation. While there is, of course, no unanimity of opinion as to man's origin among the German students, it is worthy of note that the prevalent and perhaps predominant sentiment of German anthropologists is and has been for a number of decades decidedly pro-ape. This attitude is expressed in a tendency to derive man in comparatively late geological times either from a giant anthropoid ape closely related to the existing gorilla, the chimpanzee or the orang-utan, or to a relatively proximate common ancestor of the three. It is perhaps reflected also in the inclination to refer the skull cap of *Pithecanthropus erectus* of Java to an extinct form of great ape, and the mandible of Piltdown man to a putative chimpanzee or orang. It is difficult to appraise the causes of this anthropoid obsession, but it has been manifested notably, in one form or another, by Virchow, Ranke, Klaatsch, Weinert, and many others. The habit of dissociating complementary skeletal parts found in the same deposit, and of arbitrarily assigning those which look human to man and those which present simian features to a postulated extinct ape, may perhaps be connected with a predilection for the partitive and microtomic investigation of minutiae, without due consideration of the total problem. On the other hand, it may be referable to an excess of scientific caution or conservatism. I do not suggest that this pro-ape attitude is either correct or incorrect.

If the Germans are on the side of the apes, the English have arrayed themselves almost solidly on the side of the angels. Thus the opinion of Sir Arthur Keith and Le Gros Clark separates the human stock from the anthropoid trunk as far back as the Oligocene period, while Wood Jones, the brilliant and perennial radical among physical anthropologists, will recognize no primate relative above a tarsier. Again, the typically British attitude toward *Pithecanthropus erectus* is perhaps a full recognition of human status and anatomical integrity, with some imperialistic suspicion that he belongs to an inferior species, while the Piltdown lady is at least a complete female and, apelike jaw and all, a possible

progenitor of *Homo sapiens*. Consistent with the opinion that
man early differentiated into several stocks, of variously blended
anthropoidal and human characteristics, is the view that *Homo
sapiens*, the anatomically modern species of man, emerged at a
very early period from the welter of archaic humanoid types and
co-existed with and survived the anachronistic Neanderthaloids.
The peerless champion of this cause is, of course, Sir Arthur Keith,
indomitable in his lifelong quest for a sort of Holy Grail in human
palaeontology, the skeletal remains of *Homo sapiens in situ* in an
indubitably Lower Pleistocene or Pliocene deposit.

Even more interesting is the optimistic British functionalism in
interpreting primate evolution,—a legacy perhaps from the un-
confessed Lamarckianism of Charles Darwin. Thus the late and
justly famous Sir Grafton Elliot Smith and his pupil, Professor
Frederic Wood Jones, have most plausibly delineated the process
of man evolving himself out of a tarsier by a perpetual motion
of stimuli and responses between the emancipated hands and the
expanding cerebral cortex. Of late the *neopallium* of the former
great brain morphologist, a sort of cerebral mantle of Elijah, has
descended upon the very capable shoulders of Professor Le Gros
Clark. Functional interpretations of the characters of fossil man
and of modern human types have pervaded British anthropological
thought and method, and have been employed at times with less
caution than enthusiasm.

However, it seems to me that the most outstanding characteristic of British anthropology in dealing with fossil man is the
essentially sporting attitude taken by scientists toward the discovery and acceptance of new finds, which may be contrasted
with the morbid simian suspicions which obsess the Germans and
the cynical detachment of the French. An adventurous spirit in
anthropological research and a willingness to take a chance upon
being right, have, it seems to me, resulted in many brilliant contributions to our knowledge of human evolution by British scientists, beginning with Darwin and Huxley and continuing through
a long line of bold discoverers and interpreters. It is true that this
same sporting attitude has occasionally promoted some resounding
fiascos. Thus in the case of the recent premature announcements
of the discovery of *Homo sapiens* in a Lower Pleistocene deposit,

British science behaved in a way strongly reminiscent of the spectators of John Gilpin's famous ride:

The drums were beat, the whistles blew, up flew the windows all,
And every soul cried out "Well done!" as loud as he could bawl.

The ensuing debacle is certainly attributable in part to uncontrolled enthusiasm and lack of caution in the promoting anthropological and other scientific groups. It seems highly probable, indeed, that the geological and archaeological evidence of an early glacial existence for *Homo sapiens* was actually available in Kenya. I refer to this unhappy episode in no carping spirit, but only to illustrate the well-known fact that adventures in science sometimes turn out magnificently wrong.

By contrast the French attitude in human palaeontology impresses me as constricted and noncommittal, and too rigidly adherent to the ideas of an illustrious national past in anthropological research. The myth of a Cro-Magnon race, homogeneous in physical type, gigantic of stature, with an excess of brain size and artistic gifts peculiarly appropriate to France, has been stubbornly perpetuated in the face of all conflicting evidence. It is approximately comparable with the German doctrine of Nordicism. Yet anthropological knowledge of fossil man has been munificently enriched by the work of French scientists. Probably the most nearly perfect study of a geologically ancient human specimen will continue for many years to be Marcellin Boule's great monograph upon the man of Chapelle-aux-Saints.

What I have sometimes called the Monroe Doctrine in American anthropology is a determination to refuse recognition to Old World influences in the evolution of aboriginal culture in these continents. It is by no means an interdiction against anthropological research by Europeans in the Americas. On the contrary, tourists are welcome. The attitude in question is rather a revulsion against venturesome and unsubstantiated theories of cultural and racial diffusion into the New World, blithely and irresponsibly propounded by Europeans who have neglected to acquaint themselves with the vast amount of data indicating an indigenous development of American cultures from a very simple Neolithic or Upper Palaeolithic level. On the whole I think that this American attitude has justified itself, although I must admit that it has been conducive at times to a purblind provincialism which obstructs the advance of knowledge. Now in the matter of human origins there has never been any scientific claim of American independence; we have not even an anthropoid ape, barring *Hesperopithecus,* the masquerading peccary, and *Ameranthropoïdes Loysi,* a giant spider monkey with his tail behind a box. The barriers against Asiatic human immigrants in prehistoric times have been theoretically down, except upon such occasions as nature presented them in the form of ice. The New World certainly received its first human colonization across the Bering Straits or the Aleutian Islands. There is, however, some slight disagreement as to the time of man's arrival.

The discovery of palaeolithic industries and the remains of geologically ancient man in the Old World raised the postulate of similar occurrences here and initiated frenzied and feverish scratchings for ancient man in America. It is to the everlasting credit of professional American anthropology that it has not succumbed to the itch for ancestors by giving recognition to the many dubious and spurious finds whose claims have too often received a facile acceptance abroad. No one can deny that this salutary state of affairs is due almost entirely to the righteous scientific iconoclasm of one formidable veteran, Dr. Hrdlička. On the archaeological side his adamantine position has been reinforced by the gloomy but penetrating skepticism of Nelson and the neo-Ussherian fervor of Spinden. The unhappy but deserved fate of previous fossil pretenders to geological antiquity in America, mostly at the hands of one executioner, has so intimidated the younger physical anthropologists of this country, that their attitude toward alleged fossil Americans is typically that of the poet toward the purple cow:

> I've never seen a fossil man,
> I never hope to see one,
> But I can tell you anyhow,
> I'd rather see than be one.

It now begins to appear, however, that the perennial heroism of one Dutch boy at the dyke is likely to prove insufficient to stop the increasing trickles of fossil man through the geological defenses. Dr. Hrdlička is already forced to use not only one finger but all of his capable digits to plug the holes, and still they come.

To me it seems clear that the Late Pleistocene antiquity of a human skeleton found in the New World cannot be refuted by a demonstration of the modernity of its anatomical characters alone. *Homo sapiens* was full-fledged in the Old World before the end of the glacial period. Late glacial entrants into the Americas need not prove their age by an array of archaic and simian physical features. The acid test of their antiquity must be geological. For example, even that most promising of recent aspirants, the Minnesota Lady, can evoke from physical anthropologists by way of morphological comment no more than the classic remark of Little Red Ridinghood: "Oh, grandmother, what big teeth you have!" Her physical status is wholly subordinate to the question of whether she did or did not fall into pro-glacial Lake Pelican. On the whole, it seems to me that American anthropologists, without relaxing their determination to submit each find of allegedly fossil man to every possible test of archaeological, geological, and palaeontological antiquity, should not impose unreasonable morphological restrictions upon candidates for recognition. A proper scientific caution is admirable, but it must be remembered, in extenuation of the sporting British attitude toward finds, that the battle of Waterloo is said to have been won on the playing-fields of Eton and lost by the Old Guard which died but never surrendered. We need not be either play-boys or Old Guards.

Psychology of the Individual Discoverer and Describer

The psychology of the individual discoverer or original describer of a specimen of fossil man is a very important factor in coloring the interpretation of any find. However, it is not difficult to make allowance for this personal equation, since it appears to be relatively constant as compared with the variability of national anthropological attitudes. The tendency toward aggrandizement of a rare or unique specimen on the part of its finder or the person to whom its initial scientific description has been entrusted, springs naturally from human egoism and is almost ineradicable. It manifests itself in a number of interesting and familiar ways. First of all the student is sure to realize that he is probably enjoying his unique opportunity to describe and to associate himself with a specimen which bids fair to attain the exclusive ranks of key fossils in human evolution. There are not enough fossil men to go round among the physical anthropologists. He therefore is determined to leave no bone unturned in his effort to find new and striking peculiarities which he can interpret functionally or genealogically. Unless he is very experienced, he is prone to discover new features which are partially the creations of his own concentrated imagination and partially individual variants which have been noticed, but not emphasized, by previous students in unspectacular contemporary skeletons. He may even perpetrate through lack of anatomical experience a bizarre and erroneous reconstruction which demands some preposterous deviation from the norms of human stance, gait, or morphology. However, I am not particularly concerned with mistakes due merely to over-eagerness and ignorance.

Of much more importance is the psychological conflict in which the discoverer or describer is torn between his desire to find primitive, unique, or anthropoidal features which will enable him to place his specimen nearer to the apes than any previously recorded, and his equally powerful urge to demonstrate the direct and central position of his new type in the ancestry of modern man. When the former impulse gains the mastery, the author is likely to blow the dust off his Greek and Latin dictionaries and perpetrate some horrid neologism in creating a new zoölogical species, genus, or even family, thereby committing simultaneously mortal sins in both philology and taxonomy. If, on the other hand, he is overpowered by the yearning for a type ancestral to *Homo sapiens*, he may seize upon metrically or morphologically insignificant features common to both as evidence of their genetic relationship. In my opinion Weidenreich's recent and otherwise wholly admirable monograph upon the mandibles of Sinanthropus is slightly marred by his straining for Mongoloid affinities in the mandibular torus, a bony growth on the inside of the lower jaw which is of very dubious genetic or racial significance.

Again, there is very rarely any inclination on the part of discoverers or original describers to minimize the geological age of their pet specimen, or to exaggerate any difficulties which may arise concerning the possibly intrusive nature of their positions or the correctness of assigning to one individual separate skeletal parts found at varying distances from each other in a supposedly identical stratum. In fact, one has grown to distrust the geological and archaeological descriptions and pronouncements of physical anthropologists almost as thoroughly as the anthropological judgments of geologists and archaeologists. On the whole, it would seem advisable for the different classes of evidence pertaining to any important find of fossil man to be presented by separate experts in the respective fields.

In addition to the frailties inseparable from the enactment of the rôle of original describer, one must also discount the author's previous commitments on the subject of fossil man, the ghosts of earlier opinions which rise to haunt him in the interpretation of new evidence. It is, I think, an excellent rule for a scientist to close forever the pages of his works when once published, and to try to forget their contents. Otherwise he is likely to adhere to his ancient errors and unconsciously to try to fit new data into an outmoded Procrustean bed of his own manufacture. Perennial consistency in the views of an anthropologist is synonymous with stubborn persistence in the wrong. If you do not change your mind, it petrifies. My conclusion is that a dispassionate interpretation of new fossil evidence is usually obtainable only when one awaits the reworking of the material by persons not emotionally identified with the specimen.

II. BIOLOGICAL INTERPRETATIONS OF FOSSIL MAN

Misinterpretations Due to Scanty Evidence and to Defective Appreciation of the Range of Human Variability

Thus it appears that we have to make ample allowance for contemporary human psychology before we can achieve any just appraisal of the biology of fossil man. We may now examine certain fallacies and biological misinterpretations which may be charged to scantiness of a given array of fossil evidence or to defective appreciation of the range of human variability.

In a more credulous phase of science it was popularly believed that a palaeontologist could reconstruct the skeleton of an animal extinct scores of millions of years ago from a single toe bone, and further that he could clothe the bones with flesh and integument, and give an accurate account of posture, gait, dietetic habits, mental capacity, and disposition of said animal. Such feats of creative imagination were actually accomplished and credited in an age of innocence, happily now departed. Although the anatomy of man and of the anthropoid apes rests upon a much firmer basis of factual knowledge than does that of the dinosaurs, for example, no anthropologist is justified in reconstructing the entire skeleton of an unfamiliar type of fossil man from parts of the skull cap, one or two teeth, and perhaps a few oddments of mandible and long bones. The conditions of the preservation of geologically ancient human remains usually preclude the recovery of more than a few scattered fragments of one individual. Inferences concerning the missing parts are very precarious, unless more complete skeletons of other individuals of the same type are available to support the reconstruction. Quite obviously many anthropologists or anatomists who have undertaken to describe types of fossil man have been unfamiliar with the vast range of morphological and metrical variation demonstrable within single racial groups of contemporary man when represented by adequate skeletal series. Consequently new races, species, and genera are sometimes created on the basis of defective specimens showing a few variations which may be due merely to age, sex, or individual peculiarity. Even in the case of Neanderthal man, long represented by a goodly array of incomplete skeletons, it is now evident that conceptions of the rigidity of his type, based upon Western European finds, are completely erroneous. The ever-growing collection of Sinanthropus specimens teaches the same lesson. If these specimens had been recovered in half a dozen widely separated parts of the earth and had been described by as many anatomists, the latter would possibly have created as many new species or even genera of man. The business of taxonomy, or zoölogical classification (pigeon-holing), works well enough for coarse categories, such as classes, subclasses, orders, suborders, and families. Like big business in the commercial world, it masquerades under a guise of efficiency and accuracy which proves to be illusive under close examination. Formerly I was under the impression that taxonomic indiscretions were peculiar to anthropologists, but now I am convinced that a zoölogical classificationist may be as dissolute and irresponsible as a lightning-rod salesman. Further, the more I inspect the family trees of man, so facilely constructed by students of human palaeontology, including myself, the more I am inclined to agree with the poet that "only God can make a tree."

One of the most egregious errors which has vitiated interpretations of fossil man, arises from the mistaken conception that in animal evolution all parts of the organism advance harmoniously, symmetrically, and *pari passu* in the same direction, so that a big brain is inevitably associated with reduced jaws, large brow-ridges with a receding forehead, etc. This supposition, which is refuted by the anatomy of every contemporaneous type of man, has been responsible not only for most of the rash reconstructions of the missing parts of fossils, but also for the violent dismembering of unfortunate fossil individuals whose skeletal parts include both ultra-modern and simian features. If, on the Day of Judgment, the assembling of bones incidental to a carnal resurrection should be entrusted to anatomists, I have no doubt that many of us would find ourselves skeletally defective, a goodly share of our osseous parts having been assigned to hypothetical giant gibbons or to fictitious fossil chimpanzees.

Lamarckianism and Functional Explanations

If inferences as to the form of missing skeletal parts cannot be drawn securely from the morphology of those portions recovered, deductions of function from the form of bony parts are often even more dubious. In the first place it appears that the assumption that every little process on a bone has a meaning of its own, is almost certainly fallacious. The fact that I have inherited a cow-lick where the hair grows down my neck does not mean that I keep my coat collar turned up, thus pushing the hair the wrong way, nor that my grandfather did. A supracondyloid process on the humerus is a lower mammalian characteristic, but Professor R. J. Terry found it exceedingly rare in criminals and prostitutes and present in 11.76 per cent of the Harvard Seminar in Anthropology. I find in the most recent pronouncement of Professor Eugene Dubois, the discoverer of *Pithecanthropus erectus,* this statement with respect to the Kedung Brubus mandible, attributed by him to that species:

... the extensive anterior attachment of the digastric muscle shows that *Pithecanthropus* was devoid of the human power of speech.[2]

Now I do not believe that our knowledge of the physiological correlates of anatomical minutiae justifies such a conclusion, nor that the absence of genial tubercles carries any similar implication of a lack of linguistic ability in other fossil men; nor even that the prominence of the inferior frontal convolution in this same specimen *Pithecanthropus* (discovered also by Broca in a chimpanzee which presumably could not speak) indicates, as Tilney has claimed, that *Pithecanthropus* had learned to speak.[3] I have no time here to expatiate further upon the very numerous instances in which the functional deductions from morphological features in fossil man, have been made, in my opinion, without experimental justification.

"Laws" of Human Evolution—Irreversibility, Convergence, Natural Selection, Mutation, Orthogenesis

I am also profoundly suspicious of the so-called "laws" of organic evolution, which, it seems to me, frequently "are more honored in the breach than in the observance." I should first of all like to pay my respects to the law of irreversibility, by suggesting that the real irreversibility exists not in the evolutionary processes of nature, but in the mental processes of the palaeontologists who invoke it. The re-elongated snout of the baboon, with its frontally directed eyes and stereoscopic vision, the claws of the marmoset, the supernumerary molars of the orang-utan, the high incidence of persistent metopic sutures in the White races of *Homo sapiens,* are a few of the difficulties which obstruct the enforcement of this law.

Convergence in evolution implies, as I understand it, the tendency of unrelated or of only remotely related animal groups to acquire or develop similar bodily characters in response, presumably, to identical functional needs, or to the molding force of similar environments. Many undoubted examples of this phenomenon can be attested in animals known to be genetically far apart. It is very difficult indeed to make a certain determination

[2] Dubois, Eugene, "On the Fossil Human Skulls Recently Discovered in Java and Pithecanthropus erectus," *Man,* XXXVII, 1, p. 2, January, 1937.
[3] Tilney, Frederick, *The Brain from Ape to Man,* Vol. II, p. 875, N. Y., 1928.

of convergence when the phenomena under examination occur within groups of animals belonging to the same order, or to more nearly related zoölogical categories. It may and, I am afraid, often does become a matter of one's prejudices. If the student looks upon the relationship between two animal groups as very remote, he invokes convergence to explain detailed and troublesome morphological similarities. If, on the other hand, he is desirous of strengthening and shortening the ties of blood relationship, he may regard the same similarities as due to a proximate community of descent. Since, in both cases, proof is usually lacking, the discussion is apt to degenerate into a mere exercise in dialectics.

Parallelism, as an expression of the thesis that the descendants of common ancestors tend to evolve along the same lines, provides another way of escape for those who desire to emphasize the remoteness rather than the proximity of relationship. As Le Gros Clark has recently pointed out, this principle is mainly another way of expressing that of Orthogenesis.[4] The latter implies continuous change of the organism along limited and prescribed lines, independently of, or contrary to, environmental influences. In the relation of one type of fossil man to another, or of fossil man to modern man, I see no present method of disentangling the applications of these principles or laws from the prejudices of individual interpreters.

Saltatory evolution, by way of mutation, is a very convenient means of bridging over gaps between animal forms, when the putative descendant differs radically in one or another feature from its supposed ancestral type. A mutation involves the conception of an abrupt change in some feature of the organism due to an alteration of the germ plasm, perhaps spontaneous, perhaps environmentally actuated. Under the latter interpretation it has been utilized as a method of getting round the difficulty of introducing functional adaptations or acquired characters into the germ plasm. Now I am afraid that many anthropologists (including myself) have sinned against genetic science and are leaning upon a broken reed when they depend upon mutations.[5] The

---

[4] Clark, W. Le Gros, *Early Forerunners of Man*, p. 287, London, 1934.
[5] In this connection, a quotation from Professor Dubois (*op. cit.*, p. 6) seems pertinent: ...I undertook the search for laws which regulate cerebral quantity in mammals, and entered into studies, which should furnish evidence as to the place of *Pithecanthropus erectus* in the zoölogical system. They led, finally, to the law of *progressive cerebration*

evidence of modern experimental genetics seems to indicate that most mutations are harmful, and that many of them are even lethal, and that they are attributable in the main to deterioration or weakening, affecting parts of chromosomes or genes. If this be the case, we should do well to cease our blithe references to "progressive" mutations whereby man has ascended the steps of primate evolution, with occasional exuberant bounds in which he clears two or three at one time.

In concluding this incomplete commentary upon the utilization of biological theory and of so-called evolutionary laws in the interpretation of fossil man, I should say that many anthropologists (again including myself) have employed terminology without precision, and sometimes with a woeful ignorance of its implications. We would better confine ourselves to morphological and metrical description and comparison, unless we are to educate ourselves more thoroughly in experimental zoölogy and genetics.

III. THE BIOLOGY OF FOSSIL MAN

Our actual knowledge of the biology of fossil man has been derived from inference rather than from observation. This inferential knowledge has been based mainly upon four classes of evidence: that afforded by the infra-human primates, that derived from the skeletal and cultural remains of fossil man himself, the analogy of the contemporary savage, and our own biological capacities and limitations (only partially known and realized).

The diet, posture, social habits and intelligence of the anthropoid apes and lower primates, incompletely studied as yet, nevertheless are destined to provide some of the most substantial bases for inferences concerning late prehuman and early human biology. For various reasons, but particularly because of their durability and indigestible nature, the teeth constitute perhaps the most important means of tracing the ancestry and relationships of prehuman primates. Form and pattern, particularly of the molars, have been made principal criteria of descent. It is altogether im-

by great leaps (mutations), the law that the phylogenetic growth of the cerebrum proper —or psychencephalon the most central part of the nervous system—excited by modifications of animal functions ("specialization") was automatically discontinuous, the volume, and the number of the nerve cells increasing by abrupt doubling, which implies progressive organization by degrees.

perative that the dietetic and functional implications of tooth form among existing primates be thoroughly investigated. It is almost impossible to overemphasize the importance of diet for the whole subject of human evolution. One may point with a great deal of satisfaction to the recent study of the diet of the chimpanzee, made by Nissen in French Guinea, and to other researches of Professor Yerkes and his associates, as beginning at last to lay the precise factual bases which must serve for the erection of any substantial scientific edifice of fossil human and prehuman biology. Again, more accurate studies of posture, locomotion, and the relation of anatomical form to function in apes and other primates are sorely needed for the interpretation of unfamiliar morphological features and problems of proportions in fossil remains of man and his forbears. It is hardly necessary to say that investigations of the wild life of the various primates, such as those of Carpenter and Zuckerman, are finally offering to students of social origins reliable data wherewith to attempt the reconstruction of man's social past. Similarly, invaluable researches on the psychological side by Yerkes and his school, in comparative anatomy by Schultz and others, and in primate physiology by a goodly number of skilled investigators, make the prospect of indirect illumination of man's past through these methods altogether bright.

Inferences from the Skeletal and Cultural Remains of Man Himself

I have already commented upon the insufficiency of our knowledge of the relation of form to function in interpreting the skeletal remains of ancient man. Certain other large lacunae, such as an understanding of growth rhythms and age changes, together with the extent of sex variation, are sure to be filled by the continued exploitation of such treasuries of human evolutionary data as have been uncovered at Choukoutien, in the caves of Mt. Carmel, and as will be revealed elsewhere. It is also clear that small use has been made up to now of the cultural remains of fossil man which are capable of yielding information about his biology. A brief article on the food of Peking man, recently published by Ralph W. Chaney, is a savory foretaste of the feast of information which may be available to us when botanists, archaeologists, and zoölogists turn their attention to expert interpretation of the masses of evidence found in primitive man's habitations. Dr. Chaney[6] emphasizes the amount of ashes accumulated and the use of fire in cooking the flesh of game animals, as indicated by fragments of charred bone. He also offers a very convincing argument for the use of the fruits of the hackberry tree as a part of the diet of Peking man. It should be noted that Dr. Chaney supports his contention with the results of experiments, in which dried hackberry fruits were fed to rodents and to monkeys, in order to investigate the condition in which the shells were left.

Inferences from Observations of Contemporary Savages

Contemporary primitive folk have long been regarded as a source of information to be used in interpreting the enigmatic cultural remains of fossil man. It is very hard to realize how much more information than we possess at present is procurable from modern savages, unless one is familiar with the careful and exhaustive records of the technological processes still practiced by the tribes of Western Australia, which are being collected by the anthropologists of the University of Adelaide. It is certain that much of the biology of ancient and even fossil man can be learned inferentially from a study of these tribes. The region ought to be a Mecca for archaeologists who devote their lives to the typology of palaeolithic stone implements without ever seeing a savage use an ax.

Inferences from Our Own Biological Capacities and Limitations

Possibly the greatest untapped source of information concerning the biology of fossil man lies in our own biology. Man tries to know everything but himself. He builds up a vast educational system devoted to teaching the young what he himself has done and thought and in preparing them to do and think likewise. He reserves the examination of his own vital processes for the medical profession, which is permitted to function only in the emergency of stomach aches. If a fraction of the time which is expended upon the study of history and government were devoted to the study of human biology, we should not find ourselves in the absurd

[6] Chaney, Ralph W., "The Food of 'Peking Man,'" Carnegie Institution of Washington, *New Service Bulletin*, School Ed., Vol. III, no. 25, 1935.

position of trying to reconstruct the biology of fossil man in the light of the ignorance of our own biology.

In conclusion then, we may congratulate ourselves that we have at last reached a pitch of enlightenment in which the priceless remains capable of yielding information as to our ancestry and evolution are being recorded, preserved, and scientifically studied —at least by description, measurement and comparison. We may look forward to true interpretation of these data when the entire field of biology has been more carefully and assiduously cultivated, and when human biology takes its proper place as the sharpest focus of biological research, when the human organism begins to receive a modicum of human attention, even when it is not obviously out of kilter.

PART II

The Biology of Human Races

IO.

PROLOGUE TO ANTHROPOLOGICAL INDISCRETIONS UPON RACE AND NATIONALITY

I SUPPOSE that I lay myself open to the charge of being a nasty bird which fouls his own nest when I say that many anthropologists apparently seek in their profession an escape from man and from human problems. Studying the savage is like going on a picnic; it furnishes a relief from the troublesome contacts of civilization while providing a specious satisfaction in a spurious return to nature. Of course, like a picnic, anthropological field work involves some annoyances, such as getting bugs in your food and in your system, and frequently real hardships and dangers, which may be considered "all a part of the game." I do not mean to imply that all anthropologists do field work merely because they like to play at being primitive, nor yet that they are principally gratifying a lust for romance and adventure, while pretending to themselves that their real object is serious scientific investigation. But I do think that some of them delude themselves with the idea that they are finding out things which are, or will be, useful to civilized man in some vague and undefined way;

whereas in reality they are choosing an easy way of getting out of the personality and other difficulties which beset them in civilized society.

Now I do not for a moment suggest that studies of savages are of no practical utility. Indeed in the following section I have argued quite to the contrary. As I have said in the introduction to this volume, I have a good deal of sympathy for the delight which I and my fellow anthropologists have taken in the comfortable uselessness of our studies; but I feel very strongly that in the present state of world chaos we ought not only to produce whatever we have learned of practical and social value as a result of our studies of primitive peoples, but that we should also orientate our efforts to acquire such knowledge, if we do not possess it. We are altogether too prone to confine our attention to the sort of studies which are completely innocuous and to sidestep the issues which are vital and dangerous. This attitude, of course, is partly a result of justifiable scientific caution, because we alone realize how little is positively known of the anthropological phenomena which lie at the concealed roots of human affairs. Fools rush in and make practical applications while they are still in ignorance of the actual facts. On the other hand a good deal of our remoteness is due to sheer cowardice.

It is rather significant that we have in our Government organization a Bureau of American Ethnology, which is manned by competent and highly trained anthropologists, but that this Bureau of American Ethnology concerns itself exclusively with Indians, who are of negligible importance in our national life. This Bureau has not even had any part in the actual control and administration of Indian affairs, which are directed by a special bureau of mainly political aim and personnel. It should be stated, however, that under the present administration the Bureau of Indian Affairs has been reorganized and is headed by an enlightened individual who is trying to help the Indians rather than merely to exploit them, and who, to this end, is calling into active service the anthropologists who really know and understand the American Indian.

However, the Bureau of American Ethnology is not permitted to concern itself with such infinitely more important anthropological questions as the status and future of the American Negro, and the appraisal of the contributions to our national life of the immigrants of various races and nationalities which are so facilely granted citizenship and a voice in the control of our government. The government ethnologist is supposed to stick to his Choctaw grammars. If our official anthropologists should tackle the Negro problem they would almost certainly discover many things which would arouse political opposition and result in Congress cutting the appropriations which support Government science or even in abolishing the Bureau of American Ethnology. One must not uncover in scientific research any body of facts which reflects discredit upon the wielders of ballots in our democracy.

Government anthropologists are not alone in their desire to "play safe" and to confine their research to harmless subjects. The topic of the anthropological significance of race in our national life is pretty generally taboo, partly because the tradition of the American school of anthropology is to deny or to belittle the importance of race, but partly because we are afraid of it. Racial dogmas have been utilized as political weapons to oppress and even to destroy ethnic and racial minorities in Europe until the very word "race" stinks. It certainly takes small courage on the part of anthropologists to come forward with an impartial statement of the facts pertaining to race which are known in our science, as a means of combating the erroneous theories and malevolent practices of politicians which have brought disgrace upon anthropology. Not very long ago I was approached with the request that I formulate a series of statements about race, based upon the general consensus of anthropological opinion, which should be submitted to a representative group of physical anthropologists who would go on public record as endorsers of this position. The object of such statements was to discourage attempts of any persons or factions to introduce into our national life the sort of political anthropology which is being practiced in Germany. But only one of the physical anthropologists whom I approached was really willing to sign his name to any such statement. I do not blame them; they were very wise. I finally emitted these statements myself in the address reprinted in this section (Plain Statements About Race).

If scientists shy away from the more or less general topic of race, they, in common with others, are even more timorous when it comes to the discussion of the anthropological and sociological significance of nationality.

Differences between Negroes and Whites, or between Mongoloids and Whites or Negroes, are really much greater than "racial" differences; they are almost, if not quite, sub-specific or specific differences. Races are properly physical subdivisions of these three great general groupings of modern man. Within the White division the several races have interbred to such an extent that it is difficult to disentangle them. However, certain racial types and definite blends are predominant in different nationalities. To some extent inbred national physical types have been formed in many parts of the world. Upon this physical and temperamental basis there have been superimposed unities of language, culture, thought, and psychology. Consequently, nationalities, although composed from racially diverse elements, possess a certain amount of physical uniformity which reinforces their cultural and psychological homogeneity. Thus the anthropological potentialities of present day peoples (for good or for evil) are to a great extent expressed by nationality.

Now it would be very difficult to appraise scientifically and impartially the worth of different nations—be it anthropological worth, sociological, economic, or any other criterion of evaluation. However, I suppose that no intelligent person seriously thinks that all nations are of equal worth; some of them are undoubtedly very worthy and others almost worthless. Presumably it would be perfectly feasible for a French anthropologist to study and appraise the German nation, not only from the standpoint of purely descriptive anthropology but also with reference to its quality. It would be difficult but not impossible to evaluate the Germans racially, culturally, and psychologically, and to compare them with, for example, the Portuguese. This type of national anthropological study has usually been confined to physical characteristics without any correlation of culture and with no attempt at comparison with the anthropology of other nations, except on the purely physical side.

Not even the physical anthropologist really cares a fig whether the people of a given nationality have round heads or long heads, blue eyes or brown, except in so far as these physical features may be related to the character and behavior of their possessors. What we all really like or dislike about people is the character or personality, habits and modes of thought, which we associate with their physical appearance. But we identify human groups by physique, language, and nationality. In our own country, where all have adopted a common language and acquired the same nationality, groups of diverse foreign origins are still distinguishable, partly by surnames, partly by physical anthropological characters, and very largely by their psychology, their behavior, and their various cultural traditions. There is usually some physical basis for such identification.

It is certainly a fact that Jews are racially mixed and of diverse physical origin; that they come from many different nationalities and are not even unified linguistically. Nevertheless, the majority of them are identifiable on physical grounds, because they are, on the whole, inbred, and have disseminated certain dominant features throughout the majority of individuals of their group. They have been subjected for many centuries to a rigid process of physical and social selection. In other words, they do manifest a certain measure of physical, psychological, and cultural unity. It is not exclusively racial; it is not national; it is not linguistic; but it is in some degree all of these, and it is anthropological. I cite this instance because it is so obvious; but the same is true to a lesser or greater degree in the case of national groups, as for example the Irish or the Finns.

Now in this country we have large blocs of most European nationalities which usually retain for a protracted period their national anthropological unities. Of course, we like to pretend that, as soon as they become naturalized and produce offspring who are American citizens by birth, they become *ipso facto* identical in physique, language, culture, psychology, and economic worth with all the rest of our inhabitants. Such an idea is sheer nonsense. It is perfectly possible that Irish-Americans or Italian-Americans are superior or inferior in general social and physical worth to the so-called Old American stocks of English or other descent. It is futile to deny that these various groups exhibit differences; they themselves contravene such denial by their group cohesiveness. They flock together in religion, politics, and occupation. They tend to concentrate in certain states, cities, rural districts, and urban areas. They manifest distinctive criminal proclivities and tend to be concentrated at different economic levels. Each of these national groups is likely to have its pet antipathies and affinities for one or another of the similarly integrated population blocs. Each tends to outmarry into preferred national groups. The birth rates, death rates, and fecundity of these groups also vary, as do their disease immunities and susceptibilities. Is there any doubt that the contributions of these various groups to our national life are of different average values?

I think it is the business of the anthropologist to attempt to ascertain the biological characteristics and potentialities of these American groups and to relate them to cultural characteristics. Of course, sociologists have concerned themselves to a considerable extent with studies of the various ethnic groups which comprise our population, but usually without reference to the biological side. When I began a study of the relation of race and nationality to crime in the United States, I encountered a good deal of sociological opposition, partly because criminology is to a great extent the preserve of the sociologist, as has been also the study of nationalities, but largely because of an emphasis upon the biological and anthropological aspects of the problem, to which social scientists (almost invariably environmentalists) are opposed. I have persisted in that enterprise and the data, soon to be published, will undoubtedly bring upon me an even greater unpopularity than that which I at present enjoy, because these findings reveal certain of our national and racial groups in a very unpleasant light with respect to their anti-social activities. Of course, data of this character are available in the census reports; but there seems to be a strong disinclination on the part of those who compile such reports and those who study them to discuss or to emphasize the invidious distinctions inherent in the tabulated facts. If we are to set our national house in order, we shall have to grapple with these matters.

It should be stated emphatically that there is very little probability that any studies of ethnic groups in this country, however intensive, will demonstrate the generally undesirable character of any specified national element of our population. Each is likely to manifest a complete range of physical, mental, and social characteristics, from utter worthlessness to transcendent capacity. The modal characteristics of the various groups, their average biological status, and the mean worth of their contributions to our national life are certain to vary. We ought to ascertain the nature of such variations.

II.

THE BIOLOGY OF PRIMITIVE HUMAN SOCIETIES[1]

It seems to me that many of the main trends of scientific studies are peculiar—not to say perverse. The pursuit of science and of knowledge in general is, I suppose, an idiosyncrasy exclusive to the genus Homo. Scientists are all men: they admit it and are, presumably, not altogether dissatisfied with their zoölogical status. However, in spite of the fact that science is of man, the direction of scientific endeavor seems to be mainly centrifugal or perhaps homofugal. I mean that the quantity of scientific interest in any phenomenon or in any conglomeration of matter seems to vary directly with its remoteness from man himself. Thus, there are scores if not hundreds of scientists who are looking for new stars and investigating spiral nebulae for everyone who is studying anthropoid apes. Popular interest wallows in the eccentric wake of professional science. The Century of Progress Exposition was

[1] An address given at a Symposium upon "Biology and Society," conducted by the American Naturalists, Dec. 30, 1933. Reprinted from *The Scientific Monthly*, October, 1934, Vol. XXXIX, pages 302-313.

nightly illuminated by a ray from Arcturus in the pompous setting of the Court of the Sciences, amid the applause of gaping thousands; the obscure little tent among the side shows which housed the great anthropoid apes was illuminated by such of the sun's rays as could penetrate its canvas, and was patronized during my two visits only by myself and a few straggling urchins.

Again, while one may admire the concentration of biological interest upon algae, annelids, and crustacea, he must deplore the neglect which falls to the lot of mammals, primates, and man himself. The only quantitatively appreciable biological studies which have been directed upon man are those of medicine and surgery—and these are inspired not so much by scientific interest as by fear of death and disease. Even in anthropology (the shamelessly impractical investigation of man) the vast majority of workers direct their efforts toward the careful examination of what man produces by way of material culture or social organization rather than to the determination of what he is by virtue of being a primate. So, we have archaeologists who know all about man's pottery, man's weapons, and man's implements, and nothing about man himself; ethnologists who are preoccupied with systems of kinship, terms of relationship, and the dry bones of social organization, and who care not one whit for the living flesh and blood of the social being; linguists who are willing to let him who will make out the meaning of language, as long as they can study the grammar and the syntax. And, finally, I fear that we have physical anthropologists whose interest in man does not extend much beyond caliper measurements and statistical tables of means, standard deviations, and probable errors, and who thereby commit grievous errors which are not probable but certain.

As a matter of fact, modern men living at a primitive or low level of culture—"savages"—have received a greater share of attention from anthropologists than have civilized men, although too often the sequence of cultural contact has been Christianization, exploitation, extermination, and finally scientific investigation.

It is not my present task to urge the desirability of studying the biology of modern civilized man, pressing though the need of such a study may be; it is rather my privilege to point out the special opportunities afforded to the student of evolution in the observation of biological phenomena among primitive peoples.

These special opportunities may be classified roughly in three categories, which are, to some extent, overlapping and interdependent. Under each of these categories there may be enumerated and discussed several factors which operate in various biological situations to affect or even to determine one or more of the following systems of primitive man's biology: morphology, physiology, pathology, psychology, sociology. Specifically, the three categories of factors which peculiarly affect the biology of primitive man and consequently illuminate certain obscure places in the evolutionary process are: (a) those which arise from the close relationship of primitive man to his physical environment, (b) those which arise from the geographical isolation of primitive groups, (c) those which arise from the supposed mental and physical retardation and the demonstrable cultural "lag" of modern savages. Clearly these categories are not mutually exclusive and some of the factors grouped under each might well be assigned to another. Our chief interest here is to call attention to biological phenomena in primitive man which seem to spring from these categories of causes or influences, whether or not the specific causative factors can be isolated in one of the three main categories recognized.

I have described the first group of factors which particularize the biology of primitive man as those which arise from close relationship to his physical environment. I suppose that no one will dispute the statement that primitive man lives closer to nature than our civilized *Homo insipiens*. It is incredible, for example, that we should find in primitive society hordes of savages squatting before some bare urban Mother Hubbard's cupboard, tightening their belts or their breech-clouts, while food is rotting in the neighboring fields and professors of agriculture are tinkering with the daily price of gold. The primitive agriculturalist raises what he eats and eats what he raises; he does not raise that which he can neither eat nor barter nor sell. The primitive pastoralist drinks the milk from his cows or lets the calves drink it or makes it into cheese and butter; he does not pour it out in spiteful libations upon concrete highroads. He does not, in short, behave like a civilized human being.

Granting, then, that savages are more or less what their name connotes, what are the biologic implications of their environmental symbiosis? The first of these is, I think, the untrammeled operation of natural selection. By this I mean that the individual savage survives for the most part through the hereditary toughness of his organism and through the ability of that organism to batten upon or "eat off" its environment, that is, barring accidents. The savage engages from birth in a single-handed battle against his environment, unabetted by synthetic substitutes for deficient mother's milk, without benefit of orange juice, spinach and pediatricians. He grows up, if at all, in full possession of his tonsils and his appendix. In brief, he is bereft of, or secure from, modern scientific medical attention. Consequently, the savage, in the structure of his organism and in its functioning, presents an object lesson in those physical and physiological variations which have survival value, and in those which are, at any rate, indifferent.

Another factor which arises from the peculiarly close relationship of primitive man to his environment is relative uniformity of physical adaptation. The biological effect of this factor can be illustrated best by the contrasting diversity which civilized man exhibits in this respect. In our society division of labor effects stringent occupational selection, which is, in part, physical. Thus a professional pianist will have an extraordinary muscular development of the fingers, wrists and forearms; a ten-day bicycle-racer, of the thighs and calves; a jockey must be undersized and light; traditionally a policeman is likely to have flat feet. A few years ago I undertook a physical survey of the criminals of ten states. This involved also the necessity of securing adequate samples of the civilian population of similar ethnic origin with which to compare the physical characteristics of the delinquents. It was found to be extremely difficult to round up for measurement a sufficient number of suitable subjects for inclusion in this civilian check sample. One of my energetic and ambitious young field workers managed to get permission to measure the firemen of Nashville, Tennessee, for comparison with criminals from that state. However, this check sample has proved rather unsatisfactory, principally because the firemen are extraordinarily fat. Whether this corpulence is an effect of sitting in the fire-houses all day playing checkers, or the natural result of selecting a body of men on the basis mainly of political affiliation, or what not, I am unable to say. At any rate, without laboring the point, it may be stated that the adult male population of urban residence in civilized countries is differentiated physically by occupation to such an extent as to render it quite impracticable to examine the physical characteristics of large groups without making careful allowance for the specializations which may be due to occupational composition.

On the other hand, savages are likely to show physical adaptations which are uniform in groups rather than diversified in individuals. If one of a group shows variations of the femur and tibia which may be attributed to walking with a bent-knee gait, the chances are that all or nearly all of the group will show in varying degree similar adaptations, because they all live in the same kind of country and their bodily habits are similar. Lack of occupational specialization does not bring about the multiplicity of individual variations and adaptations which are very baffling to the anatomist or physical anthropologist who is working over the skeletal parts of tame Whites. This simplifies the problem immensely for the student of functional adaptation, since in any primitive group he is likely to be presented with a large range of similar variations which he can analyze and interpret and from which he can generalize with comparative safety. It provides him with adequate and representative samples of the same modifications. Any anonymous skeleton of a White derived from a dissecting room is likely, on the contrary, to present a combination of morphological variations apparently due to physiological causes, which are inexplicable without the knowledge of the occupation of the individual who manifested them. I have an articulated skeleton in my laboratory which shows such peculiarities of the thigh bones and certain other parts that I have vacillated between speculations as to whether the man in life was a tailor, a Turk, or one of those Russian performers who do that peculiar squat-and-kick Cossack dance. Alas, these poor Yoricks! We did not know them well, or at all, and we can make very little of their remains.

Sir Arthur Keith relates that he examined the supposed mummy of the Pharaoh of the Exodus and identified him as the veritable Pharaoh who repeatedly "hardened his heart," since he showed clear signs of arterio-sclerosis. But even this exact pathological-historical correlation involves a slight difficulty, since the mummy in question was not recovered from the bottom of the Red Sea.

The uniformity of the organic regimen in savages permits us to make reasonably certain deductions as to the relationship between their diets, their habits, and their physiques. The Eskimo, for example, presents an excellent opportunity for studying the effect upon the body of an almost complete subsistence upon fish and flesh—generally raw. Many of the American Indians lived principally upon maize; others depended largely upon buffalo meat; while still others had as their staple of diet salmon or manioc. Certain pastoral tribes of Africa confine themselves almost exclusively to milk, beef, and blood; the milk of the camel is the main article of food among some desert nomads; many of the congested populations of Asia live principally upon rice. Of course, it is by no means universally the case that primitive peoples have unvaried diets consisting of one or two staple foods. As a matter of fact, many if not most savages eat almost anything which is masticable and will serve to fill an aching void and provide a slight amount of nutrition. Even the latter consideration is frequently neglected in some substances which are devoured by peoples in impoverished environments.

It is hardly necessary to contrast with the local group uniformity in dietetic habits which prevails among primitive peoples the extraordinary diversity of diets which civilized man can command and does utilize. Modern means of transportation and of refrigeration permit the individual not only to vary his diet to an almost unbelievable degree but also to indulge in many gastronomic specializations according to his constitutional type, his prejudices, and his pocketbook. This again makes the interpretation of the individual's biology difficult if not impossible, unless you know what he eats and how much he eats. Some years ago Professor E. L. Miloslavich devoted himself to a somewhat bizarre anthropometric research—that of measuring the length of the large intestine in various ethnic groups. He found that he was able to classify his material in three main categories: (1) persons with short colons (brachycolic, up to 160 cm.), (2) those possessing colons of moderate length (orthocolic, 160 cm.–175 cm.), (3) those presenting long colons (dolichocolic, over 175 cm.). Miloslavich established the fact that medium-gutted types were particularly characteristic of Central Europe (Croats, Slovenes, Czechs, Germans, German Austrians); short-gutted types were at a maximum among Magyars, Asiatic Turks, Asiatic Russians and West Poles; whereas the dolichocolic group included most of the Southeastern Europeans (Serbs, Montenegrins, Russians, Slovaks, Rumanians, European Turks, Ruthenians).

Our visceral investigator was cautious in drawing conclusions from his data, but he intimated that changes in environment may influence the length of the colon, just as head form changes in the children of immigrants born in this country. Thus European Turks tend to show Balkan rather than Anatolian types of colon, whereas East Prussians have apparently added a cubit or two to their colic length by sojourning in the Slavic region. Possibly diet has something to do with these variations—a statement which brings me to the point of this illustration. It is well-nigh impossible to make correlations of diet with anatomy and physiology in civilized European peoples because of their promiscuous feeding habits. Thus we are left in an unhappy state of uncertainty as regards the significance of our colic lengths; whether, if they are short, it is because we are or ought to be carnivorous; or if there are any vegetarian or frugivorous implications of dolichocoly. Contrast with this the pleasing certainty of deduction which attaches to recent and as yet unpublished researches of my friend, Professor George D. Williams, of Washington University, who has been soaking up the desiccated tissues of some Eskimo mummies from Greenland. Dr. Williams and his colleague, Dr. H. A. McCordock, have identified roentgenographically and histologically a large number of the calcified eggs of fish tapeworm in the liver of one of these defunct Eskimos. Now we know that raw fish is a staple of Eskimo diet. We need not worry about the individual tastes and habits of Eskimos—an Eskimo must eat fish and does eat fish, whether he likes it or not, and he often eats it raw. Therefore the incidence of fish tapeworm among Eskimos does not depend upon the idiosyncrasies of individual Eskimos as much as upon the degree of tapeworm infestation of the fishes they eat. In other words, if we find a tapeworm in a civilized individual we can infer only that the person in question has eaten something from which he acquired a tapeworm; but if we find it in a savage, we may plausibly deduce that the same kind of unwelcome guests are probably running riot or living riotously in many of his fellow savages who subsist on precisely the same diet.

A second category of factors which contributes to the peculiar instructiveness of primitive biology is that which arises from the geographical isolation of savages. The first of these factors is the intensification of hereditary traits by inbreeding. This leads to clear demonstrations of genetic factors in the production of physical types and illuminates the causes of racial differentiation. It may be that it is isolation which keeps the savage savage, or it may be that the savage becomes isolated because he is a savage. In any event it is certain that only isolation keeps the savage alive, since he is almost invariably exterminated by contact with civilized peoples. I recently heard a highly educated Pueblo Indian girl comment with gentle irony upon the elaborate celebration of Thanksgiving Day forced upon the Indian children in the government schools of the Southwest. Certainly no savage has reason to be thankful for the invention and development of modern means of transportation or for anything else which has made him accessible to the lethal White. There is even some reason to doubt whether the bringing of all parts of the world close together has been an unmixed blessing to civilized nations. Facile communication is as likely to lead to trouble as to better understanding.

Be that as it may, civil communications corrupt good savages. Isolation means salvation for the savage, and for the biologist who studies him it means that his subjects are protected within the walls of a natural laboratory. Since the only areas which remain isolated today are those which are relatively unsuitable for the maintenance of the large populations of domesticated man, the savage generally has to live in environments which do not favor or permit a great increase in his numbers. Consequently, intensive inbreeding takes place. This effects the isolation of homozygous types. The combinations of recessive characters which result are often very unfavorable, but the persons possessing such combinations tend to be eliminated by natural selection, leaving the dominants purified of abnormalities, monstrosities, and serious weaknesses. I have no interest here in arguing the relative merits of inbreeding and outbreeding in human stocks. It is my task merely to point out that the rapid isolation of homozygous factors in man as a function of the intensity of inbreeding may best be observed among savages.

It seems probable that most of the hereditary physical characteristics which we utilize as criteria of racial types are either favorable variations which have a survival value, or indifferent variations which are dominant, or variations which are alike beneficial and dominant. There is little or no chance of appraising the significance of racial variations or of other physical variations in the stew of hybridized populations living under artificial conditions of civilization. Here recessive weaknesses of hereditary origin are obscured by heterozygosity. They are overlaid by dominant traits to such an extent that probably the majority of us are little better than perambulating whited sepulchers. Recessive combinations of inferiorities are in part protected by a fatuous humanitarianism—immured in prisons, insane asylums, almshouses, and other public institutions. But many of them stalk or hobble unrecognized through the civilized scene, playing every occupational rôle, but none of them well. Under these conditions genetic observations are well-nigh impossible, on account of the lack of pure lines, the presence of an infinite variety of mixed strains, the complexity of the environmental setting, and the benevolent interference of science and social uplift with the operation of a purgative natural selection.

On the other hand, if the geneticist or the eugenist (and I do not mean by the latter a Nordic propagandist) is permitted to make his observations in a relatively homogeneous savage society, he can note the inheritance of features which appear to be racial and those which are suspected to be adaptive; he can judge to some extent whether characters are dominant or recessive, and can even hazard a guess as to the survival value of certain physical variations. If recessive features crop out he can observe the biological fate of those manifesting them, since among primitive peoples there are few if any obstacles interposed in the path of ruthless natural selection. If any physical variation is functionally advantageous, that advantage can be most readily discerned in groups which have not departed so far from the state of nature as to deprive the variation of its utility. If the woolly hair of the Negro has any survival value, that value must be determined by studies in tropical Africa, not in Harlem.

Yet another factor arising from the isolation of primitive groups and contributing to the profit of biological study of savage peoples is the range of environmental accommodations of the human organism which they present. Savages live, for the most part, in the remote places of the world. Wherever there is a place left for savages it is undesirable from the point of geographical location, climate, or other detrimental features of the environment. The fever-infested swamps, the tropical jungles with their profusion of disagreeable flora and deadly fauna, the deserts with their poverty of nearly everything except sand and heat, the chilly inhospitality of the circumpolar regions—these are all the homes of primitive man. He has to get along in the regions which no civilized man cares to inhabit. Consequently, primitive peoples live under more diverse ecological conditions than the domesticated members of the human species and of necessity exhibit a wide range of physical and physiological adaptations. Civilized man prides himself upon adapting his environment to himself and it must be admitted that he has had no little success in this direction.

The clearing of forested areas for agriculture, the irrigation of arid lands, draining of swamps and marshes, utilization of water power, destruction of insect and animal pests, are all methods whereby man utilizes or transforms his physical environment, thereby evading in large measure the necessity of adapting himself to that environment. Primitive or savage man has succeeded in ameliorating his environment to a very limited extent only. This is not necessarily because he is more stupid and less inventive than civilized man (although he may be both), but on account of the peculiarly unadaptable and recalcitrant environments to which he has been reduced. Although the savage may have "a goodly heritage," his lines have not "fallen in pleasant places." Practically all the inhabitable temperate zones and most of the endurable tropics have been wrested from him by his decidedly uncivil, though civilized, brother.

Under these circumstances the savage organism has to shift for itself in the most pestilential and dreary spots which the earth affords. Hence if you wish to find out how the human body accommodates itself to a continued existence generation after generation in tropical swamp lands, you must study certain savage tribes of the Amazon basin or of the Nile headwaters, or of other such undesirable places abandoned to the savage. If you are ambitious to discover the effect upon man of a sunless, steamy, tropical jungle, you may investigate the Negritos of Central Africa or of New Guinea. The influence of extremely high altitude upon the human animal can be ascertained among the relatively simple peoples of the Andes or of the Tibetan plateau.

Among the phenomena which arise from the geographical isolation of primitive groups is the stabilization of hybridized types. Race mixtures are most extensive in civilized society, but usually take place under conditions which make scientific observation very difficult and, frequently, impossible. In the first place miscegenation has gone on so long among civilized peoples that an almost infinite variety of mixed types already exists and pure racial types can not be isolated with any degree of certainty. The hereditary combinations have become so numerous as to defy genetic analysis. This is particularly true in the group of races which are crudely classified as "white." Dr. R. R. Marett has remarked that "a casual observer of savage life is apt to imagine it a welter of amatory confusion." [2] He might well have added that a scientific observer of civilized life is forced to regard it as a broth of mongrel promiscuity. Such a statement applies not only to mixtures between the White races in Europe and in the United States, but also to wider racial crosses between radically divergent stocks in most parts of Latin America and in many Asiatic countries.

It is not only the great diversity of racially blended types which makes the study of race mixture so difficult in civilized countries, but also the social stigma under which wide crosses take place. By a wide or radical cross, I mean an interbreeding of two physically divergent races, such as occurs when a North European mates with a Negro. Such mixtures have taken place wherever propinquity has permitted, but usually in a clandestine and surreptitious manner, because of the superior social and economic position of one of the stocks involved and the depressed status of the other. Consequently, the hybrid offspring of such marriages are socially rejected by the dominant and usually paternal race and are relegated to the subordinate stock which absorbs them by backcrossing. Thus there is little or no stabilization of hybrid types but only a small seepage of blood from the socially exalted race to that

[2] R. R. Marett, *Faith, Hope and Charity in Primitive Religion*, p. 77. New York, 1932.

which is socially abased. In course of time such a continued dilution alters the complexion of the recipient race, but only gradually and almost imperceptibly. The great reservoir of so-called American Negroes has been considerably contaminated by this steady trickle of White blood, but not in such a way as to make for the stabilization of a new and relatively homogeneous racial type.

Such a state of genetic obfuscation is not usually brought about by the contact of races under conditions of primitive isolation. One reason for this is that primitive peoples are probably not race-conscious to the deplorable or laudable extent which is characteristic of civilized populations. I mean that they are rather naïvely free from race prejudice until they have learned it from bitter experience. The American Indian was quite ready to take the European literally to his arms until he found out that a civilized embrace was inevitably throttling. Racial crosses effected on a basis of social equality between Whites and primitive races have occurred only in areas of isolation where White men have come without women and without the numerical superiority which enables them to assert their dominance and to enslave their savage hosts. Such conditions have been realized in a number of out-of-the-way places and have resulted in the stabilization of some new and biologically interesting hybridized types. Among the most important of these may be mentioned the Rehoboth hybrids of Southwest Africa, the result of marriages of the Dutch with the Hottentots; the inbred offspring of Tahitians and the English mutineers from the warship *Bounty*, on Pitcairn and Norfolk Islands; the Kisarese mestizos, descended from the mixture of a Dutch garrison with the natives of a lonely East Indian island. The study of these three groups by Fischer, Shapiro, and Rodenwaldt, respectively, has contributed more to the knowledge of the inheritance of racial characters and the genesis of secondary racial types than could possibly be derived from the investigation of any racial mixtures taking place under the congested and infected conditions of civilization.

Another of the reasons why the stabilization of racially hybridized types is likely to occur among primitive peoples in areas of isolation is that sexual necessity knows no law, and islanders can not be choosers. In small primitive groups no maiden is allowed to wither on the virgin stalk, even if she has a touch of the whitewash-brush. A considerable increment of a new racial stock in an isolated primitive population is fairly certain to result in an amalgamation which transforms the entire group, because that group is small and the population inbreeds until the characters of both racial stocks are distributed about in a new and often homogeneous blend. There is no doubt that the Polynesian race originated thus from a tri-racial mixture of some sort of White or Caucasoid stock with Melanesian Negroid and Mongoloid elements. It is still possible to observe the process of race-making by hybridization in areas where primitive races meet and where the mixture subsequently stews in its own juices.

The last general category of special biological opportunities in the study of primitive man is that which arises from the supposed mental retardation and the demonstrable cultural lag of modern primitive men or savages. I am rather dubious as to the validity of this category, since no one has ever proved that savages are in reality mentally retarded or even inferior in intelligence to civilized peoples. Even if this supposed mental retardation exists in fact, it is difficult if not impossible to relate it to biological phenomena in any significant fashion. Again, although there can be no doubt that savages are culturally backward, it is by no means clear that any causal relationship obtains between the inferiority of their material and non-material culture and certain archaic biological patterns which they preserve. On the whole, it seems the part of prudence to look this difficulty boldly in the face and pass on. For there are, at any rate, a number of vestigial biological features which still persist in savage society but have vanished in civilized communities. These are of enormous interest to the student of evolution. They include a number of certainly archaic morphological characters, some possibly primitive physiological processes, and sundry variants of the modern biological family grouping. All these may be classified as survivals. Primitive morphological features, such as protrusive jaws, large teeth, undeveloped chins and small brains, probably owe their preservation in savage groups to a lack of competition with more advanced evolutionary variants. Such scanty genetic evidence as is available seems to indicate that more highly evolved physical characters tend to dominate over those which are less advanced. Thus Negro prognathism is rapidly diminished to the vanishing point in crosses with orthognathous White stocks.

Furthermore, in spite of the vigorous operation of natural selection in primitive society, social selection appears to be in abeyance, at least as far as social selection implies the preferential mating of individuals with highly evolved racial characteristics. Of course social classes and social stratification exist to some extent in savage society, but they are not necessarily, or usually, associated with physical differences, even when the group is racially of composite origin. Correlation of racial physical features with a superior social status seems to depend rather upon the subordination of a culturally primitive people to more advanced newcomers who are racially distinct and who both mingle with the aborigines and at the same time impose upon them their own esthetic ideals of racial beauty. This is a phenomenon typical of race mixture under the special conditions described.

However, in a simple savage group, which is racially comparatively homogeneous, archaic morphological features are likely to be distributed generally in the population and are not subjected to the Mendelian dominance of more highly evolved features brought in by a new race. Nor does any stigma of social inferiority adhere to prognathous jaws and black skins when everyone possesses them. It follows that primitive ancestral traits, whether anatomical, physiological, or sociological, flourish like the green bay tree in isolated savage societies, as long as they are not detrimental to the survival of the species. "If thine eyebrow offend thee, pluck it out" is a maxim which would not be current in an unspoiled primitive group whose racial features include a thick and continuous supraorbital fringe of hair. Man in a state of nature has never learned to despise those features of his physical inheritance which may be reminiscent of an ape ancestry, nor to exalt and select as eugenic ideals bodily traits which may be the end products of degenerative evolution. This idyllic catholicity of taste in bodily beauty is in happy contrast with the perverted fastidiousness in racial characters which has grown up in certain civilized peoples of mixed racial origins.

In Germany the obsession of race has grown from a morbid inferiority complex to a national psychosis. It so happens that the Germans have fallen into the unfortunate habit of taking their science in general, and their anthropology in particular, too seriously. A most important element of their historical and political education is the conscious effort to build up in their citizens a physical ideal of the traditional German, tricked out in Nordic racial lineaments and replete with all the heroic virtues of a superman. Thus the official German is tall, broad-shouldered, lean-flanked and clean-limbed (whatever that may mean), dolichocephalic or long-headed, with golden blond hair, eyes of cerulean blue, fair pink skin (such as one loves to touch), thin, high-bridged nose, uncompromisingly straight in profile or with just a hint of the aquilinity that is aristocratic and not Semitic, thin determined lips, long horse face, and an aggressive chin.

Now this is all very attractive, but quite inaccurate. Comparatively few Germans answer this description. Undoubtedly a far more typical Teutonic portrait would be: short, squat, thick stubby limbs, protrusive abdomen, head flat at the back, bulging at the temples, brachycephalic; hair mousy brown, eyes mixed or beer-colored; skin muddy, nose bulbous, blobby; jowls pendent, lips blubbery, chin multiple. Several other descriptions different from either of the preceding would apply to great hordes of true Germans with sufficient exactitude. The facts of the matter are that the area of the present German Reich has been occupied since early Neolithic times—perhaps six thousand years ago—by three or four different racial stocks of the White division of mankind, and by a great variety of mixed types which have arisen from their interbreeding. At no time is there anthropological evidence that it was wholly populated by golden-haired Nordics, although doubtless this element was predominant in Northern Germany up to early historic times. The result of inculcating into the German people this spurious racial ideal of a supposititious Nordicism has been singularly unfortunate. First of all, it has promoted the development of a process of social and sexual selection which depreciates all racial combinations of physical features except one only. The latter certainly does not represent a crystallization of the sum total of racial virtues, whether physical, mental, or moral.

This lusting after Nordicism has developed in the German people of non-Nordic physical features (and these include the vast majority) a racial inferiority complex which has vicious outlets in several directions. The most sinister activity emanating from this complex has been the persecution and expulsion of the one element in the German population which is generally agreed by Germans to be non-Nordic, or, of late "non-Aryan"—namely, the Jews. Apart from this unfortunate people every German is his own Nordic and is allowed to explain his deviation from the official racial type in a variety of more or less plausible ways. Most of these have been invented by patriotic German anthropologists, who have been forced to the most astounding subterfuges in their attempts to derive the modern brunet, brachycephal Germans from the traditional, blond long-heads.

One of these was the famous but rather unconvincing effort of the Bavarian anthropologist, Ranke, to prove that the Bavarians owed their round-headedness and their dark complexions to a prolonged sojourn in the Alpine foothills. Another ingenious idea related the brachycephalization of the modern Germans to an increase in cranial capacity or brain size. Since a spherical container is the most economical in form, it is quite evident that an accretion of brain mass would tend to transform an egg-shaped skull into one broader relative to its length, if such an increase were accompanied by no general enlargement in body size. However, a slight difficulty in the way of accepting this explanation is the fact that no increase in cranial capacity or in brain size from prehistoric to modern times has been demonstrated in the German population. One of the most amusing efforts to prove that the German people are blond was the pigmentation survey of six million school children carried out by the government soon after the Franco-Prussian war. It is well known that in mixed races containing blond and brunet strains, light hair and eyes manifest themselves temporarily in infancy and childhood, but a subsequent addition of pigment causes darkening of hair and eyes in adolescent and adult life. Neither infantile nor Hollywood blondes can be accepted as unquestionable Nordics.

None of these expedients have succeeded in convincing the Germans themselves, or any one else, that they are predominantly Nordic in their racial characteristics. Hence, they wreak their inferiority complex upon the Jews, and still the inward clamor of their doubts by waving swastikas and by pulling the beards of ancient Israelites (who probably possess as much Nordic blood as they themselves). This lengthy digression into modern biology is not justified by my subject, except in so far as it emphasizes my point that savage societies offer superior advantages for the observation of racial characters and especially for studying archaic morphological patterns, because in contrast to civilized man the savage is naked and unashamed.

I have listed among the special opportunities offered to the biologist in the study of primitive human groups the preservation of physiological processes which are also primitive. Frankly, it is in large measure an assumption, based upon the indubitable fact that archaic morphological patterns are preserved among savages and upon the rather questionable inference of a parallelism between form and function. I take it that the strongest evidence in favor of a primitive type of physiology among savage peoples is found in the higher percentages of such remote groups which exhibit, apparently, the lack of the blood group agglutinogens, A and B, which occur as dominant mutations and have been diffused throughout the more civilized peoples. The vague and uncertain indications among savages of a partial retention of the sexual periodicity which may have characterized our protohuman ancestors are hardly worth a passing mention, since it is now known that apes and monkeys, like man, make love all the year round. Such indications are probably illusory. But the studies of the relation of sex and the reproductive cycle to the social life of baboons, recently carried out by Dr. S. Zuckerman,[3] point clearly the importance of these factors in the social organization of primitive man. The physiology of reproduction, if it does in fact condition the entire social life of man, may best be studied in the simpler savage groups.

The indubitable survival in savage society of primitive variants of the biological family grouping offers a field for research which still retains many fruitful possibilities for the social anthropologist and for the physiologist. In the minds of most civilized peoples there appears to appertain to monogamy a certain moral sanction not dissimilar to that adhering to the conception of monotheism. Both are considered to be now as they were in the beginning and ever shall be, world without end. Somewhat more liberal treatment is accorded to man than to the deity, in that the former is allowed to have, at any rate, one wife. This monorail type of belief and practice does not obtain in all primitive societies. If there has been

[3] Zuckerman, S., *The Social Life of Monkeys and Apes*. New York, 1932.

any sort of evolution of the family in man, its stages can be reconstructed only from the investigation of the higher primates and of primitive man, although the disruption of that grand old institution is abundantly exemplified in civilized society. Whether or not these familial variants in savage groups arise from mental retardation or cultural lag is a question for social anthropologists to answer.

So far you have been treated to an effusion or spattering of reasons why primitive man makes the ideal laboratory animal, supported largely by contra-indications with respect to civilized man. I do not wish to give the impression of a mere sadist flagellating civilized man over the shoulders of the savage. The foregoing pages are, rather, in the nature of a preambulatory survey—a sort of preliminary scientific sniff. The opportunities of savage biology should be discussed under the several headings of morphology, physiology, pathology, psychology and sociology. Obviously none of these subjects can be exhausted within the limits of the present essay.

12.

PLAIN STATEMENTS ABOUT RACE [1]

MAN is a predatory mammal which has achieved dominance over all vertebrates by a ruthless use of superior intelligence. From prehistoric times this ingeniously selfish biped has realized that the greatest gain of power and booty lies in preying upon his own species. It is easier to seize wealth than to create it. Yet a certain quality of benevolence has been at variance with simple brute predaciousness throughout the long struggle for survival and domination which is the history of this super-ape. Thus, man has evolved certain ideals of humanitarian behavior which often manifest themselves in disinterested and self-sacrificing acts on the part of individuals and even of social groups. This apparently innate generosity may or may not be some sort of social extension of a maternal instinct. Through centuries of painstaking cultivation and encouragement it has been built up to a point where it has

[1] An address delivered at the Conference on the Alien in America, held under the auspices of the Foreign Language Information Service, Washington, D. C., May 2, 1936. Reprinted from *Journal of the American Association of University Women*, June, 1936.

sometimes seemed to bid fair to dominate human behavior and thus to inaugurate the millennium. Unfortunately, human altruism seems to disintegrate in political and economic stress, except as an individual phenomenon. It is not a common characteristic of the large political and social groups which we call nations.

Man incessantly seeks to compromise with his conscience or with his innate humanitarianism, by rationalizing his predatory behavior. He must convince himself that the act of grabbing is somehow noble and beautiful, that he can rape in righteousness and murder in magnanimity. He insists upon playing the game, not only with an ace up his sleeve, but with the smug conviction that God has put it there.

We need not speculate upon the arguments with which primitive man presumably convinced himself that he was glorifying God by getting dominion over "the fish of the sea, and the fowl of the air, and over every living thing that moveth upon earth." Possibly the necessity of self-justification arose only when civilization had advanced to the status of cannibalism and slavery, and man had begun to make a real business of battening upon his own kind.

Certainly the specious excuse of racial difference has served ever since Ham saw the nakedness of his drunken father and Noah, awakening from wine with a bad hang-over, exclaimed, "Cursed be Canaan, a servant of servants shall he be to his brethren!" From immemorial antiquity hereditary variations of bodily form have been made the basis of charges of racial inferiority in mentality and in capacity for civilization. With this contemptible subterfuge our European ancestors justified their enslavement of the Negro and their virtual extermination of the Indian and of many other primitive peoples. The "white man's burden" has been mainly one of hypocrisy. With no more savage worlds left to conquer the White man has turned this same vicious argument to use against his own kind, committing more crimes in the name of race than have ever been perpetrated in the name of liberty.

Under these circumstances, a physical anthropologist, who has devoted most of his research activity to the study of race, desires emphatically to dissociate the findings of his science from the acts of human injustice which masquerade as "racial measures" or "racial movements," or even "racial hygiene."

I do not claim to speak for all physical anthropologists, many of whom are either too wise or too timid to speak at all upon this subject, preferring to pursue their researches in academic seclusion, rather than cry their wares in the market-place and run the risk of being pelted by the rabble. For myself, I prefer to be the target of rotten eggs, rather than to be suspected as a purveyor of that odoriferous commodity.

I therefore intend to assert bluntly and simply what I believe to be the best consensus of scientific anthropological opinion upon what races are and what they connote.

1. A "race" is a physical division of mankind, the members of which are distinguished by the possession of similar combinations of anatomical features due to their common heredity.

2. There exists no single physical criterion for distinguishing race; races are delimited by the association in human groups of multiple variations of bodily form and structure—such as amount of pigment in hair, skin, and eyes; form of the hair, shape of the nose, range of stature, relation of head length to head breadth, et cetera. These criteria are of mainly hereditary origin, but none of them is wholly impervious to environmental influences, such as the effects of climate, diet, exercise, and altitude. It follows that race is essentially a zoölogical device whereby indefinitely large groups of similar physical appearance and hereditary background are classified together for the sake of convenience.

3. Anthropologists have found as yet no relationship between any physical criterion of race and mental capacity, whether in individuals or in groups.

4. While it is conceivable that physical races may differ in psychological characteristics, in tastes, temperament, and even in intellectual qualities, a precise scientific determination of such differences has not yet been achieved. Such discrimination, if it is possible, must await the development of better anthropological and psychological techniques.

5. Race is not synonymous with language, culture, or nationality. Race is hereditary; language is a cultural acquisition. A Negro may speak English as his native tongue. There is no Aryan race; Aryan is a term applicable only to a family of languages spoken by populations heterogeneous in race, nationality, religion, and other aspects of culture. There is no "French race" and no "German race," properly so-called. Such terms imply nationality,

use of a common language, and some degree of conformity to a pattern of culture, but nothing more.

6. Physical anthropologists, as yet, are unable precisely to grade existing human races upon an evolutionary scale, upon the basis of the sum total of their anatomical deviations from apes and lower animals. Each race displays a mixture of advanced and primitive characteristics. A definitive rating of the evolutionary rank of each human race presupposes the completion of many anthropological and physiological researches which have not even begun.

7. A "pure" race is little more than an anthropological abstraction; no pure race can be found in any civilized country. Racial purity is restricted, at best, to remnants of savage groups in isolated wildernesses. The present races of man have intermingled and interbred for many thousands of years so that their genealogical lines have become inextricably confused. Physical classifications of race merely attempt to delimit groups of approximate physical uniformity, with a restricted assumption of similar heredity.

8. The composite origin of most of the existing races of man is demonstrable. Thus the Polynesian represents a stabilized blend of White, Negroid, and Mongoloid elements. The so-called Nordic race is probably a hybrid derivative of several strains present in Europe during the glacial period, to which have been added in historic times Alpine, Mongoloid, and other racial elements (carried by Lapps, Finns, Slavs, and other peoples who have mixed with the inhabitants of the "Nordic" area).

9. The study of the results of hybridization between the most physically diverse of modern races—such as the Negro and the Nordic, or the Mongoloid and the brunet Mediterranean White—has not demonstrated that fertility is decreased, or vitality diminished, by such crossings. The hybrids exhibit a wide range of combinations of features inherited from both parental races, but no degeneracy, provided that both parental stocks are normal. It is probable that racial susceptibilities and immunities to certain diseases are different in hybrids from those obtaining in the parental races, but this subject has been insufficiently studied.

10. Within each and every race there is great individual variation in physical features and in mental capacity, but no close correlation between physique and mentality has been scientifically demonstrated. Knowledge of human heredity is still far from

perfect and altogether inadequate as a basis for attempts to secure specific combinations of physical and mental features by selective breeding. A scientifically valid program of eugenics, at the present, must be limited to the restriction of breeding among the insane, diseased, and criminal, and to the encouragement of reproduction in individual families with sound physiques, good mental endowments, and demonstrable social and economic capability.

The scientific method of determining the racial composition of the United States or any other country is to appraise the distribution of type combinations of physical characters in the individual which are known to be hereditary racial features. The sorting of these types is initially made without reference to parentage or national origins of the persons studied. Studies of these physical types in the old American population, in the children of immigrants from other countries, and in residents of alien birth, do not indicate that the racial composition of the United States has been profoundly modified by recent immigrations. Incoming types are virtually identical with those represented in the population resident here for several generations, although the proportions are somewhat modified.

Each racial type runs the gamut from idiots and criminals to geniuses and statesmen. No type produces a majority of individuals from either end of the scale. While there may be specific racial abilities and disabilities, these have not yet been demonstrated. There are no racial monopolies either of human virtues or of vices.

I believe that this nation requires a biological purge if it is to check the growing numbers of the physically inferior, the mentally ineffective, and the antisocial. These elements which make for social disintegration are drawn from no one race or ethnic stock. Let each of us, Nordic or Negro, Aryan or Semite, Daughter of the Revolution or Son of St. Patrick, pluck the beam from his own eye, before he attempts to remove the mote from that of his brother. Every tree that bears bad fruit should be cut down and cast into the fire. Whether that tree is an indigenous growth or a transplantation from an alien soil, matters not one whit, so long as it is rotten.

13.

ABORIGINAL RACIAL TYPES IN AMERICA [1]

Incompatible Conceptions of Race

AMERICAN anthropologists usually deny that Old World cultures have influenced to any great extent the pre-Columbian development of the American Indian. We have set up for aboriginal America a sort of *ex post facto* Monroe Doctrine and are inclined to regard suggestions of alien intrusive influences as acts of aggression. This is probably a scientifically tenable position, although I am afraid that it has often been maintained in part by an emotional bias—an "America for Americans" feeling. Side by side with this dogma of the integrity of American Indian culture, there has grown up the principle of American racial unity, patriotically affirmed by many students of the American Indian who are native to, or naturalized in, the New World, but contemptuously dismissed by certain European anthropologists who divide up the

---

[1] Reprinted (with considerable changes) from *The American Aborigines: their Origin and Antiquity,* a Collection of Papers by Ten Authors Assembled and Edited by Diamond Jenness. Published for Presentation at the Fifth Pacific Science Congress, Canada, 1933. University of Toronto Press, 1933.

American Indian into a variable number of racial types, with the naïve irresponsibility of the cloistered savant classifying nebulous savages in remote wildernesses. It is this question of the racial type and affinities of the American Indian which I propose to examine.

There can be no profitable discussion of a problem stated in terms that are ambiguous or liable to radically different interpretations. It is necessary, therefore, to distinguish between the main prevalent conceptions of the significance of "race" and to deal with the matter from two divergent points of view.

There is one principle, at any rate, to which all anthropologists adhere, despite a diversity of opinion as to the meaning of "race." Race is a matter of physical features and not of cultural characteristics. No reputable anthropologist attempts to define "race" by the aid of linguistic criteria, nationality, social organization, or material culture. Theoretically, also, most competent authorities would probably admit that the bodily characters by which race is distinguished should be heritable, passed on from parents to children. According to this idea race is essentially a close similarity of physical features in a large body of mankind, derived from their common descent.

Here, however, we have reached the parting of the ways, for the environmentalists are unable to satisfy themselves that any bodily character is sufficiently persistent in its inheritance or resistant enough in its morphology to withstand the molding and modifying influence of physical environment and thus to endure through generations as a racial earmark. Again, this same school, which pursues a course parallel with that of the champions of independent invention in the field of cultural anthropology, logically argues that any particular variation of a bodily feature, or any combination of such variations, may conceivably originate at several times, in separate places, and among different human groups which are genetically so distinct that they cannot be assigned to the same "race" unless we broaden the term so as to embrace the whole human species. If climate, food supply, altitude, and other extrinsic forces can transform in a few scores of generations a blue-eyed, fair-haired, rosy-skinned Nordic into the replica of a black-eyed, black-haired, copper-skinned North American Indian, there is obviously no use in studying "race," since there is no such thing as fixity of physical type and no feature sufficiently permanent to serve as a reliable criterion of "race." For such students there can be no such concept as that of "a close similarity of features in a large body of mankind, derived from their common descent"; because such a physically homogeneous group might and probably would owe its community of physical characters to a common environment rather than to identical heredity. Conversely, for such environmentalists physical heterogeneity in a group of mankind could be no indication of racial diversity, since varying environments may well have created new physical types in abundance from the same stock of mankind.

Opposed to this environmentalistic school is the class of physical anthropologists who may be styled genetic physical anthropologists or hereditarians, not so much because they have studied intensively the transmission of physical features from one generation of man to another, as because they believe that there are certain bodily variations, which, appearing in any individual, may be safely ascribed to his immediate family inheritance and to his ultimate racial inheritance, since such features are relatively immune from adapting and modifying environmental influences. Their assumption is basically that of the taxonomists: that detailed resemblances in form and structure signify relationship rather than convergent adaptation. Doubtless they are somewhat prone to mistake analogous structures for homologies and to be misled by accidental or adaptive resemblances. These hereditarians judge too much from appearances, whereas the environmentalists are seemingly committed to the view that appearances are invariably deceitful.

It is quite obvious that there can be no quarter given or accepted between fanatical environmentalists and rabid hereditarians. In our present state of knowledge we cannot affirm with absolute certainty that any single bodily character is inherited generation after generation without modification, and we are equally unable to point to a single bodily character, variations of which can be definitely proven as adaptive or environmentally actuated. Nevertheless, we are on comparatively firm ground when we assert that a combination of several selected physical characters in an individual usually gives us a clue to his racial ancestry. Does anyone believe, for example, that black woolly hair, black skin, platyrrhiny, everted lips, and prognathism, can be found combined in any individual who is not of Negro ancestry? The larger the number of individual criteria employed in defining a physical type, the more certain we may be that such a type is due to inheritance, whether merely familial, sub-racial, racial, or sub-specific. A single bodily feature, such as thickness and eversion of the lips, may conceivably turn up in an individual belonging to one of the so-called White races, as an accidental variation carrying with it no implication of a Negroid ancestral strain. But a combination of characters, such as that listed above, could be due to nothing but racial inheritance. Studies of race mixtures between diverse stocks have now proceeded far enough so that we are able to gauge the persistency of certain racial features in hybrids with a fair degree of accuracy. These studies have also confirmed our suspicions that many of the peoples who have a physical status midway between, for example, Whites and Negroes, owe their position not to environmental modification but to hybridization.

We may, then, conclude that only multiple resemblances or identities of physical features found combined in individuals may be assumed to indicate racial affiliations, and even here we must beware of including as criteria characters which experience and observation have indicated to be readily modifiable by function or by environment. Thus by careful selection it may be possible to isolate a number of physical types in the New World which are immediately due to the inheritance of ancestral bodily characters, whether or not in the course of transmission through many generations these characters have varied from their protomorphs, either spontaneously or through environmental stimuli. Then if any one of these physical types is virtually identical with this or that widespread Old World racial type, we may refer the coincidence either to relationship or to an environmental miracle, according to our bias.

Physical Status of the American Indian

Let us now examine the status of the American Indian from the point of view of his unity or diversity of physical characters.

(*a*) Features displaying relatively small variability:

1. *Hair color*. This is usually stated to be black in American Indians of pure blood, including the Eskimo. It has a characteristic

blue-black sheen. However, recent extensive observations by competent physical anthropologists indicate that very dark brown hair is at least common among some tribes. To distinguish between dark brown and black shades it is necessary to view the hair against the light. By this method really black hair continues to "look" black, while the brown shades in dark brown hair are easily seen. Dr. Carl C. Seltzer, who has studied large series of Zuñi, Hopi, Navajo, and Yaqui Indians, is of the opinion that the hair color of the North American Indian is predominantly dark brown, as contrasted with the blue-black shade of pure Mongoloids, and the flat-black color of Negro hair. Actually Dr. Seltzer found 30 per cent of dark brown hair in 139 Zuñi males, but only 22 per cent in a series of female Zuñi Indians. Hair samples from Peruvian mummies and from other cadavers not infrequently exhibit reddish-brown tones, but these may be partly due to post-mortem chemical changes. That some red-gold pigment is present in Indian hair, masked by the predominance of ordinary melanotic pigment, is probably true of many types. The extent and quantity of this supernumerary pigment is unknown.

2. *Eye color*. This is nearly always dark—ranging from a medium brown to a very dark brown. Bluish tones in eyes, such as occur in some Eskimo, are probably due to pathological or senile changes, or to hybridization.

3. *Hair form and hair texture*. Hair is prevailingly straight. While I am not able to quote any substantial body of statistics on this point, it is safe to say that the overwhelming majority of Indians present this feature. However, there is no doubt that wavy hair of medium texture does occur, not only in individual cases, but probably also as a group characteristic of certain forest tribes of Central and South America. Information on this point is regrettably incomplete. The common impression that American Indians have, invariably, coarse hair is almost certainly incorrect. Dr. Seltzer found hair of fine texture in 73.6 per cent of Zuñi males, and coarse hair in only 2.9 per cent. Among the Zuñi women, hair texture was still finer.

4. *Quantity and distribution of body hair*. Whereas head hair is generally abundant in American Indians, beard and body hair is consistently very sparse. However, some Indians of the northwest coast not infrequently exhibit a fairly thick growth of the mustache. It may be possible that many of these cases occur in persons who have some recent strain of White blood.

5. *Skin color*. This ranges from a light yellow-brown through

darker yellow-brown and red-brown tones. So far as I know, it never reaches flat dark-brown tones and is never "white," except in cases of albinism. Usually ruddy or reddish shades are discernible through the yellow or brown.

6. *Malar size and projection.* Malars are usually large to very large and present considerable lateral and frontal projection. In some prehistoric skulls, however, especially those of dolichocephals, the size and projection of the malars do not exceed those commonly observed in the crania of Negroes and of European Whites living under primitive dietary conditions.

7. *Prognathism.* A moderate degree of alveolar prognathism is consistently displayed. Rarely it is slight or absent, and somewhat more frequently pronounced. Marked facial prognathism is very rare.

8. *Chin prominence.* This is usually of sub-medium development and infrequently pronounced. Exceptions to this rule are fairly common among Plains Indians and some skulls from the mounds. Genial tubercles are almost invariably poorly developed in mandibles, which as a rule are more robust than those of modern Europeans.

9. *Size of the face.* This is almost always large, both absolutely and relative to the size of the brain-case. Large facial breadth is most consistently present, but moderate to large facial length is usual.

(*b*) Features displaying relatively large variability:

1. *Cephalic index and head-form.* The length-breadth index, both on the skull and on the head, varies in groups from extreme dolichocephaly to hyperbrachycephaly. Archaeological evidence indicates that in many areas earlier long-headed populations have been replaced by brachycephals. That this phenomenon is not due to the introduction of occipital deformation is obvious from the fact that many frankly brachycephalic skulls exhibit no trace of such deformation and that round-headedness is prevalent in Indians who do not practice either intentional or unintentional deformation. Length-height and breadth-height indices show an equally wide range. On the basis of head-form the American Indian shows the greatest possible heterogeneity.

2. *Nose-form.* In the crania the nasal index varies from platyrrhiny (chamaerrhiny) to leptorrhiny. A mesorrhine index is, perhaps, most frequent. This is true also of the living. Usually the nasion depression is slight and the nasal root of medium breadth or

rather low, but the bridge may be high and aquiline or low and concave. It is usually of moderate breadth or rather wide. The tip may be depressed or elevated; the nasal wings are usually somewhat flaring. On the whole, a prominent convex nose with depressed tip and flaring alae is the commonest form in males of North American tribes, but a coarser, shorter, wider, and less elevated nose with short tip is characteristic of many females in most tribes and seems to be very common in both sexes among many of the uncivilized Indians of South America. The Eskimo nose, in general, appears to be lower in the root and in the bridge and approaches more closely an ideal Mongoloid form in its soft parts than that of most other American groups. But the nasal aperture of the Eskimo is exceptionally narrow.

3. *Eye-folds.* The inner epicanthic fold (often called the Mongoloid fold) is frequently seen in varying degrees of development in women and children of the American Indians. Traces of it may be observed in occasional adult males. It is probably most frequent among the Eskimo. However, the majority of American Indians lack this fold. An external fold is found in some old males. A complete Mongoloid fold extending over the whole upper eyelid probably does not occur in the American race.

4. *Facial index.* The commonest facial index is mesoprosopic (of medium length relative to breadth), since great breadths and large lengths are usually found in combination. However, both chamaeprosopic (short, broad face) and leptoprosopic (long, narrow face) indices occur. This index varies greatly with age and sex.

5. *Lip-form.* The mouth aperture is generally wide, but the lips vary from very thin to more than average thickness. Probably the membranous lips are on the average somewhat thicker than in Europeans. The puffy and everted lips characteristic of some Negroes do not occur.

6. *Stature.* This greatest and most composite of bodily measurements varies in tribal averages from about 153 cm. to about 174 cm. This is a wide group variation, but its remarkable feature lies in its geographical and tribal distribution. Some of the tallest and shortest tribes live side by side (*e.g.* the Ona and the Yahgan of Tierra del Fuego). The Eskimo are consistently short—a fact which may be referable in part to their unfavorable environment—but in the Southwest and elsewhere there seems to be no clear relationship between environment and stature.

7. *Body build.* The tribes of short stature are generally relatively

broad of shoulder, long of trunk, and short of leg. Tall tribes are prevailingly of medium trunk length and breadth, with somewhat elongated lower extremities. These are differences of body build which are frequently, although not invariably, associated with considerable differences in stature.

On the whole, the features in which the American Indian shows a comparative homogeneity are rather more numerous and, at first sight, more impressive than those in which a wide range of variation is exhibited.

As a result of advances in serological knowledge during the World War, the determination of racial and ethnic differences in the blood groups became a major field of endeavor in physical anthropological research. Physical anthropologists eagerly seized upon this heritable physiological feature as an attribute to be correlated with metric and morphological observations. Now, after a vast amount of data has been accumulated and is still in process of collection and analysis, I must confess that I personally am greatly disappointed in the results. If any significant and certain correlations with racial type have been established, I am unacquainted with them. An individual's blood group seems to be anthropologically less important than the form of his hair or his cephalic index. Races cannot be classified satisfactorily on the basis of this one criterion. Like any other single test of race, the blood group is wholly inadequate.

Particularly clear-cut results in blood grouping seemed to have been secured in the case of the American Indian, who, when of pure blood, was thought to belong invariably to group O which lacks the agglutinogens A and B. A number of investigators reported nearly 100 per cent of group O for various samples of different Indians. Since the peopling of the New World was supposed to have been fairly recent, the absence of these agglutinogens appeared to indicate that they may have occurred as successive mutations in the Old World in the past few thousand years. To some extent the unanimous possession of group O seemed to support the contention of the unity of the American race. This situation was puzzling in view of the considerable heterogeneity of physical type manifested by the aborigines of these continents. The prevalence of the B agglutinogen in Asia and its hereditary dominance over O, the absence of agglutinogens, were explicable only on the assumption that both A and B mutants appeared subsequent to the peopling of the Americas. However, the discovery of the blood groups among the anthropoid apes, as badly mixed up among the genera as in the human races, made it seem very improbable that these serological variations in man could be at all recent. It was almost necessary to conclude that the various agglutinogens had originated independently in man and in the anthropoids.

It soon began to appear that unique serological purity of the American group was spurious. Ruggles Gates found the B group among the Western Eskimo; Matson and Schrader found a high percentage of group A in the Blackfeet; Golden found only 23 per cent of group O in the Caraja Indians of Brazil. Now W. C. and L. G. Boyd have devised a method of blood grouping tests which can be applied to mummified tissue. These investigators have found group A in 3 of 20 Basket Maker specimens, and B in one of 8 Big Bend Basket Maker mummies. They have also discovered all four of the blood groups in Peruvian mummies. Nevertheless, the American mummy material shows, as in the case of the serology of the living, a great predominance of the O group. The authors are not absolutely committed to their findings because of certain difficulties in the methods, but on the whole the results appear tolerably secure.[2] They have also found B and AB in Predynastic Egyptian mummies, so that the very recent origin of the agglutinogens seems to be out of the question. P. B. Candela has also extended the Boyd method to skeletal material from ancient Egypt. As a result of these new findings it would seem that the predominance of group O in American Indians has no very clear bearing upon the question of the unity of the American race. To me the distribution of the blood groups "makes no sense" anthropologically, either here in the New World or anywhere else. Of course, if we accept recent evidence indicating that America was populated during the retreat of the last glaciation, or at some earlier time, it is still possible to suppose that human migrations to the New World antedated the agglutinogen mutations. But in this case it is difficult to explain A and B in the Basket Makers and

[2] Boyd, William C. and Lyle G., "Blood Group in Tests on 300 Mummies," *Journal of Immunology*, Vol. 32, No. 4, April, 1937, pp. 307-319.

in the Peruvians, although some of these groups might be expected to occur in the Western Eskimo and in the Indians who have probably had some recent contact with Asiatics.

Of the variable features the most striking is head-form, as expressed by the cephalic index. This is generally considered a heritable character of some stability, although Boas has demonstrated slight changes in the cephalic index of the children of immigrants in the United States, and Ivanovsky has shown that under famine conditions the breadth of the head in many peoples of southern Russia shrank more than the length, thus decreasing the length-breadth index. In general, however, studies of the inheritance of head-form by Frets and others seem to indicate that long-headed parents usually produce long-headed children, round-headed parents round-headed children, and that crosses between dolichocephals and brachycephals are likely to yield mesocephals, dolichocephals, and brachycephals—the last-named in much larger numbers than the long-heads. It seems probable that there is some sort of dominance of round-headedness over long-headedness, or rather of broad heads over narrow heads, but the number of characters or units involved is far from clear. At any rate, it is still reasonable to suppose that radically diverse head-form in different groups of a population probably implies a diversity of hereditary strains between these groups.

Again, the wide variation of nose-form in the American Indian can hardly be attributed to environmental factors, even if we leave out of consideration the alleged effect upon the breadth of the nasal aperture of breathing moist, warm air, or cold, dry air, respectively. It would be hard to imagine a greater contrast in the shape of the nose than that which is presented when we compare the great hawk noses of some types with the insignificant, saddle-shaped, tip-tilted nasal blobs that are not uncommon in other groups. Here again there is reason for believing that convex prominent noses tend to dominate over the low, infantile forms, and that we are dealing with hereditary features which have very considerable racial significance.

However, the crux of the question as to racial diversity or unity in the American stock is not the distribution or range of variation of morphological or metrical features taken singly. It is rather the combinations of these features into distinct hereditary types and the affinities of these types with recognized races of the Old World. Here we are faced at the outset with a dearth of utilizable data, both as regards the American Indian and also the races of Asia to whom the American stocks appear to be allied physically. So far as I am aware, no anthropologist has measured and morphologically observed and recorded a large series of living Indians and has then attempted to divide them into types, according to combinations of metrical and morphological features, testing the validity of his type differentiations by modern statistical methods.[3] An investigation of this character has, indeed, been carried out by G. D. Williams upon the Yucatecans, but his problem was one of race mixture between Indians and Spanish, and not an attempt to distinguish types among the pure Indians. Further, there is much less precise scientific material available pertaining to the Mongoloids of Asia than is at hand in the case of the American Indian. Racial analysis is a most laborious and difficult process, even when one possesses scores of measurements, indices, and accurately graded morphological observations upon long series of individuals. When such raw materials have been secured, it is necessary to establish type combinations by almost endless sortings, tabulations, and calculation of constants. If human beings had only abstained from race mixture until physical anthropologists had classified and defined the "pure races," we should at least have a *terminus a quo*. As it is, no one knows what a "pure race" is, although anthropologists are apparently the only human beings who know that they do not know.

Geographical Considerations

Apart from considerations of anthropometric and anatomical features, certain geographical factors must be taken into account when we examine the racial affinities and type differentiation of the American Indian. Up to the present there is no evidence that primate evolution in the New World has produced any form higher than the American Monkeys (the Cebidae); for, without further confirmatory evidence, I take it that no cautious student can accept the marvelous story of a South American anthropoid

[3] Since this chapter was written, Dr. Carl C. Seltzer has studied large and altogether adequate series of Zuñi, Hopi, and Navajo and has successfully resolved them into statistically validated morphological and anthropometric types. His results have not yet been published.

recently reported by de Loys, a French explorer.[4] Assuming, then, in the absence of positive evidence, that man did not evolve in either of the Americas, he must have migrated hither from the Old World. Such migration must have been accomplished by sea or by land. While it is not wholly impossible that a few canoe-loads of stray mariners afloat on the Pacific may have reached the western coasts of the American continents, it does not seem probable that any considerable portion of the American Indian population arrived by that route. A peopling *via* the Atlantic is even less in question, for the inhabitants of western Africa seem not to have developed the art of navigation to any great extent, while tradition, history, and prehistoric archaeology alike militate against the theory of European voyages to the New World before the time of the Norsemen. But even if we postulate a ship-load or two, their passengers and crews could scarcely have contributed any persistent and perceptible strain to the population which we call Indians.

In spite of current popularity of theories of continental drift and the perennially recurrent fables of sunken continents, one need not seriously entertain the hypothesis that the New World was easily accessible from the Old by land-bridges during the period that has elapsed since man's emergence from an anthropoid status. Geological evidence does not seem to indicate that the land-bridge from Greenland to Europe was available in late Tertiary or Pleistocene times, and so we are left with the Aleutian Islands and Bering Strait as the most probable route and northeastern Asia as the logical area from which the Americas were peopled. All this is, of course, trite and commonplace to American anthropologists. Nevertheless it must bear reiteration.

Thus by a trituration of rather stale pabulum, we have digested once more the conclusion that the racial affinities of the American population are to be sought principally in Asia, or, in any event, among whatever stocks peopled that area in prehistoric times. I need not here enter into the time-worn but enduring question of

[4] However, there apparently does exist in the tropical forest region near the boundary between Colombia and Venezuela a giant spider-monkey. Mr. James B. Durlacher, an American engineer whose work takes him into this region, has described this animal to me and sent me a photograph of one shot by him. This monkey weighed seventy pounds. It had a prehensile tail, rudimentary thumbs, and the wide septum between the nostrils which is characteristic of the American primates. It is apparently this large spider-monkey which was seen by de Loys.

the exact period of man's arrival in the New World, especially since no Pithecanthropi, no Sinanthropi, and no Neanderthaloids have been found in our continents. If late Palaeolithic man came here, he was probably no different in racial composition from early Neolithic or late Neolithic man.

If all or nearly all of the peoples who came to the New World had to pass through the same narrow bottle-neck, it seems probable that the earliest comers would be pushed farthest from the ingress and that the most primitive types would persist longest in the remote marginal areas. This argument has been most ably expounded by Professor R. B. Dixon in, perhaps, the most original, stimulating, and provocative treatise on human migrations produced by any anthropologist—a treatise with much of which I heartily disagree.[5] Yet, while retaining a moral disapprobation of dubious methods of acquisition, I do not hesitate to use "tainted money," and some of my colleague's results are pure gold. He has gathered together the evidence with respect to "marginal skull types" and has shown that in many parts of the New World brachycephals are in stratigraphic superimposition upon dolichocephals. His daring and ruthless suggestions regarding the racial affinities of various skull types will command our attention in a later portion of this essay. Here I wish merely to emphasize his principle that if a continent has been peopled by successive waves of immigrants, differing to some extent in racial and ethnic composition, we may well expect the most primitive and "purest" types to survive longest in areas of relative isolation, whereas the most mixed types may theoretically be found in the intermediate areas, and the latest comers, whether mixed or pure, in close proximity to the migration corridor.

Cultural Considerations

Although culture is no criterion of race, it is altogether possible that race may to some extent influence culture. Of course, one may adduce instances of peoples of apparently identical racial composition who have radically different cultures, perhaps because they live under dissimilar environmental conditions and have larger, smaller, or divergent cultural contacts. When, however, two groups inhabit

[5] Dixon, Roland B., *The Racial History of Man*, New York, 1923.

separate but similar geographical areas and differ radically in culture, we may refer these differences to race, providing that we can rule out the possibility of their having been influenced by divergent traditions and dissimilar cultural contracts. Yet in the New World it would be difficult to make much of an argument in favor of a racial heterogeneity based upon cultural differences, since one could never be sure of eliminating disturbing environmental factors. I do not think that even under ideal conditions (which are altogether unattainable) much could be made of such a method of attacking the problem. Nevertheless, the wide variation in culture found in different groups of American Indians has some bearing upon their possible variations in physical type. For such cultural differences at least suggest that the groups in question may well have been isolated for considerable periods of time and subjected as well to somewhat different environmental influences. Under such conditions local physical types are likely to develop, either through the perpetuation and exaggeration of familial features as a result of inbreeding, or possibly by mutations or adaptations. This is, of course, a cogent environmental argument, and one which is most difficult to combat. However, if we discover within the same area, and within one group in that area, individuals who have the same mode of life, the same material culture, and who yet present dissimilar physical types, these differences may be due merely to the perpetuation of family peculiarities, but they may result, on the other hand, from the mixing of different racial strains. The variations can be tested, to some extent, by comparing these individual types in sufficient samples with adequate series of the authentic races to which they seem to bear resemblances. This procedure I have attempted in the analysis of the skeletons from the Pueblo of Pecos, New Mexico; and Dixon has experimented more widely along somewhat similar lines, using, however, different methods and a smaller number of physical criteria.

Let us now abandon our general discussion and proceed directly to examine the resemblances to other races which American Indians exhibit, first in the morphology of their soft parts and external structure, and secondly in their skeletal characters. In each instance we shall deal first with resemblances in single features, and secondly with the affinities of type combinations.

Racial Resemblances of the American Indian in Soft Parts and
Bony Structure Superficially Considered

Three great groups of contemporary races may be distinguished, which possibly ought to be given the rank of sub-species. These are Negroids, Mongoloids, and (for lack of a better term) Whites. In addition, there is a composite group made up of races probably derived from intermixtures of the primary stocks. We may first attempt to establish the position of the American race with respect to these primary groups.

In pigmentation of the skin the American population is darker even than the most brunet White races, and lighter than unmixed or relatively pure Negroes. It aligns itself definitely with the yellow-brown Mongoloids. In pigment of hair and eyes, the American Indian probably also surpasses all Whites, but hardly reaches the intensity of Negroes. Here again it is to be classed with the Mongoloids. Unfortunately the range and intensity of pigmentation is so little known and satisfactory quantitative studies are so notable for their absence that this statement, while almost certainly correct, cannot be scientifically verified from available evidence.

The form of the hair in the American race is again definitely Mongoloid, as is also the texture. Nowhere among the Americans is frizzly or woolly hair to be found, nor even, so far as I know, definitely curly hair. But, as stated above, wavy hair of finer texture than Mongoloid hair does occur in some groups. This hair-form is characteristic of many composite races and of the majority of White races. Wavy hair certainly results in some cases from the crossings of straight-haired and curly-haired parents, but it may be also a primary hair-form. Sparse beard and body hair is common to both Negroids and Mongoloids. It is not characteristic of most Whites.

The size and projection of the malars in the American race is again a Mongoloid feature, but there is something of an overlap from both the Negroid and White groups, not so much in frontal as in lateral projection.

The degree of alveolar prognathism ordinarily found in the American race considerably exceeds that of Whites, about equals that of most Mongoloids, and is markedly less than the usual amount displayed in the Negroid races. However, individual Whites often show alveolar prognathism equaling that of Indians.

The chin eminence is usually less developed in Indians than in Whites and better developed in the former than in Negroes. As previously remarked, certain North American Indians have, however, strongly jutting chins. I am uncertain whether the average chin development in Indians exceeds that of Mongoloids in general.

Indian faces are commonly and prevailingly larger than those of either Whites or Negroids, but agree well with those of many Mongoloids. Especially, the faces of most Indians are much wider even than those of broad-headed Whites, and greatly surpass in this dimension average Negro diameters. The length of the face in the Indian is extremely variable, but in general probably exceeds that of most Negroids. Both Mongoloids and Whites show great variability in this feature. Faces which are at the same time very broad and very long are typical both in the American race and in many groups of Mongoloids. They are not characteristic of Whites or of Negroids.

One may conclude that in the features which are least variable and most characteristically Indian the affinities displayed are overwhelmingly Mongoloid.

The Negro races are prevailingly dolichocephalic. There are, indeed, some brachycephalic Negro tribes, especially in the Lake Chad region, and some of the pygmies or Negritoes are brachycephalic or subbrachycephalic. The White races run the gamut from extreme dolichocephaly to hyperbrachycephaly, but usually we employ the cephalic index as one of the criteria whereby different races of the great White division of mankind are distinguished from each other. In the Mongoloid groups brachycephaly is typical, but dolichocephaly and mesocephaly do occur in many peoples commonly regarded as belonging to this branch. Probably there are both long-headed and round-headed varieties of the Mongoloid form of man, but the central type is certainly round-headed. In any event the diversity of head-form among the American Indians tends to distinguish them from the Negroid division of man, but is ambiguous when Mongoloids or Whites are brought in to comparison.

The nasal index in the American race varies more widely in groups than it does in Whites and more than in the Negro races.

This index is prevailing higher in Indians than in Whites, although the Eskimo are extremely leptorrhine (more so in the skeletal index than in external nose) and leptorrhiny is not uncommon in individuals of many groups elsewhere in the New World. The chamaerrhine or platyrrhine nasal index is also of frequent occurrence, although excessively broad nasal apertures are rare so that the index never approaches the high mean values found in Negroes, except in occasional individuals. On the whole, then, the American race tends to fall midway between Negroes and Whites in means of the nasal index, but overlaps both groups, as do the Mongoloids. As far as I know, the great breadth of the nasal root, thickened tip, and pronounced alar flare typical of the Negro nose virtually never occur in the American race. Short, blobby noses, such as may be seen in many Alpine Whites, but somewhat lower and narrower at the root and more flaring in the wings, are common among the females of many Indian tribes. If one judges from photographs and measurements, these rather shapeless and infantile noses are frequent in both sexes among the forest Indians of South America and among the Yahgan of Tierra del Fuego. The very flat, saddle-shaped nose of the Mongoloid can hardly be said to characterize any American group, except possibly the Eskimo. Yet this kind of nose is by no means invariably present in Mongols. Indeed, I am not sure that it is typical of any save Mongoloid females. However this may be, the high and rather broad, aquiline noses with long, depressed tips and somewhat spreading alae, which are such a marked feature of most North American Indians and of the tribes inhabiting the highlands of Central America and the Andean region, are certainly non-Mongoloid. They do not resemble closely the ordinary convex noses of Europeans, since they are wider in the bridge, thicker in the tip, and broader in the wings. Yet they are more like the fleshy, prominent noses of some Europeans, particularly of the Dinaric type, than like the hooked Armenoid form with its very depressed tip, convex septum, and recurved alae.

The present center of distribution, and perhaps the area of differentiation of these high-bridged, convex noses is certainly the Iranian plateau. The recent anthropometric field work of Dr. Henry Field in Iran and Iraq, as yet incompletely published, makes it perfectly clear that a fundamental racial type in that area is characterized by extreme dolichocephaly, long faces and very prominent, beaky noses, sometimes straight, but usually convex. The dominant convexity of this nose has apparently been diffused into many adjacent stocks through intermixture, but there seems little doubt that it is "at home" in this Iranian Plateau race. I am of the opinion that the so-called "Armenoid" nose which has a thick, spatulate, and often depressed tip is derived from a mixture of this Iranian type with a brachycephalic, rather broad-nosed type. If this is true the Armenoid nose is a hybrid nose. It seems also probable that the very thin, aquiline noses found in many "Mediterranean" race Arabs may be derived from this source, as are also the Jewish convex noses. The prevalent habit of speaking of the Jewish nose as "Armenoid" is, on this basis, incorrect.

These prominent aquiline noses, originating, probably, on the Iranian plateau, were not only acquired in a mixed and modified form by the peoples to the west and south, but also by those to the north and east. They are distributed through Afghanistan and Northern India. Through the Turkish stocks to the north of Persia they were diffused to the Mongoloids, and ultimately, to America. We know enough about the inheritance of nose form to be fairly certain that convex, high-bridged noses are in a Mendelian sense dominant over the low, concave, short-tipped forms which are the more infantile. The fact is very notable in the study of Negro-White crosses in the United States. I do not know of any environmental influence, whether adaptive, or non-adaptive, which is likely to elongate, elevate and curve the nasal bridge to the form I am discussing. Even if one accepts the theory that the nasal aperture of the Eskimo has been narrowed by the cold, dry air of the Arctic—and I regard it with suspicion—it is certain that this diminution of width has not been accompanied in that people by any elevation or humping of the bridge. Of course you can acquire a humped nose as a result of a badly-healed fracture of the nasal bones (and I suppose some follower of Weismann might like to investigate the inheritance of such a mutilation); but the suggestion that the American Indians got their aquiline noses in such a way does not seem very helpful.

The skin-fold of the upper eyelid which may overlie the caruncula and obscure the inner corner of the eye (the internal epicanthic fold), is intimately connected with the elevation of the nasal root. This is often called the "Mongoloid fold," but, like the

"Mongoloid spot" and the "Inca bone," it is frequently conspicuous by its absence in the people whom it theoretically characterizes, and is likely to turn up unexpectedly in other races. According to my definition, a complete Mongolian fold is one which extends over the whole upper lid from the external to the internal corner, over-lying and obscuring the free edge of the lid all the way.

When this essay was written, in 1932, I had to admit that I did not know where in Asia there existed large groups of peoples pre-senting the complete combination of physical Mongoloid features: straight, coarse, blue-black hair, undeveloped brow-ridges, slit-like eyes with the free edge of the fatty upper lid covered by a complete Mongoloid fold extending from inner to the outer corner, cheek-bones both laterally and frontally projecting and covered by a pad of fat, nasal root broad and almost flat, comparatively small elevation of the bony parts of the bridge, infantile characters of the soft parts of the tip and wings, yellow-brown skin color and sparse development of beard and body hair. I was only certain that this more or less hypothetical pure Mongoloid type was not gen-erally characteristic of the Mongols proper, nor of the inhabitants of China and Tibet.

Within the past few years, however, this ignorance has been en-lightened. The Peabody Museum of Harvard University has re-ceived from Russia several hundreds of anthropometric portraits made by Soviet anthropologists. This collection from the Institute of the Peoples of the North clearly demonstrates that the present focus of the pure Mongoloid type is in Northeastern Siberia. As a rough test I have tabulated the frequency of (1) complete Mon-goloid folds, (2) incomplete Mongoloid folds, and (3) no eye-folds in this collection of portraits. The percentages of three categories in order and the total number of portraits examined in each group follow.

Gilyak—85.71, 14.29, 0, (14); Olcha—85.71, 14.29, 0, (14); Goldi—77.05, 22.95, 0 (61); Lamut—75.00, 12.50, 12.50, (8); Orochi—66.67, 33.33, 0 (6); Tungus—62.59, 31.65, 5.76, (139); Yukagir—60.00, 20.00, 20.00 (5); Chukchi—50.00, 25.00, 25.00, (8); Buriat—38.46, 53.85, 7.69 (13); Negda—40.00, 40.00, 20.00 (5); Yakut—35.71, 53.57, 10.71 (28); Samoyed—17.65, 45.10, 37.25 (51); Koryak—16.67, 83.33, 0, (6); Voguls—14.81, 25.92, 59.26 (27); Kamchadales—9.09, 90.90, 0, (11).

Of course many of these series are inadequate, but I think they are sufficient to show that the area of Siberia north of Manchuria contains populations in which the Mongoloid combination is basic and predominant. It should be added that the complete Mongoloid eye-fold almost invariably is accompanied by a full development of all the other characteristic Mongoloid features.

Certainly it is not typical of the American Indian and I doubt that it occurs at all in that race, except, perhaps, in the Eskimo. On the other hand, some development of an internal epicanthic fold is a very characteristic feature of Mongoloid peoples, is fairly common in Indians, and probably typical of the Eskimo. I used to think that this internal epicanthus was completely incompatible with a narrow, high nasal root, but I have seen it in conjunction with such a root in an European. Nevertheless, as a general rule, it is found only with a flat or low nasal root. This is probably why it is commoner in the infantile nose and among females, than in males. It is not typically associated with low, broad-rooted Negro noses, but does occur in individual cases. It is a fairly consistent feature of the Bushman-Hottentot race, which I am inclined to regard as the result of a Mongoloid-Negrito cross. As far as I have been able to observe, this internal epicanthus is not found in the hawk-nosed American Indians, except, perhaps, in infancy before the nasal root has attained its height and in some females who never do acquire full adult development in this feature. In general, however, the internal epicanthus is found oftener in the American race than it should be found in any non-Mongoloid stock.

The external epicanthus, which covers the outer corner of the eye, seems to bear about the same relationship to a flat, compressed malar as the internal epicanthus to a low nasal root. Both occur, apparently, in connection with a looseness or flabbiness of the skin caused by a lack of tension. When the skin is stretched tightly over an elevated nasal root, an epicanthus is usually absent. Similarly, an external epicanthus is unlikely to be found with large and laterally jutting malars. However, exceptions occur in both cases. The external epicanthus seems to be very common in narrow-faced, flat-cheeked Nordics, and I have at times ventured to call it the "Nordic fold," but I am certain that it occurs outside of the sacred circle of that favored race. In fact it is sometimes found in American Indians—just how often I do not know. I should by no means subscribe to the view that the presence of this external fold in Indians indicates a Nordic strain, but I do think that it implies the presence of some non-Mongoloid element. It is not a Negroid feature. On the whole, I should conclude that the types and distributions of eye-folds in the American race suggest, on the one hand, strong Mongoloid affinities, and, on the other, admixtures of some non-Mongoloid, non-Negroid strains.

The great breadth and considerable length of the average Indian face, and its great size relative to the brain-case, impress me as an outstanding American characteristic. This is certainly neither a White nor a Negroid feature. I am by no means certain that it is typical of all Mongoloids, but it seems to prevail among true Mongols, Tibetans, and probably other groups. It is not consistently present among the Chinese.

Lip thickness offers no assistance in determining the affinities of the American race, except to distinguish it from full Negro types. A well-marked lip-seam, which is typical in Negroes and very common in Polynesians, is not usually noticeable in Indians, but may occur.

Stature is of no avail for our present purposes, although its great variability in the aboriginal American population suggests heterosis (hybrid vigor) in some strains and inbreeding in others. As previously remarked, the juxtaposition of tall and short tribes in the same area (e.g. southwestern United States) makes it difficult to invoke environment as the controlling factor.

Body build is also equivocal. The American race does not conform to any one type of build, but it should be noted that the heel projection and meager development of the calves, so striking in Negroids and in Australians, is conspicuous by its absence, as is also the very low relative sitting height also common among many groups of the races just mentioned. Most of the groups of the American race which are small in stature are notable for a squareness of shoulders, deep, broad chests, and short limbs of medium development, all of which recall a type extremely prevalent among Mongoloids and Malays.

All in all, our survey of superficial bodily characters, taken singly, has not led us to any very satisfactory conclusions concerning the racial affinities of the American Indians. In all of the features which show clear-cut resemblances to any racial type, some sort of Mongoloid relationship is indicated.

When we come to consider combinations of these superficial features into types, we are baffled by the fact that an almost uniformly Mongoloid veneer has been laid over the whole American race. Pigmentation, hair-form, facial size, and malar projection bring us back to the same great group of mankind. Again, as previously stated, practically no efforts have been made to distinguish types of the American Indian on the basis of the soft parts and superficial features. Hence the exact morphological observations essential for such selection are not available.

Probably the Eskimo represent the most clearly defined type of the American race. Indeed, a good many classificationists have distinguished them as a separate race. Their crania are the easiest of all skulls to identify. Extreme dolichocephaly of a decidedly scaphoid tendency is combined with a lateral and frontal development of malars which is extraordinary even in Mongoloids. Feebly-developed brow-ridges, a low pinched nasal root with little elevation of the bridge, short tip, and spreading alae; flat, fat faces with deep jaws, projecting gonial angles, small chins, and magnificent teeth set in broad dental arches, frequent internal epicanthic folds, a ruddy-yellow skin color, and the usual lank, black hair and dark eyes—these are the familiar features of the Eskimo. Stature is short; shoulders are wide; trunk is long; and the limbs are abbreviated, but sturdy. This conventional Eskimo type seems to be most fully developed in the Greenland and Labrador Eskimo. Farther west skulls are not so narrow and the other Eskimoid features become somewhat attenuated. The presence of blood group B individuals among the Western Eskimo may mean, when taken in conjunction with their diminished Eskimoid characters and their tendency toward brachycephaly, that they have received infusions of some Mongoloid Asiatic strain in comparatively recent times, or that the present Western Eskimo are the latest arrivals in the New World.

I am inclined to think that the Eskimo are dolichocephalic because they have inherited that head-form, rather than because their heads have been pinched laterally and elongated antero-posteriorly by the vigorous action of their great temporal muscles. Nevertheless, it would be foolish categorically to deny that the peculiar

features of the Eskimo skull and face may not be in some measure
a specialization directly or indirectly connected with their environment. Hrdlička and other reliable observers report that as one goes
north among the Athabascan Indians toward the Eskimo country,
Eskimoid types increase in frequency among the Indians themselves. This, of course, may be due to hybridization, but, on the
other hand, some sort of environmental adaptation is by no means
out of the question. The same problem arises when one studies the
skeletal characteristics of ancient Icelanders. Craniologically the
skulls of Western Eskimo are to me indistinguishable from those
of the Chuckchi, their neighbors on the Asiatic side. I have had no
opportunity to make personal anthropometric observations on
either of these two groups, but from photographs the Chuckchi
seem to present the same physical type as do the Eskimo.

Taking everything together, it seems to me that the Eskimo are
the most clearly Mongoloid in their affinities of all the American
race, and I am inclined to think that they may represent the most
recent of the immigrant waves.

My impressions concerning the physiognomic types of Indians
have no scientific value, but may indicate profitable lines of investigation when physical anthropologists begin seriously to attempt
analysis of the type variations among the living stocks of the
American race. The first impression is that many Indians of the
north-west coast so closely resemble Alpine Europeans in their cast
of countenance that one could easily duplicate them among eastern
Europeans who show a dash of Kalmuck, Tartar, or other Mongoloid strains. Of course, the skin color is darker and the hair
straighter and coarser than in Europeans of the types to which I
refer. Such Indians of the north-west coast often grow fairly thick
mustaches and seem to have more body hair than most of their
race. How far such pseudo-European types are to be attributed to
recent hybridization I am unable to say. Race mixture with Europeans undoubtedly does produce similar types. I may add that in
the types to which I refer there is no such malar prominence as
characterizes, for example, the Plains Indians. The possibility to
be considered is that there is a strong non-Mongoloid element in
these stocks, possibly something akin to the brachycephalic Alpine
race of Europe.

Again, for years I have been puzzled by the types depicted in the

splendid series of oil portraits of Indians in the Peabody Museum.[6]
The majority of these represent Indians of the eastern and southeastern United States and, although the portraits are the work of an
excellent painter, the subjects look very European. The features of
most are very un-Mongoloid, with prominent noses and oval faces.
Mongoloid cheek-bones are rarely portrayed. The skin color is reddish-brown rather than yellow-brown. However, some Plains
Indians are included in the series, and these seem to be accurate
representations of types familiar today. I am, therefore, disposed
to think that the European-like types are not the result of an
artistic convention, but actually did exist. These portraits, and old
photographs of Eastern Indians, convey the impression that the
eastern dolichocephals were by no means as Mongoloid as are the
Plains and Southwestern Indians. Many of the photographs of
Indians (supposedly full-blood) from eastern Canada appear similarly non-Mongoloid.

Plains Indians, whether brachycephalic or dolichocephalic, broad-
faced or narrow-faced, seem to show the same sloping foreheads,
prominent cheek-bones, bold noses, thin, hard mouths, heavy jaws,
and firm chins. They look alike in spite of differences of head-
form and face form. The Southwestern Indians, whether sedentary
or nomadic, seem to present milder editions of the same type, which
I take to be an amalgamation of other racial features washed over
with dominant Mongoloid characters.

When we reach the Maya Indians of Central America, the preda-
tory-looking, hawk-visaged North American type seems largely
to disappear, and to be replaced by punier and less massive
brachycephals with noses even more convex, but thinner and less
flaring as to alae, adorning much smaller and weaker faces with
receding chins, thicker and flabbier lips—the whole constituting an
open-mouthed, adenoidal cast of countenance. The stern lines of
the countenance and the sombre strength of features are almost
altogether lacking. In spite of hair-form and pigmentation, these
Indians seem even farther removed from ideal Mongoloid types
than are the Plains and Southwestern tribes of the United States.

Among the more primitive and wilder types of the interior, such

---

[6] These portraits are copies of originals made principally by Charles B. King for the
McKenney and Hall *History of the Indian Tribes of North America* published in 1837-44.
The copies were executed by Henry Inman, about the years 1832-1836.

as the Lacandones, there appear individuals who have an almost pre-Dravidian look. Their photographs remind one vaguely of the Veddahs. The long hair appears to be somewhat wavy, although one must beware of mistaking unkempt, matted, straight hair for wavy hair. Noses appear flatter, with shorter tips and more circular, flaring alae; the chin is weak. The sturdy squareness of build found among the Mayas seems to be replaced by an undernourished-looking slenderness and fragility of build. Mongoloid features are not conspicuous. Is it not possible that we have here more or less pure remnants of an earlier and primitive racial element which has been submerged by mixtures with more vigorous latecomers?

In some of the South American forest tribes are more brutal and cruder-looking types with coarse noses, rather thick lips, considerable alveolar prognathism, and a hint of Negroidal admixture. But I have never seen, either in the flesh or in a photographic representation, a supposedly full-blood Indian who really could be mistaken for a Negro or an Australian. Nevertheless, I am unable to rid myself of the feeling that in the remoter parts of the southern continent there persist peoples in whom non-Mongoloid or pre-Mongoloid strains are evident, and these of a very primitive sort. Yet I doubt if any existing Indians have entirely escaped the all-pervasive Mongolization.

All of the foregoing is speculative, questionable, and probably ill-advised. It is no more scientific than racial psychology. Yet I have ventured upon it in the hope of irritating physical anthropologists into an investigation of these really important problems relating to the affinities of American Indian types. If the exposition of my own lamentable ignorance on this subject accomplishes this object, I shall not have laid bare my nakedness in vain.

Racial Resemblances of the American Indian in Skeletal Parts

I embark upon the subject of the skeletal affinities of American Indian types with few quakes, both on my own part, and on that of the ground I tread, since the skeletal remains of Indians was the chief preoccupation of my research leisure for some eighteen years.

First of all, it may be remarked that there is no single feature of the cranium which is distinctively or exclusively Indian. Probably the same statement holds true of any other race. It is the

combination of features which establishes the type. The shape of
the brain case, as I have said, is so variable as to be of little use in
distinguishing Indian crania from those of any other race. The
cranial sutures present serrations ranging from very simple to
medium when compared with those of Europeans, and, as a rule,
are less intricate than those of White races. Occipital tori and
supramastoid crests are more frequent; the temporal crests are more
strongly marked, and a greater degree of postorbital constriction
usually is present in the American race. In the vault some degree
of sagittal elevation, imparting a scaphoid appearance, is usually to
be observed; parietal foramina are often small or entirely lacking.
Brow-ridges are variable in development but average larger than in
Europeans. Further, dehiscences in the floor of the auditory meatus
are quite common; styloid processes are prevailingly small; the
petrous parts of the temporal bone show little depression below the
level of the basilar process when the skull is viewed in *norma
basalis*; the middle lacerate foramina are inferior in size to the
average of Europeans.

The face is broad and often long. Malars show strong lateral projection and moderate anterior jut, as in Mongoloids. The lateral
axes of the orbits tend to be more horizontal in Indians than in
most Europeans, but orbital shapes are not distinctive. The sub-
orbital fossae are shallower than in most Whites, and especially
poorly developed in Eskimo, contributing to the flat, Mongoloid
look of the face in that people. There is usually more alveolar
prognathism of the maxilla than in Whites. Nasion depressions, as
a rule, are poorly developed or absent—a Mongoloid feature. The
nasal root is seldom high, but often narrow. The commonest form
of the profile of the nasal bones is concavo-convex, and the bridge
is prevailingly of moderate to high development in males. The
aperture of the nose is somewhat wider than the modal form in
Whites, and the lower borders are much duller, often indistinct.
The nasal spine is usually small. The palate of the American Indian
is generally spacious; it is more likely to be constricted in length
than in width. The teeth are somewhat larger than those of Europeans, but reduction of the number of cusps of second and third
molars is common. Shovel-shaped incisors are a relatively constant
feature. Mandibles tend to be rather heavy, with submedium or

medium development of the mental eminence. Genial tubercles are almost always small.

Such a description would probably conform in most respects to that of a generalized Mongoloid skull, the principal exceptions being found in the nasal root and bridge, both of which are commonly more elevated in Indians than in typical Mongoloids, and in the larger brow-ridges of the Americans.

But in addition to a variety of familiar and Indian-looking types of skulls, there occur many crania in which unusual morphological and metrical features are so combined as to simulate types which we do not ordinarily associate with the American Indian. Mostly these un-Indian crania appear as aberrant individual members of series, the majority of which present the customary variations; but they are common enough in some cases to constitute respectable minorities. Occasionally one sees an Indian skull which recalls the cranial type of the native Australian; others appear remarkably Negroid, and rarer instances of skulls resembling those of the several White races are to be found in large collections of Indian skeletal remains. In my study of the skeletons from the ruined Pueblo of Pecos, New Mexico, I undertook to classify the 129 best preserved male crania according to morphological type and attempted to trace the affinities of these types outside of the American continents.[7] First of all, I laid out these crania in the laboratory and sorted them into groups, putting skulls which looked alike in the same group, and paying no attention to measurements. Thus I established seven type groups and an eighth which I called a Residual type, because it received all which did not seem to fit in any of the others. I then took the measurements, indices, and morphological observations previously made or calculated on each skull, found the statistical constants of each group, and tabulated the variations of its observed morphological features. The validity of each morphological type was next tested by comparing its metrical and indicial features with those of a random sample of the entire series of a size equal to that of the type subgroup, having regard to the aggregate of differences in excess of what might be expected from chance alone. Six of my eight types were clearly and overwhelmingly differentiated from the group at large, both metri-

---

[7] Hooton, E. A., *The Indians of Pecos Pueblo*, Papers of the South-western Expedition, no. 4, Department of Archæology, Phillips Academy, Andover, 1930.

cally and indicially. The seventh displayed only size differences which were significant, and the eighth—the Residual group—did not differ from a random sample of the entire series. Composite photographs of ten skulls of each type were then made in order to secure a visual record which would supplement the evidence of statistics. Finally, I gave each of these morphological types a name, according to its fancied resemblance to other Indian types outside of the Southwest or to alien racial types, and proceeded to investigate such resemblances by comparing means of measurements and indices with respect to their probable errors, or, when only raw means were available for comparative data, by using mean differences of aggregates of measurements and indices.

A full discussion of this method and the results obtained from it would extend this chapter to an excessive size. Consequently, any reader who may be interested is referred to the original cumbersome monograph. Briefly, however, the types distinguished, the names given them, and their ascertained affinities, were as follows:

(1) *"Basket Maker"* type. This type was named from a fancied resemblance to the Basket Makers of the Arizona caves. The skulls are rather small and usually undeformed. They are dolichocephalic, hypsicephalic, acrocephalic. The faces are narrowest of all Pecos types and yield leptoprosopic indices. Orbits are high and narrow, and the nasal index has a mesorrhine average. There is some facial prognathism, but the palate is broad. Mandibles are not robust. Individuals of this type, which was most numerous in the early days of Pecos, averaged in stature about 160.5 cm. It has its closest affinities in the American continent to the skulls from the Coahuila Caves and to the veritable Arizona Basket Makers. This type was compared metrically and indicially with various series of ancient and modern Egyptian crania. The Arizona and Coahuila series were similarly compared. In the measurements the Egyptian crania generally showed greater lengths and heights, broader frontal regions, and larger capacities. The American crania have broader and longer faces and noses. In indices, however, very striking resemblances are manifested. In fact, indicially two groups of southwestern dolichocephals—the Arizona Basket Makers and the Coahuila Cave skulls—resemble various Egyptian crania more closely than they resemble Pecos "Basket Makers" and Santa Catalina crania, which were judged to be racially and typologically iden-

tical with them on the basis of similar criteria. This certainly does not mean that there were Egyptians in the Southwest. At most it may indicate that one of the strains which entered into the earlier strata of the American population may have been the fundamental, Eur-African Mediterranean race.

(2) *"Pseudo-Negroid" type.* The skulls of this type show flat, broad nasal bones, platyrrhiny, pronounced alveolar prognathism, and bulbous frontal regions. They are very small, and, when undeformed, dolichocephalic, and low in length-height and breadth-height indices. The palates are long and inclined to the U-shape. Mean stature of the group (155.2 cm.) was the lowest at Pecos. This type was prevalent also in the lower archaeological strata and became rarer in the later periods. When compared with series of Negrito crania, it was found to be totally dissimilar to the types of the Andamanese and the Aetas of the Philippines. African Negro crania are invariably longer, higher, relatively narrower, and of considerably larger capacities. The Negro crania show lower orbits, shorter faces, shorter and much broader noses, and far more prognathism. The Pecos "Pseudo-Negroids" resemble most closely crania of Negro groups coming from those parts of Africa where "Negroes" commonly have some perceptible infusion of White, Hamitic blood. Nevertheless, metrically and indicially, the Pecos "Pseudo-Negroid" type is much closer to the type of the African Negro than to any of its contemporary types at Pecos. The divergences from the ordinary Pecos types are in the same direction, but quantitatively less, than those displayed by authentic Negro crania.

This again, if it means anything, probably signifies merely that in the earlier strata of the American population there was some degree of Negro or Negroid admixture, and that in occasional individuals these features are segregated and combined into a Negroid-looking cranial type.

(3) *"Pseudo-Australoid" type.* This consists of skulls with heavily marked supraorbital ridges continuous from one external angular process to the other, deeply depressed nasal roots, platyrrhiny, and alveolar prognathism. They are dolichocephalic, hypsicephalic, and acrocephalic. The malars are strongly projecting and the total face height short, yielding an euryprosopic index. Orbits are low and broad and the palate brachyuranic. There is no facial

prognathism. The average stature of this type was 162.5 cm. It occurred most frequently in the lower strata at Pecos.

The Pecos "Pseudo-Australoid" type was found to display no marked resemblance either in gross dimensions or in indices to Australians, Tasmanians, or New Caledonians. All of the Oceanic groups have much shorter and broader noses, much larger and longer palates, narrower and shorter faces, more dolichocephalic skulls, and lower length-height indices. The Pecos type lacks the characteristic prognathism of the alien groups.

A comparison for the "Pseudo-Australoids" with the Ainu showed that the latter far exceed our Pecos type in vault dimensions, but have closely similar facial dimensions and only slightly divergent vault and facial indices. My conclusions concerning the "Pseudo-Australoid" type were:

As far as my researches carry me, this type cannot be identified craniometrically with the aborigines of Australia, although it does bear some faint resemblance to them. I am inclined to the opinion that the true Australian racial type represents an archaic form of modern White man ... usually found blended with more advanced types. ... It seems quite probable that this type is represented very strongly today in the Ainu of Japan and that it exists in the Australians in combination with a definitely superimposed Negroid element which has imparted to it, perhaps, an accentuated prognathism and platyrrhiny. I do not believe that this type of man reached the New World in a pure and unadulterated form as the earliest migration, but rather that it represented in the first waves of immigrants an underlying and recessive type....[8]

(4) *"Plains Indian" type.* This was a misnomer, since I found its affinities to lie unmistakably with the eastern dolichohypsicephals. It was a tall mesocephalic type, so characteristically Indian in appearance that I made no effort to compare it with Old World groups. I regard it as an intermediate arising from mixture between the earlier dolichocephals and the later brachycephals, with the archaic elements preponderant.

(5) *"Long-faced European" type.* This is a disharmonic type in which a small, brachycephalic, hypsicephalic brain-case is attached to a moderately broad and extremely long face with leptorrhine nose and no prognathism. I satisfied myself that it was not

[8] Hooton, E. A. *Op. cit.*, pp. 355-356.

in the least like any European type which I could adduce for comparison. It also diverged widely from Armenian and Kurdish types. It approached most closely to series from eastern Turkestan and north China.

(6) *"Pseudo-Alpine" type.* The skulls of this type are short, broad brachycephals—invariably distorted by occipital deformation. They are markedly euryprosopic, somewhat platyrrhine, and very brachyuranic. They are totally unlike Alpine Europeans, but closely resemble Tibetan, Burmese, Telenget, and Kalmuck series. Nearer home, they seem intimately allied to the Apache. This is clearly a Mongoloid type.

(7) *"Large Hybrid" type.* These are large, hyperbrachycephalic crania, usually much deformed and with faces both broad and long. They are typically Indian in appearance. Craniometrically and indicially their affinities are clearly with skulls from the mounds of Ohio, Arkansas, Louisiana, and Tennessee. No effort was made to seek the relationships of this type outside of the American area. I have no doubt that it bears a close resemblance to various Mongoloid groups.

The conclusions from this study may be recapitulated briefly. The seven cranial types were distinguished by visual observation, mainly of facial features, since artificial deformation had altered the majority of the cranial vaults. Nevertheless, three dolichocephalic types emerged, which proved to be forms most numerous during the earlier periods of the Pueblo's occupation. One of these, called the "Basket Maker" type, justified its name by its clear resemblances to true Basket Makers and to skulls from the caves of Coahuila. It showed very striking similarities to Egyptian skulls of the Mediterranean race, but obviously differed from these in features which may be attributable to a Mongoloid admixture. A "Pseudo-Negroid" type was by no means identical with any true Negrito or Negro type, but, none the less, was much closer to Negro crania than to other contemporary Pecos types. A "Pseudo-Australoid" type was quite unlike skulls of native Australians, but bore some resemblance to Ainu crania. It seemed to me probable that the earlier dolichocephals of the American population may have been a blend of Mediterranean, Negroid, and an archaic White element, subsequently glossed over with Mongoloid traits due to mixture with other migrants. Three brachycephalic types showed affinities only to American Indians of other areas or to Asiatic Mongoloids. A mesocephalic type seemed to be intermediate between the earlier and possibly non-Mongoloid dolichocephals and the assuredly Mongoloid round-heads. I have no doubt that other elements, probably White, are mingled with the Mongoloid strains in the brachycephals, but they are too deeply submerged or too loosely linked in inheritance to segregate into recognizable types.

The method which I have employed in segregating cranial types differs quite radically from that of my colleague, Professor Dixon. He utilized only combinations of the conventional subdivisions of the length-breadth, length-height, and nasal indices (these being the most generally available). I, on the contrary, used morphological judgments in selecting the types, and then, after establishing their statistical integrity, sought their affinities with other crania by utilizing the means of all available cranial measurements and indices, and appraising the sum total of significant differences. He and I agree in finding that the dolichocephals came first to the New World and that there are evidences of Mediterranean and Negroid elements in these long-heads, as well as some other strain which may possibly be pre-Dravidian or Australoid. I, however, can find nothing in any of the cranial types which would justify me in stating that Nordic, Alpine, or Armenoid elements are involved in the composite race which we call the American Indian. I suspect that the aquiline Indian nose does mean a non-Mongoloid strain, but I am unwilling to identify even the Armenoid race solely by its nose.

When it comes to a choice between apes and angels, I am on the side of the apes: I subscribe also to the pragmatic doctrine of the persistence of indifferent physical traits in inheritance rather than to the mystic creed of environmental miracle-making. The American race is a composite race, but I think it is composed of heterogenous strains welded together by mixture, not of wonderfully adapted types made out of common clay by a creative environment.

14.

WHAT IS AN AMERICAN?[1]

THE question "What is an American?" may be asked and answered variously, according to the points of view and prejudices of the inquirer and the respondent. Probably it is most frequently put from an alien nationalistic standpoint and answered from the impressions of personal experience or of literary and political hearsay. Thus to an Englishman, apparently, an American is a person of certain citizenship but of ambiguous racial antecedents who, by virtue of the possession of aspirates and the lack of adenoids, degrades the English language to a singularly cacophonous dialect. The Frenchman, seemingly, regards the American as a barbarian of such simple sentimentality that his satisfaction in having said "Lafayette, we are here" makes him stop wanting to get his money back. To the Irishman, an American is a transplanted son of Erin who feeds fat his ancient grudge by ruling the descendants of the English and who enjoys the further advantage of not having to learn to speak Irish.

[1] A lecture delivered to the American Association of Physical Anthropologists at Yale University, April 30, 1936. Reprinted from the *American Journal of Physical Anthropology*, Vol. XXII, No. 1, October-December, 1936.

Aliens interpret each other's national characteristics in the light of their mutual economic, political and social relations. On the other hand, most Americans, asked to define an American, would perpetrate a Narcissian self-idealization. For example, to one numerous class of our citizenry an American is one who has fought and bled for his country and for whom his country consequently ought to be bled forevermore.

The physical anthropologist alone is qualified to answer objectively the question of this discourse, because he derives his data from caliper measurements, indices, morphological observations and statistical analysis pertaining to masses of the population. He can, at any rate, define the American zoölogically if not spiritually, if anyone is interested in the physical characteristics of the brute being.

From this restricted but definite aspect, there are a number of points upon which the status of the American requires elucidation. These subsidiary queries are as follows:

1. What is the racial composition of the older American stock and from what ethnic and national strains has it been derived?

2. Do the acclimatized Americans differ from their European forbears and have they amalgamated into new biotypes?

3. What is the distribution of physical types in the United States according to geographical areas and climatic zones, and by urban and rural residences? Are there tendencies to develop local physical varieties?

4. In the case of European groups of recent immigration and their immediate descendants, what are the facts of distribution, physical modification from the types of their homelands, and extent of amalgamation with the older American stocks?

5. What are the anthropological rôles in the United States of the Negro, the Negroid, and other elements of the population representing races radically different from so-called "White" European stocks?

Obviously, complete and conclusive answers to the foregoing questions must await the gathering and analysis of far more data than are available at present. This lack of adequate information cannot be attributed solely to the apathy, incompetence, or paucity of physical anthropologists. It is due rather to an apparently inherent revulsion from honest self-examination which afflicts men

as individuals and which expresses itself in governments by a settled policy that it is folly to be wise in the matter of the anthropological composition of its citizenry. Anthropology is an innocuous pursuit only when restricted to the study of savages.
When applied to civilized nations it has a distressing tendency to
shatter cherished delusions. Certainly, of all anthropologists, the
physical variety is most suspect and least tolerable. The cultural
anthropologist deals with phenomena which may be examined
with relative impunity, because each individual is able to dissociate himself from the institutions of his own social group, when
the latter are subjected to adverse criticism. But the physical anthropologist strips off the cultural veil and examines each individual man in his organic nakedness, for which there is no alibi.
Man wishes to know everything except himself, and nations are
only agglomerations of individuals with collective intelligences (if
such there be), functioning at a level somewhat below the deplorable group mean. All nations fear an anthropological stock-
taking, just as most men fear a medical examination. Learning
the truth is confused with "knowing the worst." Nevertheless,
we insist upon taking an anthropological glance at the contemporary American.

There are many aspects of the anthropology of this country
which I cannot discuss in this address because of limitations of
time. There are other equally important subjects which may be
omitted because the new evidence at my disposal merely con-
firms and amplifies the conclusions reached by earlier students. In
this latter category belong the changes in bodily form in the
children of immigrants, first established by the pioneer researches
of Professor Boas many years ago, and the modifications in the
somatological characters of the present generation of Americans
descended from stocks long resident in the United States, most
strikingly demonstrated in the recent work of Bowles [2] upon
Harvard sons, fathers and grandfathers. The tendencies toward
increased stature, diminished bodily fullness, elongation of the
head length with compensatory decrease of head breadth, and many
other dimensional and proportional changes, can be demonstrated
in a variety of stocks domiciled in this country. Since changes of

---

[2] Bowles, G. T., *New Types of Old Americans at Harvard*, Cambridge, Massachusetts,
1932.

this general nature are nearly as marked in the older American stocks as in those of recent immigration, it becomes apparent that we are dealing with evolutionary trends, or cyclic phenomena, and not merely with the effects of a sudden and violent impact of a new environment upon those elements of the population which have been transferred abruptly into a radically different habitat.

Because these bodily changes are by no means uniform in all stocks nor constant in their direction, it is certain that much careful study and analysis must be accomplished before anthropologists can determine their aetiology. In the meantime we may allow the medical profession complacently to attribute increases in gross dimensions to its own dispensations of orange juice, cod liver oil and spinach, without stopping to inquire whether corporeal elongation is synonymous with increased fitness and improved chances of biological survival.

Certainly the most interesting and important subject which I am obliged to defer for future discussion, is the formation of local anthropological types in sections of the older American population which have inbred in relative isolation. An incidental and somewhat disconcerting discovery of state anthropological types occurred in connection with our criminal survey to which I shall allude presently. In every one of nine states studied there is ample evidence that the metric, indicial and morphological characters of the Old American population define a state type which is different from that of adjacent states, and that the amount of difference between the Old American types of any two states seems to depend partially upon the diversity of their environments, as well as upon the variations in the ethnic composition of their interbreeding European stocks.

I am forced to neglect also the subject of the Negro and Negroid population of the United States, and the results of Negro-White intermixtures, upon which a mass of new data is available. However, these subjects have been treated competently by several anthropologists, notably Herskovits and Day.

The restricted purpose of this address is to disclose some preliminary results of studies of racial types in the United States among the White stocks—native born of native parentage, native

born of foreign parentage, and foreign born. Only the baldest
outline of a few selected findings can be presented within the
temporal limits set by a speaker's humanitarian consideration for
his audience.

Americans, for our present purposes, may be divided into four
classes: 1) Old Americans, 2) New Americans—both of whom
have been born to Americanism; 3) Immigrant Americans—those
who have achieved Americanism; and 4) Afro-Americans—or
those who have had Americanism thrust upon them. There are,
in addition, Real Americans, but these are called "Indians" and,
of course, "do not count."

Materials. I have misappropriated the term "Old Americans"
from Dr. Aleš Hrdlička's great book of that title. Old Americans,
according to his definition, were those who represented at least
the third generation born in this country. On account of the depression, it has seemed essential to devaluate this definition by one-
third, thus reducing its content of generations to two. Such measures, as everyone knows, have a most salutary effect in promoting
prosperity and in restoring public confidence. Again, while it may
be a wise child who knows its father, it seems to be a very rare
child who knows its grandfather—so far, at any rate, as concerns
his nativity and ethnic origin.

Doctor Hrdlička's anthropological study of the Old Americans,[3]
published in 1925, dealt with full sets of measurements and observations upon about 900 subjects, with additional pigment data
on another thousand. His exhaustive treatment of metric and
morphological variations, each considered by itself, has yielded
results which are unlikely to be modified except in minor detail
by subsequent investigations. There is no need of duplicating
Hrdlička's work by an enumeration here of similar results derived from later and larger series. It will be sufficient to summarize
his findings in the distribution of single characters, thus con-
fining the discussion of our own results to aspects of the subject
not exhausted by his treatment.

Doctor Hrdlička concludes that the Old Americans of the
clerical, professional and leisure classes, as compared with other
larger groups of Whites are characterized by:

[3] Hrdlička, Aleš, *The Old Americans*, Baltimore, 1925.

"intermediate pigmentation, tallest stature, relative shortness of arms, good size of head, large range of cephalic index, relatively narrow face, rather long and narrow nose with lower nasal index, moderate width of mouth, moderate height of subnasal portion of face, moderate lower facial breadth, somewhat narrow hands and feet. They differ little if at all from comparable whites in relative weight, relative height of trunk and lower limbs, height and breadth of forehead, dimensions of ears. They show at a disadvantage in muscular strength in left hand, arms, and shoulders." [4]

In general they approach most closely the people of Great Britain. Such are Hrdlička's upper and middle class Old Americans.

In conformity with his own less exalted scientific status, the present writer has sought to study humbler classes of Americans. In fact, the largest body of his material consists of criminals, who are, in a sense, a professional and leisure class of a somewhat lower order. One might paraphrase Lincoln's remark about the common people: "God must love criminals, because he has made so many of them." Certainly in a study of the anthropology of the American people criminals should not be neglected, not only because of their numbers, but because they constitute that class of the American population which costs the country most (even more than veterans); they are tenderly cherished by a host of humanitarians and sentimentalists; they indirectly or directly furnish a means of livelihood for a large proportion of our public servants, and for countless private individuals, including members of the bar, the fourth estate and writers of detective fiction.

Yet it would be hardly fair to attempt to define an American solely on the basis of the anthropological study of criminals, however appropriate it might appear to our European critics. In addition to measurements of some 14,000 criminals, the Harvard survey gathered, for purposes of comparison, a sample of some 3000 law-abiding civilians, or at any rate persons not in jail at the time of measurement. Further, it was possible through the efforts of Prof. Fay-Cooper Cole, and through the generous co-operation of a number of commercial organizations, to operate an anthropometric laboratory at A Century of Progress Exposition. This model laboratory, under the able direction of C. W.

[4] Hrdlička, op. cit., pp. 407-408.

Dupertuis of Harvard, collected in the course of two seasons complete anthropometric data on some 6000 visitors to the Fair. The complete analysis of these data awaits the attention of Mr. Dupertuis, but certain preliminary results are available. A number of other anthropometric series of the American population are in the files of the Harvard Laboratory and elsewhere, but have not been utilized for the present study. However, attention should be called to the physical data on draft recruits and demobilized soldiers of the World War, ably analyzed by Davenport and Love.

Methods. Our primary concern here is the determination of the racial composition of the White population of the United States. A race signifies a large and relatively homogeneous physical group of mankind, the members of which possess similar combinations of hereditary features by virtue of their common descent. All modern populations are racially mixed and consequently consist of a majority of hybrid combinations and a minority adhering more or less closely to the supposed physical types of the original parental races. In order to separate such a mixed population into racial and subracial groups it is necessary either for the field worker to diagnose the racial type of each subject at the time of measurement, or for the process to be carried out subsequently in a statistical laboratory by multiple sortings on the basis of combinations of racial criteria. The former method requires a very delicate and precise judgment of morphological type, the latter a judicious selection of sorting criteria, mechanical sorting and tabulating apparatus, and no end of drudgery. In the Harvard criminal survey series and in the Century of Progress series, the laboratory sorting method has been carried out. The primary criteria utilized were cephalic index and combinations of hair color and eye color; in certain subgroups a two-fold division of stature or of the nasal index was added. In general the criteria employed were those which are commonly supposed to characterize the several races of Europe, as assumed to occur in individual combinations from studies of isolated means and modes of groups. The numerous subgroups thus mechanically separated were then combined into a number of racial, subracial and mixed types— again on the basis of the consensus of anthropological opinion as to European racial composition. The next step involved complete metric and morphological analysis of each racial type thus distinguished, and the verification of its statistical differentiation from random samples of the entire series. This process establishes the anthropological integrity of the groups thus arbitrarily sorted, provided that variabilities in each group are diminished in comparison with those of the series at large. The foregoing details of technique are tedious but necessary, since they involve a somewhat novel handling of anthropological material. Physical anthropological analysis is drudgery and even a casual listener or reader may not escape utterly the abysmal boredom of the routine. Each anthropological investigation involves a protracted sojourn in a statistical purgatory, with no little doubt as to the ultimate place of emergence.

In this particular instance the issue was favorable, and consisted in the recognition of nine so-called "racial types," clear-cut and statistically validated. I wish to discant upon the proportions and distribution of these types in the American population.

The number of individuals in the criminal series utilized for this racial sorting was 5689. These persons were inmates of the penal institutions of nine states: Massachusetts, North Carolina, Kentucky, Tennessee, Wisconsin, Colorado, Texas, New Mexico and Arizona. The states were selected for the purpose of furnishing representative samples of all of the more important racial groups domiciled in the United States. Of the criminals 69% are native Whites of native parentage, 20% are native Whites of foreign parentage and 11% are foreign born Whites.

Our check sample of civilians, gathered for comparison with the criminals, numbered, so far as the racial sortings were concerned, 815 adult male individuals, all from Massachusetts and Tennessee. It is therefore more respectable but less representative than the criminal sample. Because the majority of its members were studied in metropolitan Boston, it is composed of only 36% of native Whites of native parentage, and includes 34% of native Whites of foreign parentage, and nearly 30% of foreign born Whites.

The number of adult males utilized for racial sorting in the Century of Progress series was 2664, of which 2315 are native born. Practically one-half of the latter were born in the East

North Central census district (including Ohio, Indiana, Illinois, Michigan and Wisconsin). Taking Chicago as a center, the proportion of natives of each census district represented in these visitors at the Exposition decreases with utmost regularity in all four directions. A similar distribution obtains in the case of the state of residence, except that the concentration of residents of the North Central District is greater than that of natives of that area.

In the total Century of Progress series of males, 56% are native born of native parentage, 31%, native born of foreign parentage, and 13%, foreign born. Thus the composition of this series includes nearly 13% less of Old Americans, 11% more of first generation Americans, and 2% more of aliens than occur in the criminal series. The check sample of civilians used for comparison with the criminals falls between the Century of Progress and criminal series, with about one-third of each parentage category.

It is expedient at this point to enumerate and to name the racial types somewhat arbitrarily sorted out by physical criteria and validated by subsequent statistical analysis. The description of the principal physical features of each type will be given later in conjunction with an account of its proportional contribution to the total population, its regional distribution, and a few hints concerning its sociological characteristics.

1. The Pure Nordic type of pure blond long-heads.
2. The Pure Mediterranean type of pure brunet long-heads.
3. The Predominantly Nordic type of near blond long-heads.
4. The Keltic type of long-heads with disharmonic pigment combinations.
5. The mixed Nordic Mediterranean type of long-heads with intermediate but darkish pigmentation.
6. The East Baltic type of pure blond round-heads with medium to broad noses.
7. The Alpine type of pure brunet round-heads with medium to broad noses.
8. The mixed Nordic Alpine type of round-heads with intermediate but lightish pigmentation, and medium to broad noses.
9. The mixed Dinaric type of round-heads with intermediate pigmentation and narrow noses.

The above are the so-called racial types, named with reference to their supposed European affinities, and selected on the basis of physical combinations which are anthropologically defensible, but not within the limits of this discourse.

Distribution of racial types in the American population. The proportions of the nine racial types in the three series—criminal, civilian check sample and Century of Progress visitors—are extraordinarily similar. In general, the visitors to the Chicago Exposition, with residences centering in Chicago, show percentages of the several types nearly identical with those recorded in the criminal series from the nine states. On the other hand the civilian check sample, resident largely in and around Boston, differs somewhat more widely from the criminal series in its racial proportions. This difference is perhaps in accordance with expectation. The Boston civilian check sample has about 10 to 12% more of the Dinaric type (round heads, long faces, long noses, intermediate to dark pigmentation) than the criminal and Century of Progress series. This difference arises from the larger numbers of persons from southeastern Europe and from the Near East in our Boston sample. There is also in the Boston series an excess of the Pure Mediterranean (very brunet long-heads) over the other two series, due to numerous Italians, and a deficiency of 8 to 9% of Nordic Alpines (brachycephals of intermediate lightish pigmentation and broad noses), partially attributable to a relative paucity of Teutonic peoples in Boston.

We may now consider the general distribution and ranking of the nine so-called racial types in our three series—the large series of criminals and the two smaller series of citizens unapprehended. The latter are the civilian check sample series, consisting of Nashville (Tennessee) firemen, Massachusetts militiamen, and outpatients of Boston hospitals; and the Century of Progress visitors.

Nordic Mediterranean. The ranking physical type in the combined series is the Nordic Mediterranean group of long-heads with darkish pigmentation (cephalic index under 80; dark hair and mixed eyes; red hair and mixed eyes when stature is under 170; red-brown hair and mixed eyes; light brown hair and dark eyes). This Nordic Mediterranean type constitutes about 25% of the combined series, ranking first among the criminals and a close second in each of the two civilian series. Among the criminals this type is excessively represented in the states of Kentucky and North Carolina, and somewhat deficient in Tennessee, Wisconsin and New Mexico. In the Century of Progress series it seems to have a fairly even distribution through the census districts, with a possible excess in the South Atlantic states.

The Nordic Mediterranean type is strongest among the native Whites of native parentage of whatever series, and is somewhat less numerous proportionately among the first generation Americans, and still less so among the foreign born. In these two last named parentage categories, the Nordic Mediterranean type of criminals is distinguished by a deficiency of persons of Teutonic, Scandinavian and Polish-Austrian descent. In the Century of Progress series it displays similar deficiencies of the above-named ethnic descents and is especially strong in English, Welsh, Scotch and Irish descendants. It seems to be a predominantly British type.

Among the criminals the Nordic Mediterranean type is remarkable because of its high ranking in first and second degree murder and its low ranking in burglary and larceny. Its occupational distribution among criminals is fairly even, except that it is rather high in skilled trades and transportation and decidedly low in clerical work. Educationally its achievements are very low.

The two civilian series studied are separated occupationally and educationally from the criminals by such a vast gulf that comparisons are almost ridiculous. For example, the criminal series consists of about 25% of extractives (farmers, cattle breeders, miners, etc.), and about 18% of unskilled laborers; the Boston civilian check sample includes only 1.55% of extractives and 7.10% of unskilled laborers; the Century of Progress series contains only 2.70% of extractives and no unskilled laborers at all. Again in the criminal series, 3.36% have attended college or professional school, whereas in the Boston civilian series the proportion of such educational attainment is 10.65%, and in the Century of Progress series from 50 to 65% of the various types are of this advanced status.

The Nordic Mediterranean type of the Boston check sample shows no particular occupational differentiation except a high ranking in skilled trades, in transportation, and in public service. It is fifth in educational attainment, as compared with seventh in the criminals. In the Century of Progress series this type is not occupationally remarkable, but ranks second in men who have attended college or professional school, with 64.32%.

Nordic Alpine type. The second ranking type of the three combined series is Nordic Alpine. This type is round-headed (cephalic index over 80) and moderately broad-nosed (nasal index over 63). It is of intermediate pigmentation, or of disharmonic combinations of hair and eye color, but never pure blond or pure brunet. In its pigmentation characters it tends to center around medium to light brown hair and mixed eyes (dark hair and mixed eyes, red hair and mixed eyes, red-brown hair and mixed eyes, light brown hair and dark eyes). The Nordic Alpine type constitutes 23% of the three combined series. It drops to 16% in the Boston civilian series and rises to 25% in the Century of Progress, for reasons previously stated. In the criminal series it is 24%, ranking second, as against first in the Century of Progress and third in the Boston check sample.

The state distribution of the Nordic Alpine type in criminals indicates that Massachusetts is notably strong in this type and Kentucky is markedly deficient. Probable excesses of the type occur also in Texas, Wisconsin and Tennessee. In the Century of Progress series this type seems to show a proportionately even distribution through the census districts, with perhaps a slightly excess strength in the East North Central and Middle Atlantic states.

In the parentage classification it is perfectly clear that the Nordic Alpine type has its strongest representation in persons of foreign birth, is somewhat excessively represented in native born of foreign parentage, and is proportionately deficient in the Old Americans.

In the criminal series this type is markedly deficient among Old Americans and possibly deficient in English and Welsh and Scandinavian descendants. On the other hand, it includes excesses of persons of Polish-Austrian, Russian, Teutonic, French, and Jewish birth or parentage. The Century of Progress series shows similar and almost identical ethnic excesses and deficiencies.

In the criminal series the Nordic Alpine type shows very little offense differentiation, although it is high in robbery and low in burglary and larceny. Occupationally it is deficient in extractives (farmers, miners, cattlemen, etc.), and is high in transportation. Educationally, it ranks fifth of the nine types among criminals, two places above the Nordic Mediterranean. In the Boston civilian series it drops to seventh place in educational attainment.

The Nordic Alpine type in the Boston civilians is notable because of its leading rank in public service occupations, its primacy also in personal service, and its low proportion of factory operatives. In the Century of Progress series it shows a comparatively low occupational status, and is next to the bottom in higher educational attainment.

Predominantly Nordic. Third place in the total morphological series is held by the Predominantly Nordic with 17% of the total. The Predominantly Nordic type includes all near-blonds who are long-headed (light brown hair and mixed eyes, golden and ash-blond hair with mixed eyes, red hair and mixed eyes, light brown hair and blue eyes). It is the third ranking type in the criminal series and in the Century of Progress, but drops to fourth in the Eastern civilian series, as is to be expected, with a range in the three series of 14 to 22%. In the parentage groups this Predominantly Nordic type is the most excessively represented among Old American criminals and is progressively under-represented in first generation and foreign born criminals. It is, in fact, the most generally characteristic criminal type of Old American ancestry, although not the most numerous. In the Century of Progress visitors, also, this Predominantly Nordic type is in excess among the Old Americans, although not so preponderantly, and is deficient in the first generation Americans. Taking all of the parentage groups combined, it would appear that this type has its strongest representation in native Whites of native parentage and its weakest in the foreign born.

Among the criminals the Predominantly Nordic type is especially strong in Kentucky, Tennessee, North Carolina, New Mexico, Colorado and Arizona, but is markedly deficient in Massachusetts and in Wisconsin. In the Century of Progress series, it is perhaps proportionately strongest in the West North Central District (Minnesota, Iowa, Missouri, North Dakota, South Dakota, Nebraska, Kansas). In the criminals this type includes, apart from a huge excess of Old Americans, significant excesses of English and Welsh. It is notably deficient in French, Spanish, Portuguese, Italian, Polish-Austrian, Balkan, Russian, Asia Minor and Jewish elements. In the Century of Progress series, the persons of recent

European extraction in this type are predominantly Scandinavian, English and Welsh, and British Canadian, while the ethnic groups poorly represented are those also deficient among the Predominantly Nordic criminals.

The criminals of this type are especially distinguished by being found in prisons rather than in reformatories, have disproportionately few previous convictions, and seem to have no very particularized offense propensities except a marked disinclination to rape and assault, a ranking above the mean in murder, and a high position in forgery, fraud and bootlegging. Among the criminals the Predominantly Nordic group is occupationally differentiated by its leading position in extractives (agriculturalists, miners, cattlemen, etc.). Its urban residents rank second in clerical occupations and in transportation, and are very low in unskilled labor and personal service. In educational qualifications it ranks third.

The Predominantly Nordic type in the Boston check sample ranks second in clerical occupations, as in the criminal series, is high in skilled trades, and low in personal service. It is fourth in educational rank. In the Century of Progress series, this group is high in extractives, as among the criminals, but it is also very high in professional men. It ranks sixth of the nine types in proportion of college and professional school men.

Dinaric. The Dinaric type is fourth in combined ranking with 13.33% of the total males. In the Boston civilian sample, it is, however, the most numerous type with 23%, as against 13% in the criminal and 11% in the Century of Progress series. In the criminal series this type is markedly deficient in native Whites of native parentage, and has an excess representation in the native Whites of foreign parentage, and in the foreign Whites. In both civilian series it is almost proportionately represented in all three parentage categories. This Dinaric type consists of brachycephals with nasal indices under 63 and includes pigment combinations from dark to near blond.[5] It is a rather composite type which perhaps ought to be broken up into subtypes, but it has a certain physical and sociological unity, none the less. Among the crimi-

---

[5] Dinaric type: Cephalic index over 80, nasal index under 63; dark hair and dark eyes, dark hair and blue eyes, dark hair and mixed eyes, red hair and blue eyes, red-brown hair and blue eyes, light brown hair and blue eyes, red-brown hair and mixed eyes, red-brown hair and dark eyes, light brown hair and dark eyes, light brown hair and mixed eyes.

nals it has an excess representation in Wisconsin and Massachusetts, whereas Kentucky, Tennessee and North Carolina yield unduly few. In the Century of Progress series it is excessively strong in the East North Central district and to a lesser extent in the Middle Atlantic district. Among criminals the Dinarics of recent European derivation are particularly of Polish-Austrian, Teutonic, French Canadian, Scotch and Asia Minor birth or parentage. The same is true of the Boston civilian check sample and of the Century of Progress series. The Dinaric is a type rare in the Old American males.

Criminologically the Dinarics rank second in forgery and fraud, and second also in rape and bootlegging (an offense against public welfare). In all other offenses this type is consistently low. Occupationally the group ranks first in clerical and semi-professional pursuits, second in the professions and in public service, third in skilled trades. It is low in unskilled laborers and appears to be a mainly urban type. Among the criminals the Dinaric type is the best educated. However, in the Boston check sample this type has a somewhat lower economic status and is the most poorly educated of all, probably because it is composed largely of recent immigrants from the Central European and Near Eastern region, who are still suffering the disadvantage of transplantation into a new country with a totally different language. The criminal Dinarics are more largely of Teutonic descent.

The Dinaric type in the Century of Progress series resembles the criminal type occupationally in that it ranks first in professional and semi-professional pursuits, and first in public service, and is high in skilled trades. It is fourth in percentage of highly educated men.

Keltic. The Keltic type consists of long-headed men with red hair and blue eyes, red-brown hair and blue eyes, and dark hair and blue eyes. It comprises 8.48% of the combined series and ranks fifth in each. This type is rather more strongly represented among the criminals than among the civilian check samples. It is in excess among the Old Americans, whether criminal or civilian, less conspicuous and proportionately deficient in the native Whites of foreign parentage, and decidedly rare among the foreign born Whites. Among criminals, the Keltic type is outstandingly present in Kentucky and North Carolina and is significantly rare in

Tennessee and in Texas. In the Century of Progress series, the Keltic type is especially strong in residents of the South Atlantic district (Delaware, Maryland, District of Columbia, Virginia, West Virginia, North Carolina, South Carolina, Georgia, Florida) and in the East South Central district (Kentucky, Tennessee, Alabama, Mississippi). It is also strong in New England. The Keltic criminals of recent European descent are strongly Irish, and include also a significant excess of Scandinavians. In the Century of Progress civilians, the English, Irish, Welsh, British Canadians, and Scandinavians provide nearly all of the members of the type who are not Old Americans.

The Keltic type of criminals is excessively married as contrasted with most other types. It has a marked predilection for assault with intent to do bodily harm, and it is singularly indisposed to commit robbery. It is also first in sex offenses other than rape, and in crimes against public welfare (principally illegal manufacture and sale of liquor). It is high in burglary and larceny and in both kinds of murder, but low in rape. As a matter of fact, its mean ranking for all crimes is first. It has no occupational peculiarities except a marked excess of persons in the extractive pursuits (farming, cattle raising, mining). Educationally this type of criminal ranks sixth of the nine racial types. In the Boston civilian sample the Keltic type is much more strongly Irish than in the general criminal series. Furthermore, the Boston civilians of the Keltic type include far more in public service and in skilled occupations, and fewer farmers and unskilled laborers. Instead of being in sixth place educationally it is in second place, being, as a matter of fact, nearly fifty times as well educated as the criminal Keltic type, according to a ratio which need not be explained here.

The Keltics in the Century of Progress series lead in trade, and are second in clerical pursuits and in public service. This type ranks third in higher education.

Pure Mediterranean. In the combined series the Pure Mediterranean type ranks sixth with only 402 individuals, or 4.38% of the total. It ranks sixth in both the civilian check sample and in the criminal series, and seventh in the Century of Progress series. This group consists simply of all persons with cephalic indices under 80; hair black, dark brown, or red brown; eyes pure dark brown or light brown. It is most strongly represented in the Boston civilian check sample, and least in the Century of Progress series. In the criminal series and in the Boston check sample the Mediterranean type is relatively deficient among the Old Americans and in excess in the foreign born. This condition does not obtain in the Century of Progress series.

The heavy contributors to the Mediterranean type of criminal are the states of Massachusetts, Colorado and New Mexico. Apparent deficiencies of this type occur in Kentucky, Tennessee, North Carolina and Texas. In the Century of Progress series the census districts which are unduly strong as the birthplaces of this type are Middle Atlantic and East North Central. The type is rare in the West North Central district. Ethnically, in the criminal series, the Pure Mediterranean type shows an excessive representation of Spanish, Portuguese and Italians. It is notably deficient in Old Americans and in Polish-Austrians. In the Century of Progress series there are almost no persons of Spanish or Italian origin and the Pure Mediterranean type consists of long-headed brunets from a wide variety of European descents.

In the criminal group the Pure Mediterranean type is outstanding for crimes of violence against persons, being first in second degree murder, first in rape, second in assault and robbery, and third in first degree murder. It is last in burglary and larceny and next to last in forgery and fraud. Occupationally, it is essentially an urban type of low status, ranking very high in unskilled labor and personal service. Educationally, the criminals of Pure Mediterranean type rank eighth of the nine types. In the Boston civilian check sample the occupational status of the Mediterranean type is a good deal higher, and in educational attainment the civilian Mediterraneans move up to sixth place.

The Pure Mediterranean type in the Century of Progress series is totally unlike the same type among the criminals as regards occupation. It is not occupationally outstanding among the various types and ranks fifth in higher education.

East Baltic. The East Baltic type ranks seventh in the total series, with 3.02%. It is more strongly represented in the civilian series than among criminals. This type consists of all pure blonds with nasal indices above 63 and cephalic indices of 80 and above. It thus includes persons with pure blue or pure gray eyes and ash-blond or golden hair, who are round-headed and rather broad-nosed. The East Baltic type shows an excess representation in the Old American and first generation American criminals, and is deficient in the foreign born criminals. However, in the Century of Progress series the exact reverse of excess and deficiency obtains in the three parentage groups. Among the criminals the East Baltic type is unduly strong in Massachusetts, Tennessee, Texas and Colorado, whereas in other states it is somewhat poorly represented. In the Century of Progress series, this type is outstanding among natives of the East North Central district and possibly of the Pacific and Mountain districts.

The East Baltic type of criminals of recent European origin shows excesses of persons of Russian and Polish-Austrian descent and is deficient in those of Italian ancestry. In the Century of Progress series this type is of strongly Teutonic and Polish-Austrian derivation.

The East Baltic criminals are notable for their low average age and their high rate of celibacy. In offense they are outstanding by reason of their primacy in burglary and larceny, and their low rank in every other type of crime except rape. Occupationally, this criminal type holds first place in trade, but has no professional men, no public servants, and few semi-professional and transport workers. It is rather high in unskilled labor and in factory workers, but low in extractives. It is essentially an urban type. In education it ranks second among criminals and first in the civilian check sample.

The East Baltic type in the Century of Progress series ranks next to the last in college and professional school men, and is lowest in professional occupations. It includes no transportation workers.

Alpine. The Alpine type ranks eighth of the nine types in the combined series, since it includes only 2.68% of the total. It consists simply of all brachycephals with dark hair and eyes or red-brown hair and dark eyes, whose nasal indices are above 63. It is somewhat stronger in the civilian series than in the criminal series. In all native Whites of native parentage, civilian or criminal, this type is the most poorly represented. The Alpine type is in strong excess among the native Whites of foreign parentage in all series and has its maximum representation among the foreign born

Whites. Of all racial types it is the least characteristically American.

In the criminals the Alpine type is excessively numerous among the inmates of the penal institutions of Massachusetts, Wisconsin, New Mexico and Colorado, and is rare in Kentucky, Tennessee and North Carolina. The East North Central and West North Central census districts appear to furnish an excess of this type in the Century of Progress series.

Ethnically, among criminals, the Alpine type has its greatest excess in persons of Italian birth or parentage, but also is disproportionately strong in French Canadians, Balkans, Spanish, Portuguese, Polish-Austrians and persons of Asia Minor extraction. In the Boston civilian series, this type is overloaded with Near Easterners as well as with persons of the other extractions mentioned. In the Century of Progress series, it is similarly constituted, but with a great strength of Russians and fewer Italians and Portuguese, practically none of whom seem to have visited the Harvard Anthropometric Laboratory in the Hall of the Social Sciences. Among the criminals this essentially alien type is easily first in robbery and last in forgery and fraud. It is high in assault, low in murder and rape, but high in sex offenses other than rape. Occupationally it is very deficient in farmers, miners, and cattlemen, but excessively strong in unskilled laborers. It ranks first in public service, first in professions, first in personal service and last in extractive occupations, in transportation and in skilled trades. It is evidently composed of urban dwellers from the highest and lowest economic levels. Nevertheless, among the criminals it is the most poorly educated type. In the civilian check sample it ranks eighth in education, of the nine types.

The Alpine type in the Century of Progress series resembles the same type among the criminals in that it is last in extractives, and has no transportation workers, and is first in personal service. In other occupational categories it bears little or no relation to the criminal type of similar physique. Also in the Century of Progress series the Alpine type is highest in college and professionally educated men, whereas it is at the other extreme in the criminal series and in the Boston check sample.

Pure Nordic. The Pure Nordic type is the scarcest of all types in the combined series here studied with but 2.44% of the total.

It is less common among criminals than among civilians. It is proportionately twice as numerous in the Century of Progress series as in the criminal series. It consists of long-headed men with golden or ash-blond hair and pure blue or pure gray eyes. These are the classic Nordics and they are very rare indeed. In the criminal series they are strongly in excess in the Old Americans and in first generation Americans, but disproportionately few in the foreign born. In the Boston check sample the Pure Nordic type is somewhat deficient in the Old Americans, but strong in the first generation Americans. In the Century of Progress series, this type is proportionately by far the strongest in its Old American parentage, and successively more rare in the first generation and the foreign born.

Among the criminals the Pure Nordic type is excessively represented in New Mexico, Kentucky and Colorado, and is somewhat deficient in Wisconsin, Tennessee and Massachusetts. In the Century of Progress series it is particularly strong in natives of the West North Central region (states unrepresented in the criminal series).

Ethnically, among the criminals, the Pure Nordic type shows an excess of British Canadians and a strong deficiency of Italians. In the Century of Progress series it is also strongly British Canadian and markedly Scandinavian, but still more strongly Old American.

This type among the criminals is notably youthful, celibate and distinct in its offense proclivities. It is last in both kinds of murder, assault, and robbery, and eighth, or last but one, in sex offenses other than rape. On the other hand, it is easily first in forgery and fraud and a close second in burglary and larceny. It is a type with which the pen seems considerably mightier than the sword in a criminological sense. This result hardly accords with popular impressions of the characteristics of the Nordic blond.

Among the criminals this Pure Nordic type is too small to show significant occupational differentiation, but ranks first in skilled trades and transportation, last in trade and in personal service, and has no professional men or public servants. Educationally, it attains fourth rank in criminals and third in the Boston civilian check sample.

The Pure Nordic type ranks first in extractives in both of the civilian series. In the Boston series it ranks first in clerical occupations, and in the Chicago series it has the highest proportion of students. In neither series does it include personal service workers. Nevertheless in the Century of Progress series this type has the smallest percentage of highly educated men.

Females in the Century of Progress series. The adult females used for this racial type sorting in the Century of Progress series number 2960, of whom about 60% are native born of native parentage, 33% native born of foreign parentage, and 8% foreign born. Thus the females include some 4% more of Old Americans than the males of this same series, about 2% less of first generation Americans, and 5% less of foreign born.

The distribution of the racial sorting types in the females is not very different from that of the males. The principal divergence of the females from the male distribution of types lies in an excess of about 11% in the Dinaric type of the female series, largely at the expense of the Predominantly Nordic type. As in the males, all of the long-headed types are in excess in the Old American females of the Century of Progress series, but in the females the most distinctively Old American group is the Predominantly Nordic or near blond long-head, instead of the Pure Nordic as in the males. The distribution of the racial types among the females shows, in general, an excess of about 12% of brachycephals (mainly of the Dinaric type) as compared with the males.

Age. In mean ages of the types there are no consistent differences between the criminal and the civilian series. The general average is about 30 years. In all of the series native Whites of native parentage tend to be youngest, native Whites of foreign parentage intermediate, and foreign born Whites considerably the oldest. There is no age differentiation in the types, with the exception of a marked inferiority in mean age in the criminal Pure Nordic and East Baltic types, which is to some extent substantiated in the civilian series, especially in the Old American group. Since these are the pure blond types, it is suggested that the increase of pigmentation with maturity in mixed strains tends to transfer Pure Nordic individuals into the Predominantly Nordic class, and East Baltics into Dinarics or Nordic-Alpines. This effect seems more marked in the thoroughly blended Old Americans than in the native born of foreign parentage and the foreign born.

Weight. Civilian types are consistently heavier than the same types among the criminals. Mean criminal weights center about 150 pounds, whereas civilian means for corresponding types exceed these by various amounts, usually 5 pounds or more. The racial types seem undifferentiated with respect to mean weight, which increases with mean age.

Stature. Type for type the criminals are considerably shorter than the civilians of the Boston check sample, and still further below the means of stature of the Century of Progress series. The differences in mean stature between the criminals and the Boston civilians vary about 1 cm., and between the criminals and the Century of Progress series the average type differences approach 3 cm. In each of the series the native born of native parentage tend to be the tallest, the native born of foreign parentage shorter, and the foreign born shortest. Evidently, within the same morphological racial type, stature increases with elevation of social and economic status, and with length of residence of the type within this country. Further, the younger the group, the taller it tends to be.

However, throughout the three series and the several parentage groups, the nine racial types tend to maintain more or less the same statural ranking. Thus the Predominantly Nordic, near blond, long-headed type ranks first in nearly all of the series, and the Pure Nordic type second. The Keltic type of long-head is less consistent but ranks in general third, the Nordic Mediterranean long-headed and middling dark type fourth, the round-headed blond East Baltics fifth, the round-headed long-nosed Dinarics sixth, the Pure Mediterranean brunet dolichocephals seventh, the brachycephalic moderately pigmented Nordic Alpines eighth, and the brunet round-head Alpines are invariably last.

Cephalic index. There is a general tendency for the criminal racial types to be very slightly more brachycephalic than the corresponding civilian types. In the Century of Progress series the native Whites of native parentage show least type variations from the total mean in the cephalic index, the first generations are intermediate, and the foreign born are most differentiated. For example, the actual means of dolichocephalic and brachycephalic types differ most in the foreign born and least in the Old Americans. In other words, the Old Americans tend to be the least variable.

General conclusions on the racial types. The types which have been sorted out on the basis of combinations of physical criteria and which have been described incompletely in the foregoing discussion, have been called "racial types." The use of the term "racial" is justified by the fact that the physical features used as the basis of sorting are generally regarded as, in the main, hereditary and racial characters. Nevertheless, I make no claim that these types constitute, singly, bodies of individuals of exactly the same ethnic derivation, each group composed of persons whose proportions of the several ancestral strains are identical. All that can be claimed is that mutual physical resemblances of persons belonging to the same type, establish the supposition that they are, on the whole, more closely related to each other than they are to the groups of individuals belonging to different types. It is perfectly obvious that, in such a racially mixed population as ours, individual brothers might be assigned to two or three different racial types.

So far as our data permit us to judge, the ethnic origins of the several types distinguished are identical or closely similar for the same types in all three of our series, civilian and criminal. The European antecedents, where ascertainable, confirm anthropological tradition as to the existence and provenience of certain physical races.

Our series represent fairly large samples from three markedly diverse levels of our population. The criminals are socially, economically and biologically the most debased element. The Boston civilian check sample is composed, for the most part, of urban residents representing a respectable working-class population, which has enjoyed, presumably, few of the advantages conferred by wealth and by social position. The Century of Progress series proves to be a group of persons disproportionately selected from the highly educated, and, on the whole, economically and socially superior classes. Undoubtedly this selection arose from the situation of the Harvard Anthropometric Laboratory in the Hall of Social Sciences. Probably few persons visited this hall intentionally unless they happened to be interested in education and in social problems. It required a certain intellectual curiosity and a certain pertinacity for these persons to book and to fulfill engagements for anthropometric examinations. If the laboratory had been operated in that part of the Exposition known as "The Streets of Paris," the character of the sample studied might have been somewhat different.

It is a very remarkable fact that our imperfectly segregated and classified physical types, called by courtesy "racial" types, should exist in practically identical proportions in these three widely divergent series, and that these types should show individually certain consistencies of a sociological nature, certain occupational and educational resemblances, whether they are drawn from the cream of the population, from the middle of the draught, or from its very dregs.

Certainly these findings should not be interpreted as a substantiation of any of the ridiculous and pernicious doctrines of racial inequality which have become a menace to the peace of the world and which have brought tragedy upon millions of blameless and worthy individuals. Every one of our so-called "racial" types in these series is represented by a substantial body of convicted felons at one end of the scale and a group of eminently respectable and intelligent citizens at the other.

There is no anthropological ground whatsoever for selecting any so-called racial group, or any ethnic or national group, or any linguistic or religious group for preferment or for condemnation. Our real purpose should be to segregate and to eliminate the unfit, worthless, degenerate and antisocial portion of each racial and ethnic strain in our population, so that we may utilize the substantial merits of its sound majority, and the special and diversified gifts of its superior members.

Racial purity is desirable and attainable in one sense only. Every racial strain in our country should be purified by the sterilization of its insane, diseased and criminalistic elements. The candidates for such biological extinction would not be selected on the basis of Aryan or Semitic descent, blond hair or black skin, but solely on the score of their individual physical, mental and moral bankruptcy.

One does not need to be an anthropologist to recognize that there is rampant, not only in this country, but elsewhere in the world, a selfish stupidity which reeks of human decay and degeneration. It manifests itself in some countries by brutal oppression of minorities selected for ill-treatment on account of religious, linguistic, or fancied racial differences. Elsewhere it is expressed in shameless aggression against defenseless primitive peoples or peaceable civilized nations which social disorder has weakened. Here in the United States it is horribly evident in a maudlin sympathy for criminals and in the toleration of crime which seems to characterize the mass of our population, in the looting of our national treasury in the name of patriotism, the wasting of our resources for political patronage, and even perhaps in muddle-headed efforts at national planning and reconstruction, which bid fair to reduce us to the unfortunate economic status of those fabled inhabitants of the Scilly Islands·who were "forced to eke out a precarious livelihood by taking in each other's washings."

Something has to be done to stem this rising tide of human stupidity. It cannot be accomplished by social Passamaquoddy projects impulsively initiated by little political King Canutes, who succeed only in getting themselves and us all wet. We must abandon hope of sociological palliatives and face the necessity of dealing with biological realities.

15

THE RELATION OF PHYSICAL ANTHROPOLOGY
TO CULTURAL ANTHROPOLOGY [1]

I THINK that most great men have something of the anthropologist in their make-up, and an anthropologist ought to have a certain quality of universality if he is to approximate greatness. Such a quality radiates from the mind and personality of Dr. R. R. Marett —a great teacher who, by some ingenious alchemy, has succeeded in transmuting a great deal of more or less base undergraduate metal into good anthropological gold. The assay of the product may vary, but it generally rings true.

I suppose that Aristotle, who invented the term, was the greatest of all anthropologists. His mantle ultimately fell upon Charles Darwin, and thereafter was divided into tattered but precious shreds worn by such men as Broca, Morgan and Tylor. All of these retained some measure of universality in their investigation of the human animal. Inevitably the period of spacious generalizations belongs to the infancy of a science, albeit some of the infants are

[1] From *Custom Is King*, Marett Anniversary Volume, edited by L. H. Dudley Buxton, Oxford, June, 1936.

veritable giants. There follows of necessity a long period of grubbing for facts to test these generalizations—a phase of specialization which involves the talents of men of diminished imagination, but rigorously trained, and with a cold passion for accuracy and a deadly persistence in the acquisition of data and more data. These Middle Ages of Science are not dark, but it must be confessed that they are rather dreary. If they are prolonged indefinitely in our science they are sure to produce generations of micro-anthropologists, who examine man one cell at a time and make nothing of him.

Primate evolution begins with a lowly lemuroid which has laterally directed eyes on either side of a long snout. The fields of vision are distinct; the animal sees one thing with one eye, and another with the other. The next evolutionary stage is the tarsier, whose eyes have swiveled around toward the front so that the fields of vision converge and overlap. From this animal it is but one long jump to the monkeys and apes, both of whose frontally directed eyes are focused upon the same visionary field; they have stereoscopic vision which gives depth, perspective and understanding. Now, unfortunately, anthropology seems to reverse the normal course of visual evolution in that it begins by seeing man as whole—stereoscopically—and then reverts to a monocular type of vision in which it sees only one aspect of man at a time, and that without depth, perspective or clear understanding. This wall-eyed outlook upon man and his affairs must be corrected by the spectacles of correlative and collaborative anthropology which focus the physical and cultural anthropological eyes simultaneously upon the same field of man and his behavior. The function of the anthropologist is to interpret man in his entirety—not piecemeal. We must complete the disciplinary cycle from broad, unsubstantiated and speculative generalization, through narrow and disintegrated specialization, back to an enlightened and validated system of synthesis and generalization. One cannot avoid the cynical reflection that the anthropologist, of all engineers, has been most effectively hoist with his own petard, when he forgets man the animal and studies his industries, arts, or social organization, each *in vacuo,* like any sociologist or classical archaeologist. In this paper I venture to review, discuss and deplore partitive and micro-tomic trends in physical and cultural anthropology. I then attempt to indicate the remedy, which is, in short, the application of a sort of synthetic therapy.

Trends of Development in Physical Anthropology

Physical anthropology is essentially an inquiry into man's status as an animal, and consequently presupposes some knowledge of animals in general and of the animal, man, in particular. It follows of necessity that in the infancy of physical anthropology the subject is of concern almost exclusively to zoölogists and to the members of the medical profession. Zoölogists, however, have usually been preoccupied with the lower animal forms and have been prone to leave their own species severely alone, apart from some more or less sketchy taxonomic labors. Thus physical anthropology, in its inception, tended to be principally an avocation of those physicians or surgeons who were possessed of a scientific curiosity surpassing the bounds of their primarily curative function. Physical anthropology was the handmaiden of human anatomy.

The old-fashioned gross anatomist dealt principally with skeletons and cadavers, as a dispenser of the basic knowledge required by medical practitioners. Having crammed the student with the minutiae of human anatomy, the teacher was free to observe and record the structural variations which were exhibited in the cadavers passing through his dissecting-room. From such enlightened anatomists there issued a stream of careful studies of the bones and the soft parts—at first confined largely to specimens drawn from European populations, but supplemented occasionally by examinations of the corpses of casual savages, such as that of the Hottentot Venus who succumbed to Parisian life in 1815. The appetite for racial studies of non-European peoples, thus whetted by dissecting-room experience, had to be satisfied with skeletons brought in by travelers, since this was, for the most part, the only transportable and thus available material.

From these beginnings two distinct trends of physical anthropological studies developed—monographs on the racial distribution of anatomical variations and general studies of skeletons. Since the various races of man are not distinguished by the number of their individual skeletal parts, the obvious procedure in the study of bones was to measure them. Such a method produced imposing lists of figures, whether or not they meant anything. Ingenious pioneers, recognizing the limitations of crude dimensions, quickly arrived at the idea of using indices or ratios, whereby linear measurements were also expressed proportionally. Since an index affords some vague indication of form, this innovation was valuable. Further, it became the custom to divide the range of an index into three or more named categories corresponding to low, medium and high divisions, and invariably defined without proper statistical consideration. Unfortunately these arbitrarily determined index categories were often assumed to connote eternal biological verities, or at any rate distinct biotypes.

The study of morphological variations and of metric skeletal features was ordinarily pursued without any reference whatsoever to functional significance, still less with regard for relationship to any extra-organic or cultural manifestations of man. Since these variations were not obviously connected with pathology—the chief concern of medical science—there was virtually no attempt to relate them to anything else except the vagaries of heredity.

There followed upon this period of haphazard and naïve gathering of data an interval of irresponsible and speculative interpretation, initiated, no doubt, by the anthropo-geographical method of observing man. Rationalizations about man's relation to his environment were probably current before the inception of anthropology. The simple fact that Negroes have dark skins and live in hot sunny countries, whereas Scandinavians have fair skins and inhabit cold, sunless climes, was enough to start an endless train of environmentalistic explanations whereby man's anatomical variations were attributed to this or that condition of his habitat. The anatomical facts and figures industriously accumulated by the pioneers of physical anthropology, taken in conjunction with meteorological and geographical records, economic returns, vital statistics and what not, provided an almost inexhaustible store of Chinese puzzle pieces which might be fitted together to make an intelligible picture. But most environmentalistic interpreters never tried to find out whether the pieces actually would fit together. They merely painted their own pictures with highly imaginative brushes, offering their personal impressions as realities. Some of the many fantastic suggestions offered were: that the everted lips of the Negro are referable to prolongation of the nursing period of infants; that the slim shanks of the Nilotic Negroes have developed in response to their habit of wading through the marshes like cranes; that the short legs of the Yahgans of Tierra del Fuego are an effect of constant squatting in canoes; that the lank, black hair of the Mongoloid is some sort of protective camouflage simulating the mane of the horse which he rides. Such dubious deductions are, of course, the expression of an unsophisticated and perhaps subconscious Lamarckianism.

Still another phase of physical anthropological development is marked by an inordinate employment of mathematical elaboration. The early anthropologist was prone to foist upon his readers masses of raw measurements, unanalyzed save for the presentation of occasional crude arithmetic means, and supported only by his own subjective impressions as to their significance in terms of types or differences. Statistical methods have been defined as "methods especially adapted to the elucidation of quantitative data affected by a multiplicity of causes." [2] In the application of such methods to the data of physical anthropology biometricians have rendered an immeasurable service. They have devised and exemplified the use of delicate statistical tools which render possible definitive analysis of arrays of figures.

However, these statistical tools are very sharp and quite capable of doing irreparable damage to the data when handled by an unskilled operator. No doubt a certain amount of havoc has been wrought by physical anthropologists who have attempted to employ statistical methods without a clear understanding of their utility and their limitations. Nevertheless, it would seem that far greater damage has been done by statistically inclined persons who have seized upon anthropological data as a means of satisfying their mathematical lusts. The prerequisites of sound investigation in physical anthropology are a full comprehension of the problems involved in the research and the ability to use approved techniques in the collection of data. If an investigator begins to study a racial problem without any real knowledge of the implications of race, and proceeds to collect data without adequate instruction in choice of measurements or observations and use of instruments, no proficiency in subsequent statistical analysis can compensate for his fundamental deficiencies. Even if the selection and collection of

[2] Yule, G. Udney, *An Introduction to the Theory of Statistics*, London, 1927, p. 5.

raw materials are irreproachable, the purely mathematical statistician is not equipped to study them satisfactorily, simply because he does not know what sort of conclusions ought to be sought. The inevitable result is an aimless elaboration of frequently unessential and irrelevant points. Often the research degenerates into a mere mathematical exercise, in which the biometrician taxes his ingenuity to devise and apply abstruse formulæ which divest his results of every semblance of reality. Such abuses of statistical method in every field have created a widespread distrust and suspicion aptly summed up by the vulgar saying that "there are lies, damned lies and statistics."

The use of statistical methods in physical anthropology has come to stay, but anthropologists must not turn over their data to purely mathematical statisticians with the expectation that the latter will produce satisfactory results. The anthropologist must learn his own statistics, because he alone possesses the knowledge which assures their proper application.

On the whole, the phases or trends in the development of physical anthropology which have been outlined above are such as might be expected in the normal growth of a natural science with social involvements. There is, however, a rapidly growing aspect of physical anthropology which is nothing less than a malignancy. Unless it is excised, it will destroy the science. I refer to the perversion of racial studies and of the investigation of human heredity to political uses and to class advantage. Man has long sought to excuse his disregard of others' rights by alleging certain biological differences which determine the superiority of his own race or nationality and the inferiority of others. The pro-slavery assertion that the Negro belongs to a lower species and hence may be treated as a domestic animal could be dismissed as mere specious propaganda of a pre-scientific age. However, when physical anthropology has advanced to the status of a reputable research science, its regimentation for political purposes becomes serious. Because anthropologists have studied human races intensively, the general public infers that they speak authoritatively and that there is a real basis for the racial discrimination thus anthropologically attested. The allegation of racial superiority or inferiority, previously dismissed as a mere sophistry, now assumes the nature of a valid reason for wholesale acts of injustice. Apart from the sociological consequences, such an abuse of a science results in its complete degradation. Physical anthropologists, whose sole aim in investigation and teaching should be the search for truth and its impartial dissemination, are intimidated and forced to distort their findings. Under such circumstances the output of physical anthropology may become so suspect that it is impossible to accept the results of research without looking behind them for a political motive.

The various trends in the development of physical anthropology here discussed have not been chronologically sequential in the order named; they have not been mutually exclusive, but coexistent, and all of them persist to some degree in contemporary research.

Trends of Development in Archaeology

Archaeology implies an interest in the obsolete paraphernalia of the past, which to the multitude stigmatizes its students as unregardful of the necessities of the present—the senile playboys of science rooting in the rubbish heaps of antiquity. Actually archaeology is quite as legitimate an inquiry into the past as is history, although it is documented, for the most part, with objects of material culture other than written records. Archaeology shares with history the function of interpreting the present through knowledge of the past. It must be admitted, nevertheless, that too often archaeology has been a magpie habit of collecting rather than a search for knowledge. A vast bulk of archaeological material in museums has been acquired through the efforts of persons who have made no pretense whatsoever of scientific excavation. They have simply plundered, and their loot has found its way to the shelves of museum exhibits. Such collections do not represent adequately the every day life of the people of any past age, but rather the bizarre and exotic features of their culture which appeal to the pot-hunter. The growth of archaeology as a science has inhibited to some extent the practice of digging for curios instead of for knowledge. But it has not been able to eradicate the desire of curators to fill their exhibition cases with spectacular objects, with the result that the primary purpose of the excavating parties sent into the field is to secure material and not information. The digging is indeed methodical, and the data are more or less scrupulously recorded, but the study of the collections and the interpretation of their historical significance are too frequently neglected. Digging up the past and finding quaint or beautiful objects is a glamorous business. The laborious task of dragging significant information from these inanimate objects requires more persistence, more imagination, and more downright hard thinking than most archaeologists are able to command. Hence, archaeological museums are often morgues for dead objects and undigested information concerning them.

There are other phases of archaeological development which, though less deplorable than mere pot-hunting, cannot be regarded with equanimity. One of these is an exaggeration of the importance of typology. The method of modern archaeology is based upon the principles of stratigraphy and typology. Stratigraphy determines sequence; typology defines range of variability, extent of homogeneity, and cultural trend. Stratigraphy is objective evidence which, unfortunately, occurs only sporadically. Typology, as a substitute, is too often a figment of imagination invested with a semblance of reality by elaborate nomenclature. The typological delusion is a sort of auto-hypnosis brought on by too concentrated and prolonged gazing upon a single class of archaeological objects, as into a crystal. The archaeologist begins to see things which are not there. There are archaeologists whose whole attention is focused upon the stone implements made by palaeolithic man and recovered from river gravels or cave deposits. Starting from certain variations in the forms of these tools, possibly intentional and possibly chance, they proceed to establish, as it were, phyla and all of the successively more detailed taxonomic subdivisions of stone implements. Many so-called "types" of stone implements are so crude, amorphous and variable that no sensible observer can escape the conclusion that they are the results of the uncertain fumblings of unskilled workers rather than the products of purposeful techniques. When these dubious types are called upon to define whole cultures and are supposed to be exclusive products of single prehistoric races, typology becomes ridiculous and its implications nonsensical.

Another typological excess is an over-emphasis of the study of ceramics. There are no few archaeologists who have apparently sold their birthright for a mess of pottery. The utility of potsherds for characterizing and cross-dating archaeological strata arose from the fact that earthenware is so easily and so often broken that it provides a never-ending supply of fairly durable rubbish. It is, of course, undeniable that pottery styles change from age to age, both in form and decoration. It seems very doubtful whether these facts justify the enormous amount of detailed classification and description that ceramic archaeologists devote to this class of finds. It is quite apparent that many of them have lost all perspective in looking at their potsherds and now regard ceramics as their principal archaeological objective. Thus we have culture following culture in some regions with virtually no other difference than a change from an incised technique of decoration to a cord-marked technique, or from lug-handles to loop-handles. When ceramic styles are aggrandized into criteria of ethnic or racial change, it would seem that theory has gone beyond the probabilities of the evidence, unless pottery changes are supported by correlated variations of other artifacts. The assumption that cord-marked beakers are a result of hybridization between the Bell-Beaker race and the Corded-Ware race involves an anthropomorphization of crockery which is scarcely justifiable. Races interbreed, but pots do not.

Archaeology has not escaped the tendency to specialize unduly in some areas and to neglect others. There are available for excavation numerous cultural deposits belonging to different periods and dispersed over wide areas. The great range of choice has resulted in unequal exploitation of the possibilities of excavation, according to the individual interests of archaeologists, the accessibility of sites and the potential abundance and art value of the finds recoverable. In very few instances does there seem to have been developed for a specific area a program of research designed to reconstruct the prehistory of the region.

In Egypt, in Mesopotamia and in Greece, much archaeological work has been carried on by specialists in ancient languages or in history. However skilled such persons may be in excavating and recording, it is apparent that many of them are woefully lacking in anthropological perspective and have little real comprehension of the proper aim of archaeology. The skeletal material which alone can furnish the answer to racial problems and can be used as a basis for the determination of health, vitality and longevity of the population, has usually been destroyed, discarded, or at best deposited in some museum, without any utilization. A very great deal of this work has been characterized also by the disinclination to penetrate through the treasure-bearing strata of the highly developed civilizations down to their humble origins.

In short, archaeology in general is still open to the charge that it is carried on primarily for the recovery of objects which seem desirable to the excavators and to museums rather than for the purpose of increasing knowledge.

Social Anthropology and Ethnology

Serious consideration of the origin and significance of social phenomena began very early, because man is such a self-centered animal that he usually regards his own activities as the most important of existence. Thus the mere description of forms of social organization, religious beliefs and rituals, customs, laws and material culture has commanded interest and attention from the beginnings of literate times and has invited philosophical speculation. The theory of organic evolution gave a new impetus to studies of social institutions, since the idea of higher stages of culture and more advanced types of social behavior evolving from simpler and more primitive manifestations was appropriated quickly from its original biological context. There is no need of describing and discussing here the evolutionary school of cultural anthropology. The conception of society as an organism and of a unilinear evolution from one cultural stage to another and from primitive forms of social institutions to successively more advanced types has been abandoned by most social anthropologists. If social evolution had been validated by modern research, it would have demanded, ultimately, correlative studies in the physical and cultural fields whereby the exact relationship between biological and sociological status might be established. It is probably fortunate that strictly evolutionary interpretations of cultural phenomena broke down before any such attempts were made, since it is now apparent that even in the field of physical anthropology definitive evolutionary ranking of human groups is not yet practicable.

The diffusionist school is committed to the principle that inventions or cultural innovations originate, for the most part, once only and in a single people, and thence are transferred to the rest of the world. The implication of such a concept is that the new

phenomenon is produced, presumably, as a resultant of environmental and hereditary forces acting uniquely upon a certain group
of human organisms. If this is true it ought to be possible to
analyze the interacting forces and to isolate any gross anatomical
correlate with the phenomenon which may be involved. I do not
know that any diffusionist has gone so far as to attempt to study
the racial or other physical combinations which have been concerned in the production of specific cultural innovations. However,
a logical pursuance of the underlying concept ought to demand
such an effort, fantastic though it may be.

On the other hand, it is possible to adhere to an interpretation
of cultural phenomena whereby the human organism with its
mental and physical variations is regarded as a constant, and all
social variations and changes are referred to a combination of
environmental and historical causes, with possibly some allowance
for the influence of the individual. Such a conception of the
negligible influence of organic variation upon behavioral variation
is implicit or explicit in the method and theory of most social
anthropologists and sociologists. The attitude is partially reaction
against the scientifically indefensible notions about the cultural
significance of race which seem to enjoy an unending vogue in
non-anthropological circles. Nevertheless, I believe that the refusal
to explore the scientific possibilities of the physical correlates of
social phenomena has contributed greatly to the confusion of social
anthropology and sociology and to the futility of their efforts to
become applied social sciences.

One of the new wrinkles in cultural anthropology is "functionalism." I understand the adherents of this school to maintain
that all structures and institutions of a social group operate in a
sort of physiological manner and that to understand a society,
the functional relationship of its component elements must be
ascertained. According to this conception there are no spare parts
of the machine, no superfluous and functionless elements. All
things work together for good or for evil. Certainly the attempt
to interpret societies as going concerns, rather than to produce
anatomical monographs upon their *disiecta membra*, represents a
distinct advance in social anthropological method. Whether or not
the neglect of historical data in functional studies of society cor-
rupts the method does not concern me here. It should be apparent,

in any case, that the physical and mental variations of the human organism are of great importance in studying the physiology of society, and that in modern groups comprising mixtures of racial and ethnic strains, the diverse behavior of the several elements may furnish an important clew to the interpretation of the working of the whole.

An even more recent trend in social anthropological studies emphasizes the influence of personality—the psychology of the individual—in cultural phenomena. Again this development seems healthful, if only because it departs very far from the old way of considering social institutions completely apart from the human animals which produce them, as if the former lived, died, propagated and evolved independently, like parasites upon their human hosts.

That the varying psychologies of the individuals who comprise the social group must in the aggregate determine cultural trends and shape social institutions seems undeniable to one who looks at society from the biological point of view. If the observer recognizes that individual psychology is to some extent a manifestation of constitutional proclivities—that there are bodily correlates of mental sets—the utility of physical anthropological studies of the individual with reference to his behavior becomes evident. No one, of course, supposes that the traditional good nature of fat men is a direct product of their obesity. Psycho-physical parallelisms of this sort are not causally related except in so far as they are manifestations in different activities and parts of the organism of the same forces, whether these be hereditary or environmental. Gross anatomical features may be symptomatic of mental states, although they do not stand in a parent or child relation one to the other.

In summary, my only quarrel with the ethnologist and with the social anthropologist is that they willfully abstract social phenomena and divorce man's activities as a social animal from man himself. The members of each school mount their own particular breed of hobby-horse and ride it with blinders toward some far-off and invisible goal, looking neither to right nor to left, and missing not only the setting of their journey, but possibly also the objective.

The Synthesis of Physical and Cultural Anthropological Studies

From my own research experience, I have come painfully and slowly to a realization that Anthropology behaves very stupidly when it does not let its right hand know what its left hand is doing.

Many years ago I undertook an investigation of the archaeology of the Canary Islands, which present an interesting problem of cultural variation and diversity of skeletal type. In this archipelago the tabulation of archaeological evidence in relation to cranial type facilitated the reconstruction of a plausible and probably correct sequence of migrating peoples from the mainland. Considered apart, neither the archaeological nor the physical data were particularly illuminating.

In a later study of the large skeletal series from the ruined Pueblo of Pecos, New Mexico, excavated by Dr. A. V. Kidder of Phillips Academy, Andover, the value of co-operative work on the part of archaeologists and physical anthropologists was again demonstrated. The stratigraphic data pertaining to each skeleton made possible an examination of the physical characteristics of the population through the successive archaeological periods, and also estimates of the number of inhabitants. The rise and decline of several physical types was traced.

In studies of the physical characteristics of racially mixed peoples in various parts of the world, the most striking results have been the intimate correlations of physical types with sociological status. Such physio-sociological associations are closer than those of physical type with ascertained degree of blood mixture. In other words it seems possible to predict from the physical type of a racial hybrid his occupational, educational and social status, more easily than the proportions of bloods of the parent stocks which he represents.

Finally, in a very extensive survey of the physical and sociological characteristics of American criminals, the results of which are not yet published, physical differentiation seems invariably to accompany sociological differentiation. Hereditary and environmental forces apparently combine in selecting specific physical types not only for distinct offenses, but also for various occupations, degrees of educational attainment, et cetera. The interpretation of physical differences lies, for the most part, in their relation to sociological facts. It seems certain that the converse is also true.

It is my firm conviction that physical anthropology is not a study which can be pursued profitably with utter disregard for its sociological connotation. As long as it works in isolation, with its attention directed solely to bones, teeth, viscera, and physiology, it is comparatively trivial. We are really not much interested in man considered purely as a lower animal. It is rather his higher animalistic functions which render the lower features significant. Physical anthropology is properly the working mate of cultural anthropology. Indeed I should advocate a marriage for better or for worse of these male and female principles of anthropological research, since the one, if working in celibate seclusion, makes of man nothing much more than a mysteriously gifted and altogether inexplicable brute, whereas the other, if condemned to spinsterhood, indulges in precisely those meddlesome and sterile investigations of human activity which too often characterize the female in public affairs.

On the other hand, if these two join, they bring to the union their individual capacities, which, mingled, facilitate an adequate performance of the biological, sociological and economic functions which such a mating should subserve. Combined in some sort of scientific, bi-sexual reproductive process, they may give rise to a real anthropological science, capable of understanding man.

PART III

Humanity Halts:
The Need of Evolutionary Guidance

16.

THE EUGENICS BOGY

WHILE democracy is making the world safe for morons and fascism is making it unsafe for everyone else, there are in this country and in Europe some few organizations composed of persons sincerely interested in human welfare which are striving to improve the quality of the human animal by biological measures. Many anthropologists and biological scientists have tended to look down their noses at the eugenists, although they ought to be in the forefront of workers in a science of better breeding if they pretend to have any social responsibility. One can allege many plausible reasons for staying aloof from such movements, but I suspect that the fundamental causes of our non-participation do us little credit. In the first place, apart from a few public scientists, laboratory and field workers in biological subjects are usually so immersed in research that they are disinclined to be active in organizations which are attempting to promote the practical application of biological principles. Such organizations are necessarily to some extent propagandist, and their membership is largely recruited from interested laymen and enthusiastic amateurs, with the inclusion of not a few fanatics. A great many scientists are temperamentally averse to the atmosphere of emotional fervor and "uplift" which is likely to pervade such groups; they dislike reformers. More than this, they are afraid of associating themselves with societies which are likely to overstep the bounds of actual knowledge in their statements urging the adoption of legislative or other measures. They fear to lose caste in their profession by identifying themselves with cranks. I think that this attitude of timorous withdrawal is pusillanimous and reprehensible, although I have it myself. If anything is going to be done to improve the human species, the actual burden and heat of the day will be borne by these missionary zealots who are carried along by their almost religious convictions—these executive amateurs at whose perspiring efforts fastidious scientists sniff. Personally, I am thoroughly ashamed of myself for wincing and cringing at the pseudo-scientific stuff put out by eugenic organizations, because their moral rightness and their driving vigor are of much more social value than the cold-blooded, inhuman detachment of the pure scientist.

However, there is one really sound reason why eugenics and eugenists are rightly suspected, and why many anthropologists cannot force themselves into activity in a movement which, on the whole, they approve. Eugenics has, in this country and elsewhere, been mixed up with a great deal of vicious racial propaganda, especially the nonsense of Nordicism. A certain number of persons who have been prominent in eugenics here and elsewhere are really attempting to promulgate measures of racial discrimination under the guise of "race hygiene" and "race betterment." They seem to think that being well-born is synonymous with being a "Nordic," although many who talk the most loudly along these lines are neither the one nor the other.

A good many years ago I attended an International Eugenics Congress, the president of which was one of our most celebrated public scientists, an aristogenist if there ever was one. At the formal banquet which is an inevitable and depressing feature of scientific congresses, this genial, erudite, and justly famous scientist made an introduction of the foreign speaker of the evening in terms which I recall as follows:

"Twenty thousand years ago, when the ice sheet had retreated sufficiently to lay bare a coastal strip of Scandinavia, there landed upon those frigid shores a band of intrepid adventurers, who have remained there to this day, who have pioneered in all of the arts of civilization and yet have maintained the purity and integrity of their Nordic racial blood and physical heritage. And tonight, I am privileged to introduce to you one of the most famous scientists of this Nordic race, who is foremost in research upon racial hygiene and in the promotion of measures to insure racial integrity."

From my obscure and remote table of uncelebrities, I peered myopically to catch a glimpse of this dolichocephalic, blond Viking who was to embody the physical, intellectual, and scientific ideals of the "Great Race." At first I got the elevation of my sight too high and saw no one standing at the speaker's table except the blandly smiling president who had made the eloquent introduction. Then I heard sounds of broken English, and, lowering my gaze a foot or two, I was able to discern its source. It was a sawed-off, rotund person with a head round as a bullet, black hair, a blobby nose and a face reminiscent of the full moon—in short, the complete Alpine. I thereupon decided that every man is his own Nordic, and I am afraid that I leaped to the conclusion that eugenics is a lay form of ancestor worship. If eugenics is going to command the support of disillusioned anthropologists it will have to divest itself entirely of its Ku Klux Klan regalia.

Now the hostile criticism of eugenics arises mainly from the following classes of persons: (1) supercilious geneticists and cautious anthropologists, (2) those who suspect it to be an undercover weapon of fascists, anti-Semitists, and other perpetrators of racial and ethnic injustice, (3) proletarians who believe that "the Lord must love common people because he has made so many of them," (4) surreptitious ax-grinders, such as demagogues whose hope of domination lies in the stupidity of the majority, industrialists who want an ample supply of cheap labor, and clerics whose followings are recruited from the irresponsibles who gratify their brute instincts by incessant breeding.

I am going to discuss the principal measures advocated by the proponents of eugenics in the light of the objections against them raised by these several classes of antagonists. These measures are birth control and sterilization. Both are negative in that they can serve only to restrict undesired and undesirable reproduction. They can improve the quality of the population only by eliminating the procreation of a certain proportion of potential inferiors. One may as well admit at the outset that the widespread application of these two measures is unlikely to check degenerative evolutionary processes or to effect any sudden and marked elevation of the average physical and mental status of man.

Birth control is, of course, a weapon which cuts both ways. While the sins of contraception are by no means equal to the sins of conception, the restriction of offspring in families of sound heredity and economic efficiency presents a very serious population problem. The need of an increase in the proportion of the superior is almost, if not quite, as pressing as the necessity of checking the multiplication of the inferior. It is hard to deny that birth control up to now has had the principal effect of diminishing the numbers of the desirable, because it has been restricted in practice mainly to the families which possess a sufficient sense of economic responsibility to be unwilling to produce more children than they are able to support and to educate. These same families are called upon by direct taxation and voluntary contribution to maintain the offspring of the socially inefficient, who do not practice birth control. Thus the lack of birth control where it is desirable promotes its use in the very groups which ought not to limit reproduction. In this country, at any rate, and under the present political administration, public policy involves the penalizing of the successful in order to reward and encourage the human failures.

Perhaps the most serious objection to birth control, apart from its utterly perverse application, is that raised by economists in connection with the decline of populations in civilized countries. The evidence of diminishing birth rates and of the insufficiency of declining death-rates to compensate for this lessened fertility has been presented in so many population studies that it need not be recapitulated here. The argument is that progressive diminishing of the population will bring about increased unemployment, because the lessened demand for goods will disrupt industry, starting apparently with the manufacture of equipment for infants' and children's toys. Of course I am not an economist, but it seems to me that this is tantamount to worrying about the unemployment of those who are not going to be born. However, there is reason in the supposition that a decline in the population will not in itself relieve unemployment, since it is likely to carry with it a proportional decline in consumption and production of goods. However, if it were possible in some way to increase the consuming power of the economically depressed by improving their quality so as to make them self-supporting and productive, the situation might not prove to be serious. Surely our economic system is not dependent upon the maintenance and increase of that section of the population which has to be supported at the public expense. It is unthinkable that industry should not be able to accommodate itself either to an increase or a decrease of consumption.

There is really no point in attempting to combat the arguments of those who object to birth control on moral or religious grounds. One can only offer as a counterblast the moral and religious convictions which are equally strong among the advocates of the measure. Those who obstruct progress have no monopoly of conscience. Behind the allegations of religious scruples and moral objections there are often the ambitions for power of scheming individuals and organizations. Dictators want teeming populations composed mainly of weak-minded individuals whom they may use for cannon fodder. The quality which someone has called sheep-through-the-gapishness is the essential characteristic upon which despotic rulers build their dominance, whether it be in labor organizations, or in political parties, or in the church. One can expect no sympathy for any movement which aims to decrease the proportion of the stupid, the feeble-minded, the insane, and the economically ineffectual on the part of those who owe their success to their ability to use this moronic mass for their own aggrandizement.

As a humanitarian measure for relieving sick and exhausted women from the strain of excessive childbearing, as a means of lightening the economic burden put upon the heads of uncontrolled families by too many offspring, as an indirect method of increasing the environmental opportunities of the children who are "wanted," birth control seems absolutely essential. Since it is not injurious to the health of those who practice it, and since there is no good evidence that it is productive of increased sexual immorality, it ought to be supported and promoted on grounds of social expediency.

However, I am not particularly hopeful of voluntary birth control as an effective agency for improving human stocks as a whole, or for elevating their evolutionary status. The classes of people among which reproduction ought to be discouraged will hardly be taught or persuaded to limit their families for any nebulous ideals of the social good. Only a week or two ago I read the statement of the proud father of some fifteen children upon the occasion of the birth of (as I remember it) his third set of twins. It was to the effect that birth control was ruining the country. Many of us have been edified by the news of the so-called Toronto "baby Marathon" and have seen in the news-reels pictures of a number of the competing families—all of them obviously breeding in an environment of dirt, disease, poverty, and ignorance. It seems to me that stupid and ignorant persons are far more anxious to crowd the world with their kind than are the intelligent and socially responsible. It is quite probable also that the latter are less fertile, quite apart from the practice of contraception. On the whole, then, it seems as necessary to encourage the reproduction of more offspring by the superior families, as to promote restriction in size of the inferior families. I do not know how this can be done. It has been pointed out by close students of the subject of birth control that the knowledge of contraception, first disseminated among the upper classes (economic and social), is gradually spreading to those less favorably situated, so that the decrease of the reproductive rate among the latter is inevitable, irrespective of legislation and propaganda in favor of birth control.

Sterilization is a more radical measure and perhaps offers better possibilities for improving the human stock. Not a few highly intelligent persons are strongly opposed to compulsory sterilization because they fear that unscrupulous governments and individuals will use it as a means of eliminating elements in the population to which they are antagonistic—such as Jews in Nazi Germany. I think that this fear is well-grounded, and there are perhaps many of us in this country who would not feel entirely comfortable if we knew that our present national government could exercise its discretion in the matter of having any one of us sterilized.

The brilliant researches of modern geneticists who are occupied with mathematical considerations as applied to human heredity are decidedly discouraging with regard to the probable effect of sterilization as an evolutionary panacea. Taking, for example, the matter of feeble-mindedness and mental defect, it is argued that very little is known of the inheritance of these undesirable conditions. The indications are that, if they are hereditary, they are probably not dependent upon single gene substitution, but are extremely complicated. Sterilizing all of the feeble-minded would not eliminate the production of persons suffering from this weakness. This contention is undoubtedly true. The assertion that we are ignorant of the extent to which environment may be a causal factor in mental defect is equally valid. Certainly the present meagerness of our knowledge does not justify us in attributing to heredity the exclusive rôle in the production of the mentally inferior. Still less are we in a position safely to neglect attempts to ascertain the environmental factors which may be operative in the situation and to relinquish our efforts to improve the social conditions which may contribute to the production of mental defect.

Lancelot Hogben, apparently drawing upon the researches of J. B. S. Haldane, offers some very cogent mathematical considerations of the effect of selection in breeding upon the genetic constitution of a population.[1] If generations did not overlap and the recessive type alone was allowed to breed, all dominants would be exterminated in a single generation. But if selection favors the dominant type, the elimination of the recessive type is different for selection involving autosomal and sex-linked gene substitutions. In the latter case it is much more rapid. I do not intend here to enter into the details of the demonstrations of these scientists of the slow and relatively minute effect which could be expected of complete selection in the case of complicated recessive characters which are not sex-linked. They are sufficient to convince any reasonable person that the complete regeneration of mankind is not to be achieved in a few generations by sterilizing some thousands of the insane, the feeble-minded, and the criminalistic.

"If seven maids with seven mops swept it for half a year,
    Do you suppose," the Walrus said, "that they could get it clear?"
"I doubt it," said the Carpenter, and shed a bitter tear.

[1] Hogben, Lancelot, *Genetic Principle in Medicine and Social Science*, pp. 156-166, N. Y., 1932.

Nevertheless, it seems to me that we ought not to neglect the opportunity of securing some improvement of our population, albeit infinitesimal, by adopting such measures. However vague and incomplete may be our knowledge of human heredity, and however potent the influence of environment may be, I cannot see that the status of man can be lowered by preventing inferior human animals from propagating, even under the improbable assumption that the resulting offspring will not be like their parents, but will be an improvement upon them. I think that we can afford to accept the chances of losing any potential geniuses or superior specimens of mankind which might arise from the re-productive efforts of those tainted with hereditary disease, of those who are insane, feeble-minded, and antisocial. If we limit sterilization (or at least compulsory sterilization) to specimens of humanity who really ought to be exterminated, we shall probably achieve some slight gain.

Of course the answer to the whole problem of improving man's status (if anyone thinks it needs improvement) lies in the acquisition of more knowledge about the interplay of hereditary and environmental factors which make the man, rather than in the immediate application of any crude and drastic social or biological measure. There are perhaps those who think that the millennium is either here or just around the corner. To such, of course, all of the opinions and statements here offered will be wildly wrong.

17.

AN ANTHROPOLOGIST LOOKS AT MEDICINE [1]

Introduction

AN anthropologist looks at medicine very humbly, much as a cat may venture to look at a king. Moreover, the anthropologist, like Kipling's cat, walks by himself and all people are alike to him— even doctors—at any rate as long as he is feeling well. It happens that physical anthropology is the only field of knowledge which concerns itself exclusively with human biology, except medicine. Therefore, from the dim obscurity of speculations upon man's past, present and future, the anthropologist sometimes turns an appraising eye upon the practitioners of human biology—those who are not only studying man, but are also doing something to him.

Differences Between Physical Anthropology and Medicine

Certain differences between the methods and purposes of physical anthropology and of medicine condition the status of

[1] Address before the Harvard Medical Colloquium, Dec. 12, 1935. Reprinted from *Science*, March 20, 1936, Vol. 83, No. 2151, pages 271-276.

each and merit brief discussion. Medicine enjoys a uniquely favorable position among the sciences, because its activities are of immediate or potential concern to every human being. "How do you do?" is a conventional form of greeting, perfunctorily reechoed by way of response to everyone except a doctor. There appertains to the healer a certain supernatural sanction, a legacy from the medicine man and the shaman. He works magic—not public magic, which is the province of the priest, and, as such, religion; but private magic for the benefit of the individual, which commands a fee. As the fearful sinner recognizes in the priest the personal agent of his soul's salvation, so does the suffering patient see in the doctor the instrument of his corporeal rehabilitation. Thus, each man's preoccupation with his own carcass—a sort of physiological egocentrism—gives medicine a distinct advantage over all other sciences. Medical research receives and deserves the most lavish financial support, since it is an investment which promises and pays the sort of dividends appreciated by all.

Physical anthropology, as I have intimated, is an unobtrusive and possibly innocuous growth in the field of human biology, a lonely and disregarded tare among the wheat. If it may aspire to be called a science, it is a pure science, in the sense that it is not applied—if not indeed purely useless. It is entirely untainted, because it has virtually no pecuniary contacts. Physical anthropology concerns itself with man's origin, present status and future evolution—problems which are of little or no concern to the individual in his pursuit of personal health and happiness. Physical anthropology is neither ultilitarian nor idealistic, it is merely skeptical and speculative, in the etymological sense of each. It holds up a mirror to man and lets him look at himself, with the result that he likes neither his reflection nor the agent of its production. Medicine teaches, for whatever age or sex, what every man should know, and is discreetly silent upon matters of which a lay understanding is inexpedient. Anthropology reveals many things which most persons prefer not to know, since it harps upon humble and even bestial origins, regards the present status of our species without approbation, and can predict for the man of the future no apotheosis, but only a multiplication of psychoses, dental caries, malocclusions and fallen arches, together with a full retention of his aboriginal cussedness. Under these circumstances, anthropology not only misses the material opulence achieved by an applied science, but even the comfortable circumstances of a "popular science." Not for the anthropologist is the contemplation of the celestial grandeur of the expanding universe; he looks at one animal "bereft of his tail and grown weary of climbing"; he wonders why that animal carries so much excess baggage in the way of apparently unutilized brain, and whether he would not be better off with a smaller hat size and a set of lower and upper teeth which hit.

Now there are marked contrasts in the methods of physical anthropology and of medical science, arising no doubt from their diverse approaches to the problems of human biology. Medicine must focus upon the individual, for whom something has to be done, and that right quickly. Contact with suffering evokes sympathy and engenders an attitude of noble humanitarianism, rather than one of disinterested contemplation and appraisal. It is hardly a question of not seeing the wood for the trees, but rather one of sawing wood and selling timber or of giving it away. Since life is real, and ridiculously earnest, and the grave is a goal which the patient must be led to miss at all costs, medical science is nurtured in the fetid atmosphere of pathology, and has no chance to breathe pure ozone in the congregation of *mentes sanae in corporibus sanis* (sound minds in sound bodies). All of which is a cumbersome way of saying that doctors are so preoccupied with the sick that they do not know the well and are forced to evolve the normal from their inner consciousness, as the German scholar evolved the camel. Just as New England, according to Mark Twain, has no weather, but only samples, so medical science has no subjects but only patients. Inevitably this restriction results in a faulty conception of the range of "normal" human variation, a tendency to base conclusions upon the study of numerically inadequate samples and a failure to develop and to utilize valid methods of group analysis.

In contrast, the physical anthropologist is as little concerned with the bodily welfare of any given individual as the individual with that of the anthropologist. The anthropologist is interested in groups (the larger the better). Any member of a group commands his attention merely as a component unit, exhibiting a greater or less deviation from the mean. His business is to determine the range of variation of physical characteristics in large samples of the population, classified on an ethnic basis, a sociological basis or by whatever criteria the purpose of his specific investigation may suggest. Thus, a physical anthropologist may undertake to study Italians, an ethnic group; criminals, a sociological group; babies, an age group; mountaineers, a geographical group, *et cetera*. Or he may study Italian criminals, infant mountaineers or any group selected on the basis of several categories. In every instance, however, he must avoid confusion of categories by subdividing his material into groups which may be presumed to exhibit a certain physical homogeneity. There are, for example, certain physical variations which are determined by racial heredity. Therefore, the anthropologist, in studying criminals, would not throw Negroes and Whites into the same statistical series; he would analyze them separately and eventually compare the constants and characters of their respective series. He would not include Italian and American babies in the same series, nor would he lump two-year-old infants with infants of three years, nor mountaineers with lowlanders. In the last two examples, differences of age or physical environment affecting bodily traits necessitate a careful sorting of material, if group characteristics and trends are to be determined in any clear-cut fashion. Having delimited his group by such essential sortings in order to avoid confusion of issues, the anthropologist then proceeds to an examination of each component member of the group. He next advances to seriation and statistical analysis of the group data thus obtained, calculating the constants, recording the distribution of observed morphological characters, the intercorrelation of various features, and in every case taking into mathematical consideration the range of error introduced by the possibly inadequate size of the sample studied. He is then finally in a position to describe scientifically the physical characteristics of the group investigated. If, however, he wishes to go further and to differentiate between Italian criminals and Italians who are law-abiding citizens, or between mountaineers and plainsmen, he must repeat his analysis for each group adduced for comparison and must finally derive their differences from their respective arrays of characteristics.

Thus, if the anthropologist were investigating pneumonia, he would require: firstly, a large body of persons suffering from the disease; secondly, a sorting of the sufferers into statistical groups based upon race; thirdly, a further subdivision of the group, based upon age, and a possible fourth, based upon sex. All these sub-groups would be subjected to separate statistical analysis before pneumonic characteristics could be scientifically isolated from con-fusing factors introduced by certain irrelevant biogenetic differ-ences. But this is not all. The anthropologist would not feel that he really knew about pneumonia until he had compared his several subseries of affected subjects with similar groups of the non-infected population, each measured and analyzed in the same way. Then at last he would be in a position to reach scientific con-clusions. Of course the doctor can not proceed along such inves-tigatory channels. Before he had finished gathering his data, all his patients would have died or recovered—in either case without benefit of medicine. Such deliberate research can scarcely be under-taken by a practitioner who functions only during a crisis, and who is scientifically apathetic and professionally inert during peri-ods of that condition described by the detestable term, "normalcy."

Nevertheless, the pedestrian methods of the anthropologist may eventually lead medical science to certain desired goals, possibly unattainable through mere utilization of the cumulative clinical experience gained by guidance of individuals through their bodily emergencies. I should like to discuss a few of the possibilities of practical contributions to medical science through the employment of anthropological methods.

Problems of Medicine Which Might be Illuminated by Anthropological Methods and Co-operation

(a) *Constitution.* The problem of constitution in its relation to medical science may be defined as the extent to which gross body type is correlated with immunity and susceptibility to various diseases. The relation of body type to disease is obviously only a part of the larger problem of the correlation of morphological variation with physiological variation, with psychological variation, and with sociological behavior. Medicine has no immediate concern with some of the broader aspects of this question, although all of them engage the attention of the anthropologist. Lack of time, lack of knowledge, and lack of inclination combine to prevent me from entering here into a history and critique of constitutional work in medicine, the substantial results of which, according to my possibly erroneous impression, are as yet regrettably slight. Nevertheless, I have the greatest confidence in the ultimate productiveness of research in this subject. My own positive findings respecting body build in its much farther-fetched relationship to type of crime have merely confirmed a conviction, gradually reached on other anthropological grounds. It is feasible, however, to define the essentials of correct scientific procedure in the investigation of the medical aspect of the problem—essentials, some of which, I fear, have been consistently disregarded in much of the work heretofore done. It is first of all imperative to diagnose completely and correctly the disease to be investigated. Foggy symptomatology will not do. If dementia praecox is a residuary legatee of all the bequests of psychiatric perplexity, it can hardly serve as a clinical point of departure for constitutional research. Assuming, however, that symptoms are clearly defined and diagnosis certain, it is next and equally essential that a valid scientific determination of body type be effected. Now, an actual establishment of an anthropological type, statistically demonstrable and irrefragable, is the most difficult and complex task which ever confronts a physical anthropologist. To attempt it with no more equipment than a clinical hunch and a pair of borrowed calipers is sadly ingenuous. Experience and a little mathematical knowledge will dissuade the most sanguine caliper-wielder from efforts to establish morphological types by a few raw measurements or crude indices, arbitrarily selected from the infinity of possible mensurable combinations. Type is a total morphological impression, a composite of dimensions, proportions and immensurable qualitative variations, synthesized by the brain, but through the eye, of the trained observer. Discernment of type is the ultimate acquirement of the anthropological observer; its mathematical expression and demonstration, the most refined accomplishment of the expert biometrician. The former is useless without the latter. I can conceive of no more futile exercise than bandying about the clinic anthropometrically unsubstantiated concepts, with dubious Greek names such a "pyknic."

The last prerequisite of a successful investigation of the problem of body build and disease is a competent method of statistical analysis, controlled by common sense and a full realization of the limitations of the data and of the ends to be achieved. The satisfactory application of such a method implies, of course, modern mechanical equipment for statistical reduction, plenty of computing assistance, together with sufficient resources, financial and moral, to carry on through years of arithmetic drudgery. There is no royal road to anthropometric analysis. The data must be sorted and analyzed, then resorted according to other categories and completely reanalyzed. This process of trial and error must continue until the possibilities of the data are exhausted. The investigator must be prepared ruthlessly to discard masses of data found to be inaccurate or irrelevant, and, if he is mathematically gifted, he must beware of the temptation to fiddle with formulae while research funds burn.

The requirements for success in constitutional study, as here laid down, are severe but not prohibitive, in view of the potential importance of the results.

(b) *Orthopedics.* The specialty known as orthopedics deals, in some degree, with bodily difficulties due to man's imperfect adaptation to an erect posture and to a biped mode of progression. Man is a made-over animal. In the course of evolution, his ancestors have functioned as arboreal pronogrades and brachiators or arm-progressing tree-dwellers—not to mention more remote stages involving other changes of habitat, posture and mode of locomotion. This protean history has necessitated repeated patching and reconstruction of a more or less pliable and long-suffering organism. The bony framework has been warped and cramped and stretched in one part or another, in accordance with variations in the stresses and strains put upon it by different postures and by changes in body bulk. Joints devised for mobility have been readapted for stability. Muscles have had violence done to their origins and insertions, and have suffered enormous inequalities in the distribution of labor. Viscera have been pushed about hither and yon, hitched up, let down, reversed and inverted. In making a new machine out of an old one, plenty of obsolete spare parts have been left to rattle around inside. There are no few evidences of ungifted, amateur tinkering.

That the specialty of orthopedics should be based upon the very broadest knowledge and understanding of these evolutionary changes seems to me so obvious that I need not labor the point.

The problems of body mechanics are in themselves tremendously complex. I suppose that no one lacking the training of an engineer can grapple with them effectively. Unless I am greatly mistaken, an adequate comprehension of bodily mechanics has not been achieved, as yet.

Two comparatively recent developments in experimental scientific facilities point the way for orthopedic progress. The first of these is the possibility of rearing the semi-erect and quadrupedal anthropoid apes in the laboratory, and of studying their postures and gaits from the point of view of bodily mechanics. These apes unquestionably illuminate the path of man's adaptations for erect posture and biped progression. It is hardly necessary to add that man himself, from infancy to senility, ought to be studied in the same way. The second modern development which facilitates orthopedic advance is the use of the x-ray photograph and the slow motion picture for the study of posture and gait and their mechanical implications. A full utilization of these technical devices for the observation of ape and human subjects, combined with anthropometric and clinical methods, can not fail to result in revelations of great practical value. Success will, however, necessitate protracted and expensive labor and a full employment of the resources of medical and anthropological science.

(c) *Pediatrics.* The study of the medical or hygienic treatment of children is, of course, an immense and valuable field of specialization. Pediatrics can pluck the heart-strings and the pocketbooks of the populace with greater facility than perhaps any other branch of medical science, because nature furnishes every normal human being with a special fund of sympathy for the young. An integral part of pediatrics is the study of human growth, which is indubitably bound up with the physiological crises and the pathological infestations of infancy, childhood and adolescence. No one, indeed, can claim that the study of human growth has been neglected of late in civilized countries. I fear, however, that much of this study has been ill-directed and purposeless, relegated for the most part to specialists in education or educational psychology (who are ready to try anything on someone else's child), to instructors in physical education and to anthropologists. Huge masses of statistics have been compiled and innumerable growth curves have been drawn, but the correlations of these data with nutritional status, with infections and with constitutional diseases are, I think, still to seek. Many growth studies have been carried on by persons who have not been trained in the technique of anthropometry (which is by no means easy to acquire), and the measurements are consequently unreliable. The bulk of the subjects studied has not been assorted racially or even on the basis of national origins, so that the conclusions derived from the heterogeneous material are of dubious value. There are, of course, many exceptions to these generalizations, but, in my opinion, much of the effort expended in growth studies has been unintelligent and pointless. Such studies, unless undertaken for the simple purpose of demonstrating racial differences, should be so intimately associated with pediatrics as to furnish the controls and the knowledge of individual development with which to correlate the diseases and nutritional variations of childhood. This contention does not require further elaboration, because it has reached a status of almost general recognition.

However, I should like here to enter a plea in behalf of the study of age changes subsequent to adolescence. It is a lamentable fact that comparatively little is known of the terminal phases of the growth cycle (approximately between 21 and 25 years of age in males, and between 18 and 22 years in females). Actually we do not know when growth stops, nor when senile changes begin. There is a sort of general assumption that the final period of growth is succeeded by a resting phase, lasting for perhaps five years or more, after which senile decay insidiously sets in. Now it seems to me very probable that the physiological changes of middle life and old age are quite as intimately associated with disease, and consequently with medicine, as those of the advancing years of youth. The world is largely run by middle-aged and elderly individuals whose dispositions, bodily health and mental processes are presumably affected by senile changes. Consequently, it would seem that these age changes bring upon the population of every age-grade, wars, financial crises, diplomatic incidents, new deals and every other sort of social and economic evil. Hence, I venture to suggest the need of a science, or at least a medical specialty, of geratology, or the study of old age changes and their relation to disease. If the course of world events is to be altered because this old man has an enlarged prostate, that one has high blood pressure, and the other has gastric ulcer or a wife going through the menopause, we have reason for desiring a somewhat fuller knowledge of the range, exact nature and general implications of bodily decline.

I will refrain from enlarging further upon relationships of anthropology and medicine, although there are many of an importance fully equal to those which I have discussed.

Proposal for an Institute of Clinical Anthropology—A Foundation for the Investigation of Well Beings

All the foregoing considerations lead to a proposal which might profitably engage the serious consideration of medical science and of those great philanthropic foundations which alternately establish and allow to perish through inanition institutes for research to promote human betterment. In my opinion, the world is in sore need of an institute of clinical anthropology or, if you like, an institute of anthropological medicine, a foundation for the study of the biology of well beings. One might define such an institute as an organization devoted to the purpose of finding out what man is like biologically when he does not need a doctor, in order further to ascertain what he should be like after the doctor has finished with him.

I am entirely serious when I suggest that it is a very myopic medical science which works backward from the morgue, rather than forward from the cradle. I can see no bright future of scientific achievement for the healing art, if it persists in dealing only with those men who have stomach aches, and hypothecates its norms from them exclusively. The institute which I have in mind, would, of course, include physical anthropologists, whose techniques, methods of analysis and points of view I conceive to be essential to the enterprise. It would provide applications for their exact methods, too often wasted upon investigations which are, from a mundane point of view, relatively futile. The entire subject of human biology, apart from pathology, can not be investigated adequately by the physical anthropologist without the co-operation of medical science. There are in this country less than a dozen physical anthropologists who are paid to devote their entire time to this specialty, and there never will be a supply sufficient to cope with the task until an alliance with applied human biology is effected. On the other hand, there are enough and probably too many young men who are preparing to enter the medical profession, and a considerable number of them might advantageously be diverted from practice to clinical anthropological investigation. But I have intimated, and I now say quite flatly, that a medical education does not make its possessor competent to undertake research in physical anthropology, and that there seems little prospect of sound cultivation in the great field of human biology wherein may grow the nutritive plants essential for a greater materia medica, if that field is to be abandoned to the anthropologists rooting for something entirely different, and to the casual scratchings of medical leisure.

The purposes of such an institute for research in applied human biology might be enumerated as follows: to establish ranges, norms and variabilities in the fields of human morphology, physiology, psychology and neurology; to investigate age changes in man from his conception to his dissolution; to determine racial susceptibilities and immunities; to test the assumption of parallelism between human physiology and that of the higher mammals; to investigate human heredity and to apply the results of such research to medical practice; to lay the foundations for a rational science of eugenics. All these studies and many more might be undertaken with the avowed purpose of obtaining knowledge bearing directly upon medical practice, and it is medical science which would profit largely from them.

This paper is not intended to exhort medical sinners to an anthropological repentance; the anthropologist does not cast himself in the rôle of a John the Baptist, crying aloud in the wilderness— far less of a Messiah. Without any desire to crash the gates of a great profession, he peeps curiously between the bars, and comments—no doubt rashly—upon the laudable efforts of the inmates.

18.

MAN AS DIRECTOR OF HUMAN EVOLUTION [1]

ON THIS occasion one should perhaps attempt some sort of synchronization of evolutionary knowledge with the founding of Harvard College. I am able to produce but one pregnant coincidence—namely, that the first living anthropoid ape to visit Europe, a chimpanzee, arrived in the Netherlands in 1641, when John Winthrop, Jr., was also abroad, looking for a Master of Harvard College.[2] Winthrop went to the Netherlands in the summer of 1642, where he may have met the chimpanzee and forgotten his mission. Whether or not because of such an anthropoid divagation, he found no head for our infant institution. The first scientific description of the chimpanzee was published in 1641 by Nicolas Tulp from observations of Winthrop's contemporary

---

[1] The Charles A. Brackett Lecture. Delivered at the Tercentenary Conference of the Harvard Dental School on September 15, 1936. Reprinted from *The Harvard Dental Record*, Vol. 11, No. 2, January, 1937.

[2] Huxley, T. H., *Man's Place in Nature and Other Anthropological Essays;* On the Natural History of the Man-like Apes, New York, 1902, p. 10.

Morison, Samuel Eliot, *The Founding of Harvard College*, Cambridge, 1935, p. 245.

visitor. A scientific account of the gorilla did not appear until 1847, but here at last Harvard registers, because it was published by Professor Jeffries Wyman, first Curator of the Peabody Museum, together with Thomas S. Savage, a Boston Missionary.[3] Hence, in spite of the recent intimate association of Yale with the anthropoid apes, Harvard may claim here, as elsewhere, historical priority.

In this lecture I propose to discuss man's rôle in directing the course of human evolution, beginning with the extent of such evolutionary self-determination in prehuman and protohuman times, continuing with an appraisal of its importance in primitive and ancient human society, and culminating in specific suggestions concerning the necessity of an intelligent control of man's future evolution through medical science.

The later stages of human evolution certainly, and those of the other higher primates possibly, stand in contrast to the evolution of lower animals in at least one important respect. Infraprimate evolution is characterized by passivity of the organism, which evolves through a sort of environmental determinism. In man, on the contrary, evolution has become autodirective. The balance of power has shifted from the environment to the organism. Whether or not intelligently, the animal has taken the bit in its teeth and is bolting. Natural selection has been tossed out of the saddle and is prostrate somewhere back in the muck. It behooves us to consider this phenomenon—man running away with his own evolution.

The Dawn of Organic Self-Assertion

It is unnecessary in this assemblage of biological practitioners to embark upon an elaborate definition of the factors in organic evolution. These are ordinarily classified in two categories: variation and selection. Variation has to do with changes in the organism, selection with the sifting of these variations by environment. Those which slip through the meshes continue in the stream of life; those which are too coarse-grained are relegated to the dump.

We are wont to fall into the habit of deifying natural selection,

---

[3] Savage, Thomas S., and Wyman, Jeffries, "Notice of the External Characters of and Habits of Troglodytes Gorilla, a New Species of Orang from the Gaboon River ... Osteology of the Same..." *Boston Journal of Natural History*, 5, 1847, pp. 417-43.

as if it were an omniscient guide and controller of biological affairs, instead of a concatenation of purposeless forces, the resultant of which for any animal species is survival or extinction. Probably it would be better conceived like Justice, blindfold, equipped with a primitive set of scales and slashing about in the dark with an unwieldy sword. It is difficult to avoid teleological interpretations of natural selection, but less so, perhaps, if one contemplates the noxious character of many of its triumphant survivors—as for example the sixteen of thirty-five species of the Genus streptococcus which are pathogenic. Of course, such a viewpoint is essentially anthropocentric; a streptococcocentric evaluation might be different. Apparently, the more primitive organisms merely sit and submit to the bludgeonings of chance environmental forces, or, at a somewhat higher level, dash about hither and yon, caroming off one environmental obstacle and against another, and surviving or perishing by a mainly unintelligent trial and error process. The passivity of the organism and the activity of the environment are alike purposeless and interchangeable, but the organism is a vital entity, whereas the environment is a mere assemblage of physical forces and matter—inert and animate.

Here I shall distinguish artificial selection from natural selection in a completely unorthodox manner. Natural selection is purposeless as regards the environment, and in its operation the organism's response to that environment is purely instinctive. In contrast, and for my present purposes, artificial selection commences when the animal attempts consciously to order its life and its habits in such a way as to promote its chances of survival, and when it begins more or less intelligently to try to adapt the environment to its own needs, or to seek one more favorable. It is, of course, impossible to determine when the organism begins consciously to strive to dominate its environment. There may be, at first, mere assertion of organic individuality, an idle monkeying with nature, without purpose, and serving merely for the satisfaction of errant impulses arising from within. Such organic self-assertiveness, accompanied by casual experimentation, and partially inspired by a sort of superorganic curiosity, is increasingly observable in the successively more highly developed members of the primate order.

Prerequisites of Autodirective Evolution

The prerequisites of an autodirective evolution for the individual may be stated as follows: high development of curiosity and imitation; learning ability; definitely directed, sustained, and concentrated attention; behavioral adaptation on the basis of insight and foresight; memory and delayed response; creative imagination; ability to manipulate and to adapt the environment; mechanical skill; dominance; speech or other means of communication. Every one of these traits is said to be present in a more or less highly developed state in one or another of the anthropoid apes, with the sole exception of articulate speech.[4]

However, it is equally essential for an autodirective evolution that the individual exist in society and that the society possess certain attributes. For the creation and continued existence of society the following characteristics are essential: gregariousness, dominance, socialibility, and mutual dependence. These are again found to be present in increasing measure as one ascends the primate scale, according to Yerkes. Zuckerman finds, however, among baboons an excessive development of individual dominance, and although mutual aid is often observed, there is, among these poor relations of man, a distinct absence of altruism.[5]

If an animal is to direct his own evolution he must exist in a society in which there is not alone marked dominance of the more intelligent individuals, but also subordination of the individual to the social good, a clear conception of past evolutionary history, a knowledge of the measures whereby evolutionary defects may be eliminated and gains consolidated, and the social sanctions to put such measures into effect. Certainly, however closely the anthropoid apes may approximate such individual capacities and social characteristics, it may be stated categorically that autodirective evolution appears possible for man alone.

Adoption of Terrestrial Life

From a genetic viewpoint it is probable that a series of mutations in an isolated, inbreeding group of progressive, generalized anthropoids initiated the protohuman line of development. Eco-

[4] Yerkes and Yerkes, *The Great Apes*, New Haven, 1929, pp. 547-550.
[5] Zuckerman, S., *The Social Life of Apes and Monkeys*, New York, 1932, pp. 292-305.

logically this phase seems to have coincided with the abandonment
of arboreal life by the forerunners of man. The adoption of a terrestrial life was the turning-point of evolution toward humanity.
The declaration of human independence was signed at the foot
of a tree. The simplest explanation of this phenomenon assumes
a change of climate which killed the forests in the abode of the
ancestral anthropoids, and forced the latter to the ground. This
postulated deforestation has been plausibly connected with the
formation of the Himalayas and the uplift of the Central Asiatic
plateau region. Such a view, it seems to me, both exaggerates the
compulsive influence of environment and underestimates the
organic self-assertiveness of the progressive primates. I think that
it may be assumed that deforestation was a gradual and not a
cataclysmic process and that there must have been ample time for
progressive but mobile anthropoids to follow the retreating tree
line, as did undoubtedly the conservative ancestors of the gorilla,
chimpanzee, and orang-utan. Apes can brachiate more rapidly than
forests can recede. Some may imagine our ancestors squatting on
their haunches in the primate Garden of Eden, watching the trees
shrivel up, and saying amongst themselves, "Fellow apes, we must
now arise upon our hind legs and earn our bread in the sweat of
our brows, instead of eating of the fruit of the trees." Is it not
more probable that some intrepid anthropoid adventurer, fed up
with a diet of shoots, berries, fruits, and nuts, having descended
to get a drink and stretch his legs, decided to take a chance on
the ground, questing, no doubt, for ampler supplies of Vitamins
A, B, C, D, and E?

Seriously, I am of the opinion that it was the desirability of an
enlarged dietary which furnished the motive for adoption of terrestrial life, and that an already enlarged brain and superior intelligence was the catalytic agent that produced this radical change.
All of the organic qualities which make for evolutionary advancement by the formation of new and more advantageous modes of
life, may be summarized under the term "initiative." Of course,
initiative means the capacity for "starting something"—whether
or not you can finish it. It is this complex of traits which all of
the higher primates possess in some degree, and in which man and
his protohuman ancestors are and have been supreme.

A Chain of Organic Consequences

This crucial experiment set in motion a chain of organic consequences of which the end is not yet in sight. The first of these had to do with posture and method of locomotion. It is obviously impossible to brachiate on the ground; so, save on rare occasions, a quadrupedal pronograde gait is preferred by the great apes. Any ape can walk erect if he chooses, but such gait and posture are awkward and fatiguing for the giant arboreal primates, because they lack the requisite bodily adaptations. These latter are: a stabilized supporting foot with a consolidated tarsus, instead of a mobile prehensile foot; a hypertrophied lower extremity with complete extension of the leg upon the thigh and of the thigh upon the pelvic girdle; a lateral expansion and anterior recurvation of the iliac blades to provide suitable attachments for muscles used in balancing and in orthograde progression; a sharp anterior convexity of the lumbar column to facilitate erection of the spine upon the pelvis and to bring the axis of the center of gravity into coincidence with that of the lower limbs; a reduction in relative weight and size of the jaws, arms, and thorax, in order to lower the center of mass and to reduce top-heaviness. The presence of these modifications characterizes man, and their absence, the great anthropoid apes. Only the small gibbon resembles man in the elongation of its legs and in the slenderness of its torso, although it lacks the other anatomical adaptations for orthograde posture. This animal, nevertheless, has an occasionally bipedal gait upon the ground, running with bent knees and uplifted balancing arms. Oftener it moves in an erect quadrupedal posture, since the enormous length of its arms permits the knuckles of the hands to touch the ground and to supplement pedal support, while the trunk is maintained in an almost perpendicular position.

Millions of years were probably required for the development and genetic consolidation of the somatic changes essential for erect biped progression. Since most of these changes must have been acquired at first in the lifetime of the individual, it is hard to understand how they could have become fixed in the germ plasm and hereditarily transmitted, unless one either rejects orthodox Weismannism or takes refuge in a hypothetical series of mutations.

Much more important than the bodily modifications directly

induced by the mechanical exigencies of the new posture and gait were the secondary changes resulting from new functions of certain parts of the organism. Even the lowliest of the arboreal primates are equipped with pentadactyl hands and feet, terminating in more or less flattened nails instead of claws, and with thumbs and great toes partially opposable to the outer digits. The primitive grasping hands, used at first primarily for maintaining a hold upon branches, gradually develop tactile, exploratory, and food-conveying functions, even among the tree-dwelling monkeys. This process proceeds apace in the ascending stages of primate development, although inhibited in the brachiating apes by coarsening and elongation of the fingers and regression of the thumb, due to their weight-suspending function. It is not until the duties of bodily support and locomotion have been placed squarely and finally upon the legs and feet, that the emancipated hands fully realize their evolutionary destiny. The fingers now become motor extensions of the brain. Tactile and exploratory use of the digits of the hands is undoubtedly correlated with the hypertrophy of the primate brain. Scratching, massaging, pinching, and flea-picking, however greatly contributing to bodily comfort or to the satisfaction of sensation, are nevertheless not particularly conducive to evolutionary advancement. The use of the hands for the conveying of food to the mouth does, on the contrary, so conduce, since it relieves the jaws of their prehensile function and encourages regression of the snout. But this hand-feeding is highly developed among the lower primates without consistent association of dental reduction. It is the preparation of food by the hands which seems to have contributed most to the regression of the dental apparatus, presumably as a result of the fabrication of tools. Anthropoid apes and even monkeys are incipient and half-hearted users and contrivers of tools, but they lack in their arboreal existence both materials and incentive for a persistent and habitual utilization of any extra-organic implement. What is more important, they possess intelligence insufficient to motivate them to a tool-using habit, and even to the recognition of the continuing and future utility of an implement once employed.

Dominance of the organism over its environment is achieved only by setting the environment to work through the instrumentality of tools, the raw materials of which it furnishes. The organic prerequisites for the fashioning and employment of tools are a pair of free and mobile limbs with prehensile extremities, suspended vertically with ample clearance of the ground, a stable support and an easy balance upon the sustaining limbs, stereoscopic vision, and last but most important a brain capable of an intelligent grasp of the principles of mechanics. Such a combination seems exclusively human.

The evolutionary advantages of tool-using accrue from the fact that such use increases the strength and efficiency of the animal many times beyond its natural physical capacity. Specifically, these advantages are increased command over food supply and enhanced ability of self-preservation. Indirectly, the use of tools not only leads to the fabrication of clothing, when the climate requires it, but ultimately also to the construction of windbreaks, shelters, and other artificial habitations. Settled abodes consolidate the family and help to establish permanent social groups, without which man is unable to survive. They promote mutual aid and the division of labor and stimulate the development of social institutions. Probably the origin of agriculture is to be traced to observation of the chance sprouting of seeds thrown or spat upon the ground outside the hut or cave.

The Organic Concomitants of Tool-Using

The repercussions of tool-using upon the organism merit discussion. You cannot revolutionize the habits of an animal without causing organic ructions. The effects in order of magnitude and certainty pertain to the alimentary system, the nervous system, and to the endocrines.

The teeth of large primates are specialized for a double duty. The deeply implanted, tusk-like canines serve as the principal weapons of offense and defense and for piercing the tough rinds of certain tropical fruits; the molars and premolars with their expanded crowns are suitable for the crushing of nuts and very coarse vegetable food; the bevel-edged incisors bite off the food in lengths convenient for chewing and swallowing. Now suppose that you begin to hack off bits of food with a stone knife or chopper, instead of tearing at them with your front teeth; suppose that you crack your nuts with a stone instead of your molars; and your enemy's head with a club, instead of chewing his ear.

Your teeth lose their job, or, at any rate, are relegated to the
Public Works where they merely go through the motions. Atrophy
of function deteriorates the disused part, just as relief of the un-
employed rots their moral fiber. The masticatory muscles shrivel,
the jaw bones shrink, and the less plastic teeth become too large
for the dental arcades; they jostle each other out of position and
erupt hither and yon; functional equilibrium is disturbed; mis-
placed stresses and strains bring endless aches and pains. Broad-
crowned, blunt-cusped teeth suitable for crushing tough vegetable
fibers become entangled in the gelatinous strands of gobbets of
meat; decaying morsels become lodged in the dental interstices
and set up acid reactions, bacteria proliferate and dental caries
embarks upon its fell career.

Regressive Evolution

Of course the organism makes shift to accommodate itself to
changing conditions. Symmetrical reduction in the size of the
dentition with adequate preservation of occlusion and function
seems to mark the transition from the frugivorous, toolless ape to
the omnivorous or carnivorous artefactual man. Regressive evolution does not immediately involve the onset of pathological condition. Moreover, it would be folly to assume that function dictates
the direction of every evolutionary change. Thus the third molars
are reduced and degenerative in all three of the great apes, although supernumerary molars are very common in the gorilla and
in the orang-utan. Therefore the reduction of the third molar,
which is evident in some very early types of fossil man, cannot be
attributed to the change from anthropoid to human habits of diet
and food preparation.

Among the fossil men, Sinanthropus (the Peking Man),
Heidelberg Man, and all of the Neanderthaloids exhibit the enlargement of the pulp cavities of the molars which has been called
"taurodontism" because of similar conditions manifested by rumi-
nants. In modern man this condition is an infantile phenomenon,
gradually modified with advancing years. It is absent in adult
anthropoid apes. Some students infer from taurodontism that early
man was specialized for a herbivorous diet. J. R. de la H. Marett,
a recent and brilliant theorizer on the etiology of human evolution, has suggested that the enlarged pulp cavities of Neanderthal

man may be ascribed to an initial deprivation of Vitamin C, caused by the change from fruit- or leaf-eating to the consumption of roots and seeds, bringing about the swelling of the pulp cavity in the individual and encouraging the development of larger teeth, which would be more efficient for grinding down vegetable food, and whose capacious pulp cavities would secrete more secondary dentine, thus prolonging the lives of their possessors.[6] Unfortunately we do not know that Neanderthal man was a root- and seed-eater, nor that he suffered from Vitamin C deficiency, but only that he had "taurodont" teeth. The opposite condition—small pulp cavities—is called cynodontism, because it is prevalent in carnivores. However, it is found also in the fruit- and shoot-eating great apes and in *Homo sapiens*, the morphologically modern species of man. Marett regards *Homo sapiens* as a meat-eater and supposes that a reduced intake of Vitamin C, consequent upon a change from a fruit to a flesh diet, is compensated by an alleged carnivorous power of manufacturing or storing Vitamin C. Hence this deficiency in morphologically modern man would not enlarge the pulp cavities but would initiate a change toward smaller teeth more serviceable for meat-eaters.[7] My own feeling is that to infer the unknown diet of an extinct form of man from the type of his teeth, and then to refer his tooth form to his diet is nothing more than chasing one's own tail. I doubt the validity of the assumption that all variations in animal organisms originate in environmental stimuli and are selected for the purpose of supplying some functional demand essential for survival. It seems probable that many variations, indifferent or even harmful, arise spontaneously from the germ plasm and cannot be related to function. Thus the details of cusp pattern and such variations in tooth form as the shovel incisor may be merely the vagaries of a versatile germ plasm, perpetuated by the inertia of heredity.

A Shift of Diet

A shift from the frugivorous and herbivorous diet of the arboreal anthropoid to the omnivorous or carnivorous diet of man may not have required either profound anatomical modifications

---

[6] Marett, J. R. de la H., *Race, Sex, and Environment, a Study in Mineral Deficiency*, London, 1936, pp. 205-07.

[7] Marett, *op. cit., loc. cit.*

of the ancestral digestive system or any physiological revolution.
Yerkes states that "the gibbon and siamang are vegetable feeders
of a high degree of adaptability, which take in nature, as opportunity offers, such animal products as eggs, insects and other small
mammals." The orang-utan is also a vegetarian, but can be taught
to accept human diet and to thrive upon it. The highland gorilla
is stated to be primarily herbivorous, whereas the lowland form is
more largely frugivorous.[8] Nissen's field study of the chimpanzee
is the only first-rate source for the food habits of anthropoid apes
in a state of nature. He was able to list thirty-four foods proved to
have been eaten by the chimpanzees, of which twenty-eight could
be classified as fruits, three as stalks or stems, two as blossoms, and
one as leaves.[9] This observer was unable to secure evidence that
chimpanzees ever eat roots or tubers, or that they catch and eat
birds, rodents, and fish, or eat eggs, but he thinks it entirely
possible.

Examination of the scanty evidence concerning the alimentary
system of anthropoid apes does not indicate that their digestive
organs differ profoundly from those of man. An index which expresses stature relative to length of the large intestine places man
close to the omnivorous animals rather than in any dietetically
specialized category. Thus we have: Insectivores, 2.5; Carnivores,
3.7; Man, 5.0-6.3; Omnivores, 6.8; Frugivores, 7.1; Granivores,
8.7; Herbivores, 15.1.[10] Now the Genus Semnopithecus of Old
World monkeys possesses an enormously enlarged and sacculated
stomach, which has displaced to the right and deformed the liver
and spleen. Since these animals are primarily leaf-eaters, it has
been suggested that the modification of the stomach is analogous
to that of herbivorous mammals of other orders, that the stomach
is capable of providing for rumination, and that its first sac substitutes for the cheek pouches of other Old World monkeys which
are absent or diminished in this group. Moreover, sacculated stomachs of the Semnopithecine form have been recorded in adult
human beings. Further, the human foetus in the fifth month shows
a diverticulum at the cardiac end of the stomach, lined with a

[8] Yerkes, op. cit., p. 539.
[9] Nissen, Henry W., A Field Study of the Chimpanzee, Comparative Psychology Monographs, Vol. 8, No. 1, Serial No. 36, December, 1931, pp. 52-72. .
[10] Duckworth, W. L. H., Morphology and Anthropology, 2nd ed., Vol. I, Cambridge,
1915, pp. 148-50.

specially corrugated mucous membrane. The modification of the stomach of adult Semnopithecus monkeys consists of a dilatation of the fundus which includes this diverticulum. It therefore is deduced that the simplicity of the human stomach is not primary, but secondary.[11] It seems, then, to follow, that both man and the anthropoid apes may have descended from monkey ancestors with alimentary systems particularly adapted for herbivorous diets, and that the organic modifications which facilitate omnivorous propensities were accomplished long before the human stage.

Consequences of the Enlarged Dietary

It would appear, however, that less direct but more important consequences may have followed upon the enlarged dietary secured by terrestrial life, upright posture, and the use of implements. Nissen estimates that a chimpanzee spends a net period of from three to six hours per day in feeding. The volume of food ingested must be enormous, but the food concentration value of the fruits, stalks, leaves, and blossoms eaten is so low that it may be insufficient to maintain the animals near their maximum potential weight.[12] Now, there is little opportunity of cultivating the higher faculties when it is necessary to spend half one's waking hours scrambling from tree to tree in search of food, and most of the remainder in attempting to digest and eliminate a vast bulk of unnutritious fodder. Subtract, further, a modicum of time for one's love life, for quarreling and other social amenities, and there is nothing left.

Ground-dwelling with erect posture and tool-using gave early man a food supply which created the leisure essential for social and cultural progress. Of course some quantity of brain was also necessary, but as long as the digestive system is chronically overworked, the brain has little chance of a blood supply adequate for anything more than a maintenance of its evolutionary *status quo*. Again, the amount of muscular work required by the arboreal life of a giant primate is enormous, and it is known that pound for pound the muscles of anthropoid apes are several times stronger than those of

[11] Loth, E., *Anthropologie des Parties Molles*, Paris, 1931, p. 288, citing data from Magnan, M. A., "Le Regime Alimentaire et la Longueur de L'intestin chez les Mammifères," Comptes Rendus hebd. d. Sc. D'Acad. d. Sc. Paris, Vol. CLIV, 1912.

[12] Nissen, *op. cit.*, pp. 65-66.

human beings. Expenditure of energy in work and of nutriment in muscle repair must starve the nervous system of the ape.

The subject of mineral deficiency, vitamins, the endocrine glands, and their relation to human evolution has been illuminated recently by the ingenious speculations and deductions of the young British anthropologist, J. R. de la H. Marett.[13] He argues that lime-rich soils, resulting from climatic aridity or from the nature of the parent rock, are alkaline and inhibit the retention and absorption of iodine, necessitating in animals every means of economizing the basis of the thyroid hormone. Conversely, lime-deficient areas, which are almost always humid, demand an economy of calcium and phosphorus, together with the capacity to utilize an abundance of iodine and potash and to cope with a deficiency of sodium. Mineral economy is held to have been secured through an increase of sexuality. The sex having the greater need of reproductive efficiency carries a full quota of genes for physiological efficiency, whereas the other is better able to develop specialized and progressive features. When food is scarce or ill-balanced, a full bodily expression of the sex-linked genes for food economy would confer survival upon the feminized individuals of either sex, whereas under reversed conditions survivors would tend to be those who manifested bodily characteristics least hampered by sex-linked repression. Genes for liquid and iodine economy are believed by Marett to have become sex-linked on account of their reproductive importance, and to have secured their results through size and tissue hydration. Lime-economy is assisted by small size, because of enlargement of the areas of gut and skin relative to body bulk, encouraging the intake of lime and the autosynthesis of Vitamin D and reducing the ratio of skeletal-to-body weight. On the other hand, cold and aridity may be countered by the large size and metabolic activity produced by hyper-secretion of the anterior lobe, on account of inhibition of moisture and heat loss from relatively reduced skin surface. Dry soil provides an abundance of lime and probably of phosphorus and fluorine for the building of a large strong skeleton and teeth. Vitamin E, considered as the raw material of the anterior lobe hormone, is thought to be most plentiful in arid habitats. Thus anterior lobe activity is greatest in arid and iodine-deficient situations, whereas rainfall reduces

13 Marett, J. R. de la H., *op. cit., passim.*

this need by providing more iodine. In brief, Marett suggests that the small-boned "feminized" species of *Homo sapiens* has evolved in a humid tropical area, under conditions of lime-shortage, whereas the older massive-boned types, as represented in Neanderthal man and other fossils, are the products of arid regions with iodine deficiency. The mechanism of such differentiation is held to be environmental selection of genes, based upon nutritional conditions and acting through the endocrines.

Correlative Research Needed

Such hypotheses seem to deny to man's ancestors even an infinitesimal amount of organic initiative and dietetic instinct. A vast quantity of correlative research must be accomplished before we can appraise the value of these adventurous theories. Man's prehuman ancestors, from the time of their adoption of a terrestrial habitat, must have been widely migratory animals, not constrained to "stay put" in any restricted geographical environment and to survive only by a painful and elaborate process of self-adaptation, but free to roam the world in search of diets adapted to the needs of their hereditarily varying organisms.

Deductions concerning the effect of diet upon prehuman evolution are highly speculative, but experimental studies of nutrition, such as those of Wolbach and Howe, enlarge not only our knowledge of normal and pathological growth, but also of evolutionary processes.[14] Lawrence W. Baker's recent demonstration of madderstaining in the skeletons of foetal rats, whose mothers had been fed with this substance, opens up a conspectus of possibilities for the study of bone growth, and indicates the intimate relationship between maternal nutrition and prenatal development. The researches of Weston A. Price upon the diets of primitive peoples and civilized groups in isolated environments, illuminate both the etiology of dental caries and the differentiation of modern physical types. This investigator has apparently come to grips with the evolutionary paradox of savage immunity and civilized susceptibility to dental caries and malocclusion. Briefly, Price has shown that the Eskimo, the Polynesians, and the Melanesians, when living

[14] Wolbach, S. B., and Howe, Percy R., *Vitamin A Deficiency in the Guinea-Pig,* Archives of Pathology and Laboratory Medicine, Vol. 5, 1928, pp. 239-53; *Intercellular Substances in Experimental Scorbutus,* Archives of Pathology and Laboratory Medicine, Vol. 1, pp. 1-24.

in a state of nature, are forced to utilize to the full the food resources of their environments, and thereby secure a sufficiently balanced ration in both energy-producing materials and those needed for growth and repair. Civilized man has modified natural foods and obtained a greater latitude of choice. Appetite still determines the quantity of food eaten, but is satisfied mainly by the energy-producing foods. Progressively exhausted soils produce foods which are not only deficient in minerals but also lower in activating substances. As soon as modern primitive peoples begin to get civilized foods they become subject to caries, malocclusion, and other conditions due to defective nutrition.[15] These generalizations are supported by chemical analyses of diets of caries-immune and caries-susceptible civilized and primitive groups, and also by studies of the physico-chemical state of saliva which provides the dental environment.

Seemingly, man has directed his dentition and possibly his whole alimentary system into digressive and pathological evolutionary by-ways by securing an almost unlimited variety of foods, by tampering with natural foods, thus removing from them certain essential elements, and by exerting his dietetic choice so ignorantly as to make himself the victim of deficiency diseases and to establish as apparently stable human breeds what may be in reality different deficiency types.

Dental Science Strategically Situated

It seems to me that dental science is strategically situated in its constant supervision of the most accessible part of the alimentary system, to observe, to study, and to experiment upon this all-important question of nutrition as affecting form and function. The dental practitioner should equip himself to become the agent of an intelligent control of human evolution, insofar as it is affected by diet. Let us go to the ignorant savage, consider his way of eating,

---

[15] Price, Weston A., "Additional Light on the Etiology and Nutritional Control of Dental Caries with Its Application to Each District Showing Immunity and Susceptibility," *J. Am. Dent. Assoc.*, Vol. XX, 1933, pp. 1648-79; "Acid-base Balance of Diets Which produce Immunity to Dental Caries among the South Sea Islanders and Other Primitive Races," *Dental Cosmos*, September, 1935, pp. 841-46; "Studies of Relationships between Nutritional Differences and (a) Facial and Dental Arch Deformities and (b) Loss of Immunity to Dental Caries among South Sea Islanders and Florida Indians," *Dental Cosmos*, April, 1935, pp. 1033-45; "Eskimo and Indian Field Studies in Alaska and Canada," *J. Am. Dent. Assoc.*, Vol. XXIII, March, 1936, pp. 417-37.

and be wise. Let us cease pretending that tooth-brushes and tooth-paste are any more important than shoe-brushes and shoe-polish. It is store food which has given us store teeth.

Man has unwittingly directed the course of his own biological evolution by means of social selection. Such selection manifests itself firstly in the family, then in the larger social group, and beyond that in the state.

Darwin was not convincing in his effort to show that secondary sexual characters have been developed and intensified and that racial differentiation has come about mainly through the agency of sexual selection. His overemphasis upon masculine display and combativeness and upon female coyness, aesthetic sensibility, and discriminatory choice of the most virile appearing potential mate recalls the fact that Darwin himself was a mid-Victorian and boasted a luxuriant beard, tufted eyebrows, and a somewhat Neanderthaloid physiognomy. It seems probable that the proto-human female, instead of sitting by to await the outcome of the conflict between hairy-chested males in fond anticipation of the attentions of the battered survivor, would sneak off into the bush with some sinuous and smooth-cheeked precursor of the modern gigolo.

In the London baboon colony studied by Zuckerman, the most important social feature was the dominance of certain powerful and aggressive males, who owned all of the females. Mature and unmated bachelors were often attached to monogamous or biga-mous family groups. Female baboons were generally passive in the matter of their disposal as sexual objects. Occasionally the monog-amous females committed infidelities. Zuckerman observed one instance in which a female was left alone for forty seconds while her overlord chased a bachelor round Monkey Hill. During this interval the female made advances to, and had relations with, two other males. Sexual activities of the adult females with immature males were frequently observed to take place under the eyes of the complacent overlords.[16] The battle is not always to the strong.

On the whole it appears to be impossible to estimate the extent to which man, or woman either, has guided his own evolution by sexual selection. Its operation must always have been capricious, erratic, and unpredictable. In our own society perhaps the most

[16] Zuckerman, S., *The Social Life of Apes and Monkeys*, London, 1932, pp. 229, 237.

notable example of sexual selection is the tendency for the successful male American Negroes, of whatever pigmentation, to choose as mates the lightest-skinned Negroid girls. There was also a time when Harvard football players married Back Bay heiresses, but, for aught I know, the preferred males may now hail from Holy Cross.

It is indeed possible to make some sort of prediction as to the sexually selective effect of one of your own specialties, orthodontia. It is probable that many, if not most, malocclusions are due to hereditary tendencies. Now, the young lady afflicted with the condition which is vulgarly called "buck teeth," requires the ministrations of the orthodontist before she can be a promising candidate for preferential mating. But after such treatment, owing to the consummate skill of the profession, she becomes speciously beautiful, presenting an appearance entirely at variance with her probable genetic constitution. Hence she is chosen by the most desirable males and proceeds to present her husband with bevies of buck-toothed offspring. Thus the effect of sexual selection in this character is to make business better for the orthodontist.

Three Paramount Forces

Since this lecture should not exceed in minutes the number of millions of years which have elapsed since the emergence of the lowliest primates (estimated at sixty), lack of time forbids me to dilate upon all of the socially selective forces which man has set in motion to act as non-purposeful directors of his own biological evolution. I cannot, however, refrain from a few comments upon the operation of three paramount forces in the modern world: war, medical science, and social ethics as embodied in education.

In the colony of Hamadryas baboons which Zuckerman studied in the London Zoo, intestine warfare invariably originated from sexual rivalry. Scuffles over the possession of food did not usually lead to serious fighting. On the other hand, the "sexual fights" for the possession of females were extremely deadly for the members of the fair sex involved. Of the thirty-three females who died, thirty lost their lives in fights, in which they were the prizes.[17] Only eight of fifty-eight deceased males were killed in battles. When thirty-six males and only five females were left alive, the fatal beauties

[17] Zuckerman, *op. cit.*, p. 220.

were removed. However, Zuckerman does not believe that such a large proportion of females would be killed in a natural community as succumbed in the civilized environment of London. A vast initial disparity in the numbers of the sexes and the confined quarters perhaps contributed to a situation which had all of the ruthless ferocity of a Spanish civil war.

I do not believe that the baboon warfare in a London Zoo bears any close resemblance to protohuman strife nor to the fights of primitive peoples. In spite of romantic traditions, it seems probable that warfare among savages and barbaric peoples is not usually motivated by sexual considerations, but arises from economic causes. No scholar today blames Helen for the Trojan War. "The face that launched a thousand ships" has probably always manifested a physiognomic range between the lineaments of Der Führer and Il Duce.

From what is known of primitive warfare it may be deduced that it was slightly more dangerous, and possibly more enjoyable, than modern football, but considerably less hazardous and probably less painful than childbirth. The active participants in this sport were, ordinarily, the young and middle-aged males, but the victims included the old and the young of both sexes. As an agency of selection it probably contributed to the survival of the strongest, but perhaps little more than the risks incident to the chase, and considerably less than the diseases of childhood. With the rise of civilization and the increased size of human groups consequent upon the domestication of plants and animals, war began to play a more important part in selection. Organized states now began to wage warfare on a large scale with armies levied from the males most physically fit and between the age limits of youth and senility. Such a conscription, of course, tended to enlarge the paternal functions of the infirm and the senile stay-at-homes. However, as long as survival in warfare depended mainly upon individual strength and prowess, it seems probable that the hardy veterans, either returning home or sojourning among the conquered, performed their full biological function in the propagation of the fit. But with the invention of firearms and the development of wars of aggression in far-off lands, fighting became a drain upon the hardiest stocks of nations. In modern times this dysgenic effect of war has been enormously increased, because the chances of survival probably do not favor the strong and the courageous as much as the small, the weak, and the pusillanimous. Veterans of foreign wars become bonus-seekers and breed pensioners.

The Rôle of Medicine

Doubtless, man began to be preoccupied with his physical ailments long before he achieved sufficient intelligence to attempt to do anything about it. One may safely postulate the genesis of medical science from the individual's distressful contemplation of his own belly-ache. Beginning with groans and writhings, and proceeding through spells and prayers, the ability of this super-ape to profit by experience soon brought into being a set of practices designed to relieve himself of pain and ultimately to insure a reversion to that state of corporeal well-being which we call health.

However, it seems very doubtful whether man's curative efforts interfered seriously with the operation of natural selection in primitive society and in ancient times. Even though home treatment of human diseases was early supplemented by the professional ministrations of the medicine man or witch-doctor, it is wholly probable that these combined therapeutic activities merely increased the ordinary hazards of life. Only the most vigorous could survive the treatments. The efficacy of the healing art and the extent of its practice were so limited that they merely served to usher individuals into and out of the world under proper ceremonial auspices. Medicine provided spiritual consolation for all concerned, but its effect was mainly to speed the parting guest.

Obsolescence of Natural Selection

Even if we make the most liberal allowance for precocious medical skill, it is certain that wars, epidemics, famines, and the routine risks of life continued, up to very recent times, to exert a dominating control over the increase of the population and the character of the surviving stocks.

The obsolescence of natural selection is largely due to humanitarianism and to the efficacy of modern medical science. It is obvious that the most skillful and successful medical practice could have little effect for good or for evil upon the population, as long as it was restricted to those few who could afford the luxury of high fees. When, however, there arose enlightened leaders among men who taught the nobility, not only of casting out devils, but also of healing the sick, making whole the lame, and causing the blind to see, the doctor began to yearn to be the savior of all mankind. This did no harm at all, as long as his miracles were imaginary and his nostrums continued to waft his patients to the Elysian Fields. But when he really began to succeed, Pandora's box was open.

Studies of the individual age composition of ancient and primitive skeletal populations indicate that an increase of longevity is a marked phenomenon of modern civilized life. Statistics of infant mortality show that the constitutional inferiors of today stand a much better chance of surviving to adult years, and of reproducing their kind, than they have presumably enjoyed at any previous time. Again, modern advances in sanitation and in the knowledge of communicable diseases have done much to control the epidemics which periodically have decimated the populations of times past. What are the consequences of such preservation and prolongation of human life?

In the first place the effect must be to increase proportionally that section of the population which is helpless because young, and also that section which is relatively helpless because old. Both increases place additional burdens upon the family and the state. The economically depressed, who seem always the most prolific, have larger numbers of offspring who must be fed, clothed, and educated, and probably more surviving children of inferior bodily and mental endowment. Familial care and earnings must be distributed among a greater number of less fit young. There follows the tendency to dissipate the family resources upon the inferior offspring and to neglect those who are better fitted in individual hereditary endowment to cope with the world. The major portion of parental energy is exerted upon the effort to make the best of bad reproductive jobs. Instead of saving the bacon, we misdirect our hog-raising efforts to the futile task of attempting to make silk purses of the animals' ears. The more active and able-bodied children are left to fend for themselves—an abandonment which for many of them leads to delinquency.[18]

---

[18] Sheldon and Eleanor T. Glueck have found that the juvenile delinquents studied by them come from families appreciably larger than the average of Massachusetts. Glueck, Sheldon and Eleanor T., *One Thousand Juvenile Delinquents*, Cambridge, 1934, p. 77.

At the other end of the curve we have the increase of the population of advanced age. Let us consider the effect of the continued activity of these elders. It is perhaps most clearly manifested in the modern gerontocracy, or the rule of old men. One of the most constant characteristics of old age is an inability to recognize its own obsolescence and an unwillingness to relinquish its direction of the life of family and state. The dominion of senility in the family increases the conflict between generations, since three instead of two are involved, and must be one of the factors tending toward familial disruption. In the political and economic world, it means that those who have attained the seniority requisite for leadership are likely to be a generation behind their times in thought, relatively impervious to the advance of ideas, and completely unsympathetic with the world of the middle-aged and the juvenile which they dominate.

Add to this the fact that these elderly potentates perform their public functions in a personal aura of corporeal and mental disintegration, being indeed not immortal, but subject not only to ordinary human ailments but also to those of old age. I have said on a previous occasion that it is impossible to estimate, for example, to what extent the miseries of nations may have been enhanced by the vagaries of the enlarged prostates of their senile rulers, or by the climacteric mental disturbances of the latters' wives. If indeed we are to tolerate the sway of those debilitated by age, it would seem necessary at least to make some appraisal of the extent to which their functions are impaired by disease, in order that our entire public policy may not be moribund. For those who retire from active life with the onset of senility, there remains public care in the form of old age pensions and homes for the aged, or alternatively, retirement to the family chimney corner.

Now I am not arguing in favor either of a policy of infanticide or of senicide. I am merely calling attention to the fact that the benevolent and efficient labors of modern medicine are raising new and grave population problems. I may here state what I believe to be the anthropological view of pathology. Man is a made-over and makeshift organism, the end product of many adaptations and unsatisfactory compromises between heredity and environment. Early in the life of the average individual, various working parts of his organism begin to weaken under the attack of infections or through sheer constitutional inferiority, but, in some way or other, functions are partially maintained, and the animal goes limping along through life, aided by the crutches of medical science and sustained by that brutal tenacity of life which seems to be an inheritance from lower evolutionary stages. By some saturnine gift of nature the reproductive system of the human animal continues to function when the nervous system is completely disintegrated, the alimentary and excretory systems thoroughly disorganized, and virtually the entire organism is in a state of morbidity. By super-skillful tinkering and patching, life and activity are maintained, and the animal continues to exercise one of its strongest instincts and to produce more and more of worse and worse offspring.

Education and Ethics

The pathway of degressive human evolution, like hell, is paved with good intentions—medical, educational, and ethical. The fallacy of social ethics lies, I think, in the assumption that all human life is inherently good and worthy of preservation, and that by a process of environmental tinkering, fools may be transmuted into sages, criminals into saints, and politicians into statesmen. Surely this conception is nothing but a secularized belief in conversion and personal salvation. The clergyman of yesterday is the unfrocked sociologist of today.

When are we to realize that a great proportion of mankind continues to be as stupid, unteachable, bloodthirsty, predatory, and savage as we are wont to imagine that maligned and regrettably extinct precursor—Neanderthal man? Is it because the precepts of Christianity have not been sufficiently disseminated, or because the blessings of plumbing and mechanical transport have been too narrowly restricted, or because there are still a few persons who lack the degree of Bachelor of Arts? I think it is because no little of the human germ plasm is poisonous slime, and we have not had the intelligence and the courage to attempt to find out anything about human heredity. We have imagined universal education, mutual understanding, and improvement of the social environment to be the ingredients with which we can concoct the human millennium; we have mixed them up and stirred them in, and turned out a horrible mess. There must be something the matter with our basic element—man himself.

It is not yet too late to begin the studies of human inheritance which are essential for man's wise and efficient control of his own evolution. Such studies should begin with genetic researches upon the gross anatomy and general physiology of the human animal, his pathology, his psychology and mental capacity, and should proceed ultimately to his sociability—or fitness to function in human society. Of course environment is important, but we cannot exercise an intelligent control of environment without a fundamental knowledge of the range and restrictions of hereditary variations.

The Banner of Equality

When Mr. Midshipman Easy was called to account for a serious breach of naval discipline, he replied that it was "all zeal," and when requested to explain why he had flown the silk petticoat of a señorita from the masthead of a prize of war, he stated that "it was the banner of equality and the rights of man." We have adopted this easyish philosophy without its saving grace of humor; we have been plunging zealously ahead under a banner of equality and the rights of man, which turns out to be less significant than the señorita's lingerie.

It might well have been said to Luke: "Thou art the physician, and hast the keys of life and death," for that precisely is the responsibility of the medical profession, of which dental science is not the least important division. In medical science lies the only practicable control of human evolution and of biological progress. Medical science must cease to regard its function as primarily curative and preventive. It must rid itself of the obsession that its chief responsibility is to the individual rather than to society. It must allocate to itself the function of discovering how the human animal may be improved as a biological organism. The future of mankind does not depend upon political or economic theory, nor yet upon measures of social amelioration, but upon the production of better minds in sounder bodies.

19.

WHAT MUST WE DO TO BE SAVED?[1]

Introduction

IT MAY seem to some of you that I have selected for the subject
of my discourse a belated and hence superfluous question—What
must we do to be saved? For have we not survived, during the past
year, a political campaign in which, nightly, by long waves and
by short, the atmosphere has vibrated with alarmist viewings of the
necessity of salvation and prideful pointings of the single means
of its attainment? And have we not answered the question with
one accord and secured for ourselves that necessary salvation by
the virtual unanimity of our ballots? Decidedly, then, it is no fit
time for anyone to raise the issue of political salvation—and least
of all for a puttering professor of the unfashionable and impolite
science of man.

The kind of salvation with which I am concerned is not political,
but biological; not economic and material, but rather mental and

[1] Address delivered before the Harvard Club of Kansas City, February 19, 1937.

spiritual. Now, at the very outset, I wish emphatically to disclaim any intention of assuming the function of a prophet prepared to point out the one true road of biological salvation. I am much closer in temperament and intellectual position to the calamity-howling Jeremiah as, in figurative garb of sack-cloth and ashes, I preach the need of biological repentance and reformation. Indeed, I should prefer to be regarded as a mere wringer of hands, hysterically shouting "What *shall* we do?", rather than as an omniscient diagnostician of evolutionary ailments, all ready to prescribe a sure-fire panacea.

It is my intention then, principally, to disclose to you modern man's need of an evolutionary salvation, by reviewing his biological progress from prehuman times and by appraising his present status. Since, however, man's behavior is a function of his organism—perhaps the most important function—it is within the province of the physical anthropologist to survey also the cultural and psychological symptoms of the well-being or ill-being of the human animal. Finally, it is better to avoid the ignominious attitude of the defeatist by attempting to suggest remedial measures, however little expectation one may have of their adoption, than to lead one's auditors into a Slough of Despond, and leave them there, bogged down and splashing about in the slime.

REVIEW OF THE BIOLOGICAL STATUS OF MAN

Man's Physical Emergence

Let us begin with the record of man's successful capitalization of his originally meager animal assets, his brilliant extension of a narrow evolutionary prospect. It has required some sixty millions of years to develop man from a small, long-snouted, quadruped tree-dweller, equipped with a simple brain and mobile, five-digited, grasping hands and feet. Such an amount of time in the life of the world is as trifling as that sum of dollars to a federal budgetary officer. In this brief period the six great steps of primate evolution were ascended by man, who left some breathless poor relations stranded at each stage. Man belongs by structure, function, and descent to the zoölogical Order of Primates, which includes also the anthropoid apes, the monkeys, the tarsiers, and the lemurs. Man and the rest of these animals can trace their ancestries back to the common arboreal primate stock within this span of sixty million years. We may not like our kinship with these animals, but probably they do not either. Blood relationship is not a matter of choice.

The humble ancestral lemuroids ran about the trees on all fours, clasping or encircling the boughs with thumbs and fingers, great toes and lesser toes, eating nuts, leaves, fruits, shoots, and occasional insects and grubs, producing litters of two or more young at a birth, and behaving in a thoroughly lower class mammalian fashion. In their tree-top homes they developed agility and keenness of vision, but not much intelligence. Almost at the beginning, some of the smarter of these animals began to sit up on their hind legs and to use their free upper limbs for scratching, exploring, and conveying food to their mouths, thereby relieving their protruding snouts of the duties of grazing and of tactile investigation. Thus they reached the second primate stage—that of the erect-sitting, hopping, hand-feeding tarsier. These diminutive and monkey-like little beasts have shrunken snouts, enlarged brains, and eyes which have swiveled round from the primitive position on either side of the muzzle, so that they are directed more nearly forward.

Another step brings us to the monkey level, with much larger and more complicated brains, enhanced skill and complexity of manual movements, perfected stereoscopic vision, and many organic refinements. Here we find curiosity, imitativeness, increased emotional expression, and intense sociability, with dominance, subordination and mutual assistance in the individual members of the social group. Our evolving primates have now become very playful and significantly noisy and quarrelsome. This is the stage of the *Bandar-log*.

Twenty to twenty-five of our total span of sixty million years were required to reach the monkey level. In the same geological deposits occur the first remains of small anthropoid apes which stand upon the fourth of the six steps of primate development and are represented in a modified form by the gibbons of today. These animals have ceased to progress upon all fours in the trees. They move from bough to bough by arm swings. The body is now held upright and the viscera are hitched up by sheets of membrane so that they do not slump toward the bottom of the body cavities. The arms have become greatly elongated in response to their increased function; the shoulders broader, and the chest flatter; the snout has continued to recede but is no more reduced than in some groups of monkeys. The brain, however, has grown remarkably, and, in the pattern of the furrows and convolutions of its nervous covering, manifests a much higher stage of organization. In most anatomical details these small anthropoids are much closer to man than is any monkey. It seems probable also that these gibbons surpass monkeys in intelligence, although it has never been proven. We think that they ought to be more intelligent than monkeys, because they are more like ourselves.

It seems to have taken another fifteen or twenty millions of years to produce the giant primates—the large generalized anthropoid apes whose remains were found first in the Libyan desert, and later in the foothills of the Himalayas and in various deposits of the Miocene period in Europe. Some of these creatures were the size of a man, and some much larger. The skeletal parts recovered are mostly teeth and fragments of jaws. We have to reconstruct them by reference to the anatomy of their modern descendants, the gorilla, chimpanzee, and orang-utan. These giant fossil primates had become powerful, massive-boned creatures, with molar tooth patterns like those of man, with jaws markedly projecting, with brains huge in comparison with those of their predecessors, but still less than half as large as those of the lowest extant human types.

Our ancestors, progressive anthropoid apes, not only abandoned arboreal life and committed themselves to a more adventurous existence upon the ground, but gradually developed the habit of standing upon their hind legs and moving with a bipedal gait. There is no need of reiterating here the bodily changes which were involved in these shifts of habitat, posture, and method of locomotion. A prodigious expansion of the brain provided the protohuman being with so complex a nervous system and such a superabundance of nervous energy that he simply had to do something with it. He proceeded to initiate a material culture which he, alone of all animals, possesses; to develop a super-animal social organization, and to use the spare rooms of his capacious brain for the storing of complex impressions, associations, memories, and ideas which ultimately burst forth in vocal and articulate symbolizations. Linguistic communication had begun.

Fossil Man—Status and Fate

Our first absolute proof of the existence of man upon the earth occurs about at the completion of the fifty-nine millionth year of primate life, just before the onset of the great glacial period. Stone implements, very crudely chipped, but evidently fabricated by human hands, afford mute evidence that our ancestors were in existence, at work, and apparently making a rather poor job of it.

It is not until the first quarter or possibly the first half of the million year glacial period has elapsed that we actually find the bones of man. When we piece them together, we get individuals of various types, doubtless worthy persons, but certainly not prepossessing. There was *Pithecanthropus erectus* of Java, an ape-like creature who got himself involved in a volcanic eruption some half a million years ago, and left the top of his skull, three of his teeth, and a diseased thigh-bone strewn about in a deposit cut through by the river Solo. He was called *erectus* because his femur shows that he walked as we do, but he had only two-thirds of modern brain ballast, and at least that proportion of excess jaw projection. He fashioned and used some rough but effective stone tools, and was doubtless monarch of all he surveyed. At about this same time, in the neighborhood of Peiping, China, there existed a group of primitive human beings with big teeth and protruding jaws, beetling brow-ridges, almost no foreheads, and decidedly exiguous brains—little if any larger than those of Java ape man. However, their brains were much too large for any anthropoid ape and their teeth are of primitive human pattern. They also made crude stone tools, and doubtless their elders and matriarchs shook their heads over the younger generation and wondered what the world was coming to. Again at this period, the first half of the Pleistocene or glacial period, there resided on the banks of, or fell into the bed of, a German river, the creature called the Heidelberg man. Eighty feet of sands and gravels have accumulated over his massive jaw bone since he employed it to mouth his last utterances about Nordische Kultur and Rasseneinheit. He had perfectly human teeth of no excessive size, set in a chinless mandible of quite extraordinary strength and dimensions. Max Schmeling could probably have swung at that jaw until he pulped his knuckles, without landing a knock-out or even evoking the most perfunctory "Heil

Hitler!" The English contemporary of this ancient Heidelberger, called Eoanthropus, may have been a female with a brain as capacious as that of Lady Astor or of any other American female who has played a dominant part in the affairs of the British Empire. But while Dame Eoanthropus had a lofty brow and a modernesque brain, she seems to have had a face like a chimpanzee—no chin at all, and projecting tusk-like canine teeth. Hers was no countenance for which a king would renounce his throne.

I have no time for detailed descriptions of the many odds and ends of Pleistocene fossil men which have been turned up in the geological deposits of the Old World. The last group of these pioneers of human form and culture were the Neanderthaloids, who inhabited, or perhaps infested, the caves of western Europe and the Near East during the latter part of the glacial period. Short, stocky, barrel-chested, with protruding jaws, rudimentary chins, broad and blobby noses, low brows, and massive flattened braincases, with shuffling bent-kneed gait, the Neanderthalers were nevertheless upstanding men who made well-chipped and efficient flint implements, hunted successfully the huge and formidable fauna of the period, preserving intact the sanctity of their cave hearths against the depredations of the cave bear (*Ursus spelæus*), the saber-toothed tiger (*Machairodus latidens*), and other beasts whom palaeontologists have extinguished with polysyllabic names.

Rise of Homo sapiens

We do not recognize any of these simian-looking Pleistocene men as our direct ancestors, because their bodily specializations seem to have carried them along evolutionary paths divergent from those which have led on to modern races, with the possible exception of the native Australians. It seems quite probable that an anatomically modern type of man had already evolved outside of Europe before the last brutal Neanderthaloids relinquished their leases of the European caves—perhaps forty thousands of years ago. For they seem abruptly to have been ejected from those damp and drafty abodes before the end of the last great advance of the ice sheet. There is no doubt whatsoever of our direct relationship to the succeeding tenants, since these were men with straight faces, jutting chins, noble brows, and the entire array of modern anatomical features which we esteem as beautiful and symmetrical, but which would impress any nonhuman mammal as an unnatural combination of pathological overgrowth with degenerative dwarfing.

These new men built their hearths in the upper strata of the caves, directly above the vestiges of Neanderthal meals, of Neanderthal men themselves, and the debris of their stone industry. The immigrant intruders seem to have brought with them new and improved techniques of stone and bone working, and an itch for artistic expression which made them scratch drawings of animals and plants on ubiquitous soup bones and rocks, daub paintings on the walls and roofs of caverns, and even model bas-reliefs in clay, and sculpture figurines of bone and stone. Some of this cave art is really very good. Graphic, plastic and mimetic arts find their most enthusiastic cultivators and perhaps their most appreciative connoisseurs among unwashed savages.

Probably the makers of the cave murals do not represent the first incursion of modern types of man into glacial Europe, but they do mark a permanent settlement which has endured. There is reason for thinking that several of the types of flint implements found by thousands in the gravel deposits laid down by European rivers, in the three long interglacial periods of genial climate, are the work of Neanthropic or new style man. If so, he managed to keep his bones out of the water, unless they have been ground to bits. It seems likely that the modern type of man went south for the winter at the onset of each succeeding glacial period. As a matter of fact, cave occupation by human tenants is only demonstrable for the fourth or last glaciation. Neanderthal man seems to have hung on through most of the winter, but yielded to our ancestors before the ice went out in the spring. The new men almost certainly came into Europe from North Africa, although their original home was probably somewhere in the western Asiatic plateau region. Why was Neanderthal man thus supplanted and what became of him?

The simplest solution of the problem would be to derive the modern type—*Homo sapiens*—directly from the archaic Neanderthaloids or other ape-like men known to have existed in the early Pleistocene. But Neanderthal man had certain specialized anatomical features, such as enlarged pulp cavities of the molar teeth, a

flattened brain-case, and huge brow-ridges, which represent variations divergent from those characteristic of the modern type. Also
in Western Europe modern man follows Neanderthal man
abruptly and without any anatomically transitional forms. These
difficulties may be resolved in part by recent finds in several regions
of the Old World which seem to indicate that the Western European Neanderthaloids were a specialized and conservative variety,
as contrasted with other representatives of the same or of kindred
species in Palestine, in Java and elsewhere, some of whom combine
large brow-ridges and other Neanderthaloid features with anatomical characters approximating those of *Homo sapiens*. It is
therefore possible that the new type of man, originally developed
from some progressive Neanderthal-like stock in Asia, advanced to
a modern anatomical status and displaced in Europe an obsolete and
conservative Neanderthal survivor who stood in a sort of avuncular
relationship to him—or, perhaps, more like that of a spinster
grand aunt, doggedly outliving her evolutionary generation and
flaunting her anachronistic features until she drove the exasperated
moderns to senicide. It is not entirely clear that the modern type
of man possessed any particular anatomical advantage over Neanderthal man whereby he was enabled to survive at the expense of
the latter. Neanderthal man had quite as large a brain as is found
in most races of *Homo sapiens*; he had bigger and better teeth than
any; the weapons and tools he used may have been somewhat inferior to those of his successors, but there could have been no such
disparity of armaments as enables a Fascist to subdue an Ethiopian.
The count of skeletons in the European caves does not suggest that
the modern type of man conquered the Neanderthaloid by sheer
force of numbers; the newcomers were at first very few. As a matter of fact, I am not acquainted with any conclusive evidence that
modern man really came into contact with the Neanderthaloids.
He may simply have moved into their abandoned homes after a
few thousands of years.

Neanderthal man may have succumbed to epidemics or diseases
conveyed to him by *Homo sapiens;* he may have committed race
suicide, or with protean facility he may have transformed himself
into modern man in one evolutionary quick change. However, on
the whole, it seems most probable that *Homo sapiens* practiced

upon him the same sort of virtuous extermination which we have so frequently employed in ridding ourselves of contemporary primitives—professedly for the advancement of civilization. It is very easy to convince ourselves that this replacement of Neanderthaloids by modern man was a triumph of superior intelligence. Inasmuch as our species was victorious, the better man won. It was our ancestors who carried the torch of civilization, and if the Neanderthalers got burned up through our handling of this precious legacy, it was just too bad. "I weep for you," the Walrus said, "I deeply sympathize."

Diversification and Spread of Homo sapiens

The diversification of *Homo sapiens* into modern races and their diffusion over the world had begun before the end of the glacial period. We must suppose that the process of racial differentiation came about principally through variation and selection. New characters or modifications of old features are forever arising in organisms and some of these are heritable. When a group of animals becomes isolated within its geographical habitat and inbreeds intensively, the small variations and larger mutations which arise from time to time within it are subjected to a process of germinal selection. Local peculiarities of bodily form are diffused through the inbreeding populations, with combinations of hereditarily dominant characters surviving. These again are sifted by natural selection so that, on the whole, only those animals survive which carry the hereditary peculiarities least disadvantageous in the struggle for existence. But the modifications which adapt the animal's organism successfully to its environment vary according to the nature of the physical and geographical environment itself. Consequently if virtually identical groups of fauna are isolated in radically different environments, in the course of time they will diverge widely from one another in their bodily form, partly because of the idiosyncrasies of hereditary variations within the confines of the isolated groups, and partly because of divergent environmental selective forces which operate upon them. All of this sounds very complicated. However, some of the complexity of this explanation, like almost any other, lies in the fact that we do not understand the phenomena which we are trying to explain.

The most archaic, physically, of the existing races of *Homo sapiens* is certainly the aboriginal Australian. The ancestors of this stock wandered from the Asiatic mainland as far as the island continent of Australia, where their descendants remained for a long time in isolation. The primitive skeletal features which the Australians have retained include: very large ridges of bone above the eye-sockets associated with extremely low and receding foreheads and small brain-cases, protrusive jaws, poorly developed chins, large teeth, and broad nasal apertures. Archaic features of the soft parts comprise many muscular variations, an unspecialized wavy form of the head hair, and a more abundant growth of body hair than is found in most other stocks of recent man. One can only suppose that the Australians represent an evolutionary group conservative in the production of new bodily variations, and that, as a result of isolation and freedom from intermixture with other more variable and progressive stocks, they have become stagnant. It is probably more than a coincidence that the infra-human fauna of Australia is also out of date and non-progressive. The mammals belong to an antiquated pouched or marsupial type, except the dingo dog, which trailed over with man, a few rodents, and those two living fossils, the egg-laying duckbill and the spiny anteater, which are still standing with reluctant feet where the reptiles and mammals meet. It is significant also that the material culture of the aboriginal Australian is well nigh as obsolete as his physical type.

Our own great physical group of mankind, called Whites for want of a better term, was, seemingly, one of the earliest divisions of *Homo sapiens* to differentiate and has in some respects proceeded farthest in diversification. Most of the so-called Whites are not really white in skin color, but of shades varying from olive to light brown. It is probable that they have retained about the amount of skin pigment possessed by the generalized ancestral human stock. In one or two races of the group a marked reduction of the pigment in skin, hair, and eyes has taken place, presumably as a result of mutations (abrupt hereditary changes), followed by inbreeding and selection. In this group, as a whole, the principal tendencies toward skeletal modification lie in excessive retraction and shrinkage of the face and of the teeth, with a narrowing of the nasal aperture and a bizarre pinching up and hooking of the nasal roof; a diminution in size of brow-ridges and in slope of forehead. Enlargement and extreme specialization for support of the foot bones, widening and massiveness of the pelvis, and increased size of the bones of the hand are also notable. This White group shows a stronger inclination to vary in head form, face form, and bodily build than is probably manifested by Mongoloids or Negroids. Heads of medium breadth in relation to their length are exceedingly numerous, together with the extreme variants of long, narrow and short, broad brain-cases. Similarly, squat, broad faces and long, narrow faces have developed, and are likely to be found in combination with every form of the cranial vault. Stature, trunk, and limb proportions are also exceedingly diversified. In the soft parts, extreme progressive differentiation is noticeable, with the retention of some primitive ancestral features such as wavy hair, profuse body hair, and less degenerate and reduced external ears than are found, for example, in Negroids. This wide variability of the White group is doubtless due in part to the extreme diversity of its physical environments, together with the development of means of transportation which have facilitated interbreeding over wide areas and among large populations. In part the multiplicity of White physical types may be caused by greater tendencies in this stock to produce organic variations. Lastly, the antiquity, richness and diversity of its cultures are an indirect evidence of organic versatility, adaptiveness, and initiative. It is this division of mankind which, pre-eminently, has acquired the habit of "monkeying" with its own bodily processes of evolution.

There are indications of two distinct evolutionary experiments in the production of the Negroid division of modern man. Negroid types were evolved as specializations for tropical existence, notably in respect of a profuse pigmentation of skin, hair, and eyes, which tends to cut off certain destructive rays of the vertical sun and thus to protect the underlying tissues from overheating and scorching. Other evidence of specialization is found in the multiplication of skin pores and sweat glands, the sparsity of body hair, greatly flattened and tightly curled head hair, the extreme breadth of the nose and wide open nostrils, and the puffy and everted lips. Primitive features retained include: a considerable protrusion of the jaws (prognathism), narrow pelvis, elongation of the forearm, and a somewhat generalized foot structure with certain ape-like characters.

All races of *Homo sapiens,* with the possible exception of the
Australians, represent, in some degree, what is called the fœtaliza-
tion of the human stock. This term implies that the adults retain
certain bodily features which normally occur in various stages of
prenatal development, both in human infants and in those of apes
and monkeys. Such fœtal characters include: large size of the head
as compared with the trunk and limbs, short and underdeveloped
limbs with arms long relative to legs; a disproportionately large
and swollen brain-case with a bulbous forehead, a small, short face,
and a flat nose. Many of these fœtal characters attain their highest
development in the Negroid group, and especially in the pygmy
or Negrito division of that group. These Negritos were almost
certainly evolved before the full-sized Negroes. They are found
today only in remote parts of the African equatorial forest, in the
jungles of the Malay peninsula, in the Andaman Islands, in certain
parts of the Philippines, and in the interior of the great island of
New Guinea. Everywhere they stand at a very low level of culture.
They are food collectors and hunters, usually with no knowledge
of agriculture. The African pygmies are not known even to possess
a language of their own. They speak the tongues of neighboring,
full-sized Negro tribes. The physical features of the pygmy
Negritos which distinguish them from the larger Negroes are:
extremely short stature (averaging less than four feet, nine inches
in males), lack of differentiation in head form (both long and
round heads occur, with intermediate types perhaps predominating), absurdly infantile and bulbous foreheads without brow-
ridges; exaggeratedly broad and swollen noses, thin chimpanzee-
like lips, very wide mouths, feeble chins, long arms and bodies but
very short legs, frequent fuzzy or downy hair on many parts of
the body, pot bellies, lightish skin color, heavier beards, and hair
more tightly curled and in tinier spirals than that of the Negro.
Not all of these features are primitive; some are specialized. In contrast the more highly evolved Negro varies from short to gigantic
stature, with tallness predominating. The legs are lengthy, with
especial elongation and attenuation of the shin segment; skin color
is darker and body hair much more scant than in the pygmies;
heads are usually very narrow and long, foreheads more sloping
with a central eminence and larger brow-ridges, faces relatively
shorter and broader and more protrusive, noses finer, lips thicker,

and chins better developed, feet and hands longer, narrower, relatively smaller but more highly specialized. The full-sized Negro stocks have apparently developed from the pygmy Negritos on the periphery of the densely forested Negrito habitat. This process of evolution has been influenced and accelerated by admixture with non-Negro stocks—in Africa with a brunet White stock, and in New Guinea with an Australoid stock. Everywhere the large Negro shows an ability to develop civilization which far surpasses that of his primitive pygmy relative.

In central or northeastern Asia there has evolved the great Mongoloid division of mankind, probably the most recent and in some features the most specialized of human physical groups. This stock overlies more ancient Australoid, Negroid, and White elements in Asia, in America, and in eastern Europe, and has scarcely penetrated Africa and southern Oceania. In stature and bodily proportions the Mongoloid types tend to adhere rather closely to average, with a preference for the squatter and broader builds. Characteristic features are: a very broad and exceedingly capacious brain-case, somewhat flattened vertically, with a steep or slightly sloping forehead, almost completely undeveloped brow-ridges, cheek bones flaring laterally and jutting forward, a very low-bridged and infantile nose of moderate breadth, medium lips and pointed chins, very square jaws—the whole constituting an extremely large, flat face, which lacks any great forward protrusion of the jaws. In the soft parts a yellowish or yellow-brown skin color is associated with blue-black hair and dark eyes. The head hair is highly specialized in its straightness and coarseness, while the body hair is even more sparse than in Negroids. A very notable feature of the Mongoloid group is the accumulation of fat in the eyelids and over the cheek bones. The upper eyelid characteristically has a loose fold of skin hanging over its free edge, which cuts across and conceals the inner corner of the eye opening. This flap of skin is commonly called the Mongoloid fold. It is possible that both the fatty covering of the eyelid and the extra fold of skin serve to some extent to protect the eye against the light, since the eyeball is protruded and comparatively exposed, as contrasted with its recessed position in races with deeper eye-sockets and overhanging bony brow-ridges. The forward jut of the cheek bones may also offer some advantage of position to the masticatory muscles in working the broad and powerful jaws of this blunt-faced type.

In addition to the Australoid, Negroid, White and Mongoloid divisions of mankind, many composite breeds have arisen from the intermixture of these main physical varieties. Notable among these are the Polynesians, a smooth blend of Negroid, Mongoloid, and White; the American Indian, probably derived from minor elements of archaic White and other strains heavily overlaid with dominant Mongoloid features; and such mixtures of White with various Negroid stocks as are to be found in many parts of Africa and in the Indian peninsula. Moreover, there also exist in various out-of-the-way parts of the world a few enigmatic odds and ends of types left over from Nature's early and unsuccessful experiments in *Homo sapiens*—such as the Bushmen-Hottentots of South Africa, the Veddas of Ceylon, and the now extinct Tasmanians.

New races are built up by cumulative transmission of the bodily peculiarities which arise from time to time in an inbreeding stock. Most of these anatomical variations which combine to form racial types are wholly unimportant from the standpoint of function and neither contribute to the chances of survival of their possessors, nor detract from them. So far as we know, there is no biological advantage in having a long, narrow head, as contrasted with a short, broad head, or in having curly hair instead of straight hair, except that the former requires no permanent waves. A jutting nasal promontory subserves the olfactory and respiratory function no better and probably no worse than a retroussé and insignificant blob of a nose, although the beaky type is more liable to frost bite, fracture, skewing, and adenoidal obstruction.

There is, however, among students of man, a suspicion amounting to virtual certainty that the numerous anatomical variants are sorted into racial physical combinations through the activities of certain glands in the body—the pituitary, thyroid, parathyroids, thymus, adrenals, and gonads. The secretions of these glands are the regulators of growth and sex differentiation and perhaps of metabolic and other vital processes. These are their real jobs, but they amuse themselves in their spare time by shaping variously the nose and the head, fooling about with the form of the hair, making blonds or brunets, and otherwise disporting themselves in the fabrication of meaningless anatomical variations.

Equipment for Biological Survival and Obstacles Thereunto

Now that we have concluded our little sixty million year saunter, in which we started out with a tree shrew and ended up with Mrs. Simpson or what have you, we are confronted with the more important task of inquiring how we have managed to get so far and where we go from here.

The sequence of animal remains yielded by the fossil-bearing beds of successive periods of the earth's history, clearly reveals that the majority of animal forms die out and the survivors achieve their continuance only by acquiring variations and adaptations which give them some sort of biological advantage. The fate which overtook the dinosaurs hangs over every living species. Before we ask ourselves what we must do to be saved, we may profitably inquire what our ancestors, animal and human, have done to perpetuate their germ plasm up to the present. Obviously our temporary survival has been attained by hereditary gifts of physical and mental equipment which have worked out some sort of *modus vivendi* with the physical environment in which we have developed. We have to consider the relative importance of physical and mental equipment in this struggle and of the utilization and choice of an environment which the organism makes. We need not retraverse the entire course of primate evolution, but can begin where a generalized anthropoid primate took to the ground. The physical requisites for survival of a terrestrial mammal vary somewhat with body size. The very small animal has to keep out of the way of larger predatory beasts by use of its olfactory sense, or by development of some sort of organic accessories which will enable it to burrow in the ground, for example the ever-growing incisor teeth of rodents or the shovel-like feet of the mole. Or it may develop an undigestible protective covering, such as the spines of the hedgehog or the carapace of the armadillo. A somewhat larger mammal has to depend upon speed and cunning (which latter, on the physical side, implies a highly organized brain and nervous system). But a really big animal must ordinarily rely upon defensive and offensive strength such as is possessed by the gorilla, the tiger, and the elephant, or upon the rapid locomotion for which many of the hoofed, herbivorous animals have become narrowly specialized. Now, man's ancestors, when they took to the ground, were certainly no larger than we are today, and they may have been much smaller. It is improbable that they were as powerful as the modern chimpanzee, which, of a bulk and weight similar to that of man, is certainly two to three times as strong. Yet the chimpanzee unquestionably owes its evolutionary success to its agility in the trees. It is not terrestrial. Man is a comparatively weak animal and could never have survived on the ground by strength of arms, hands, or teeth. Again, the adaptation of man's body to the erect posture and biped method of progression, however advantageous in other respects, is pitifully inadequate for the development of speed. Almost any kind of animal of moderate size or of large size can easily outrun a man. Jesse Owens, the fastest modern human, a few weeks ago managed to outrun a race horse for one hundred yards, with the aid of a thirty-yard handicap. But Nature does not hand out yardage handicaps in the race for survival by speed.

Man has had to survive by cunning rather than by strength or speed. His big brain has allowed him to utilize his free prehensile forelimbs to develop weapons and mechanical devices which augment enormously his natural quota of organic strength. He had to skulk only as long as he relied upon bare fists and cudgels and unworked stones. However, he very soon developed edged stone axes and projectile weapons, whereby he was able to conquer the largest beasts of prey—facts amply attested by the bones of these great brutes which form the mass of kitchen débris in human habitations of the glacial period.

Man's perspicacity in selecting his habitat and his organic adaptability were even more potent factors in his survival than his manual achievements in the way of weapons, tools, and beast-proof shelters. Perhaps the most important human characteristic is dietetic versatility. Man, even in the prehuman stage, avoided the fatal error of becoming specialized for an exclusive class of food, vegetable, or animal. He retained the primitive omnivorous habits of the lower primates. Thus, when our ancestors took to the ground, they were not enslaved to the vegetarian habits of the gorilla which require him to hang about the tropical forests, consuming vast quantities of relatively unnutritious fodder such as leaves, shoots, berries, and nuts. Man ate all of these foods, but he also thrived upon flesh, without having to develop or retain long tusk-like canines and sharp claws wherewith to kill his prey, or great speed whereby to catch it. The animal which has become dependent upon one class of food is inevitably tethered to the environment which produces that kind of nutriment. If the climate changes and the food gives out, there remains for the luckless brute a long quest on an empty stomach with starvation at the end. Again, man's very early discovery of the use of fire in the preparation of food has been one of the most important means of enlarging his dietary, particularly in relieving his jaws and teeth of a vast amount of laborious work and in taking the strain from a long-suffering digestive system.

The obstacles to biological survival are either animate or inanimate. The latter class includes climatic, meteoric, and geophysical conditions and phenomena. The ability to wrest from the habitat every possible aid to the maintenance of human existence is a great deal more useful than mere organic plasticity. The secret of man's diffusion into every conceivably habitable zone of the world lies in this very fact that man does not have to adapt his organism, because he adapts his environment. The successes of the Eskimo in the frigid Arctic zone, and of the Bushman in the arid wastes of the Kalahari desert, are supreme biological achievements. Here it may be noted that the White man prides himself upon his superior intelligence in occupying what he considers the most livable and desirable region of the earth—the temperate zone. However, a modern follower of Hippocrates, Dr. William F. Petersen, has accumulated a mass of evidence which indicates that an abode in the cyclonic storm tracks of the northern hemisphere actually places more strain upon the organism and precipitates more pathology than does the frigid zone or the enervating tropics. Perhaps we are not so clever when we select a region of violent and sudden changes of temperature and barometric pressure; when we build our habitations in the flood plains of great rivers (even Noah knew enough to build an ark); when we undertake to live by dry farming in places where the odds are about seven to one against the production of a crop.

Although there is a frightful wastage in human life in the struggle against physical environment, there is no real doubt of the issue. The cataclysmic phenomena, such as floods, hurricanes, earthquakes, and volcanic eruptions, are too occasional and too limited in their spheres of influence to be any serious menace to the survival of the far-flung human species.

The animate competition which man has to meet may be classified as non-human and human. Non-human rivalry involves, on the one hand, the large-sized vertebrate fauna and the insects; on the other, the micro-organisms. Man has completely mastered his large animal competitors in every area except a few remote spots inhabited by feeble, backward human groups. Elsewhere the more formidable animals have been exterminated or continue to exist only upon human sufferance. Insects are pests, more dangerous as carriers of disease than as actual competitors. A limited control of this class of invertebrate fauna has been achieved, with great difficulty, by civilized man only in very recent years and within certain areas. In the tropics human multiplication and dominance is, to some extent, restricted by insect life. However, there is little real danger of human extinction through insect competition.

Man has had to fight his battle against the micro-organisms—plant and animal—without any aid except the resistance of his own body cells and their products, up to the late dawn of bacteriological and immunological science. In spite of the remarkable progress made against these previously invisible enemies, they constitute, seemingly, the greatest menace to the survival of our species. The more we know about the pathogenic bacteria, spirochetes, fungi, filterable viruses, and protozoa, the more we marvel at the success of man in combating these rapidly evolving, highly adaptive, and predatory organisms by his own internal resources. The unspectacular headway against these insidious enemies made by medical science constitutes probably the greatest human achievement.

Except microbes, man's worst enemy is himself. Extermination of the later fossil species of man by the aggression of early types of *Homo sapiens* is indicated. Within the recent period there is no doubt of the sequence of events. The more highly evolved and predatory human stocks have deliberately destroyed their poor relations whose weakness is manifested in simpler cultures. The retention of primitive physical characteristics is commonly associated with cultural inferiority. Together they make a combination which spells extinction for their possessors. The Tasmanians have vanished; the Bushmen and Hottentots are virtually gone; another generation will probably witness the end of the Australians; the pygmy Negritos will disappear as soon as more advanced human types choose to move into their forest refuge areas. Several of the more highly evolved and cultured physical races can read their own obituaries with the disagreeable assurance that these will presently be inserted in the historical record. The comely and pleasant Polynesians have almost completed their earthly course; the accomplished, courageous, and philosophical American Indian race is destined to survive only in hybridized stocks with borrowed or composite cultures. One fears that the same fate must be predicted for the more highly specialized Negro type, which, however, is endowed with far more biological resistance and tenacity, and is consequently more capable of surviving that process of sapping and attrition which we pharisaically call acculturation.

It is scarcely necessary to discant upon the methods whereby one type of mankind perpetuates itself at the expense of another. The most straightforward of these is warfare, whether waged under some hypocritical pretext of Christianization and taking up "the White man's burden," or with brutal frankness as to its acquisitive motive. Contrasted with the sanctimonious smugness of the Anglo-Saxon in his wars of aggression against primitive peoples, the unconcealed avarice and ruthlessness of the Italians and the Japanese have at least the merit of sincerity.

Far more potent and less obtrusive factors than warfare in the suppression of one physical and cultural group by another are germinal selection, disease infection, and social subordination. The White races have interbred amongst themselves so extensively that they present combinations of hereditarily potent and dominant physical and mental characters, which have survived by natural and social selection. When these genetically tough Whites interbreed with other racial stocks which have been more isolated, more protected, and less exposed to germinal competition, the hybrid offspring are likely to show a majority of physical features leaning toward the type of the dominant race. Thus, in the course of time, many of the physical characteristics of the suppressed group are covered over, or have become "recessive." They appear to have been bred out.

Even more important is the introduction of so-called civilized diseases among the more primitive groups. The aggressor has achieved a certain measure of constitutional resistance to, or relative immunity from, diseases to which his stock has been exposed for many generations. These diseases introduced among primitive peoples decimate or totally destroy them. Of course, the primitives have their own immunities from diseases endemic in their own habitats, and these often take a heavy toll of the invaders. In fact, racial contacts sometimes reduce themselves to a question of which group carries the meaner microbes and the stronger antibodies.

The most important and insidious destroyer of a race which possesses its own culture is the civilization of the conqueror. Man has become such a highly artificial animal that he cannot live by bread alone. His whole existence is bound up in his language, his social institutions, his religious beliefs, his habits of life, and his material paraphernalia. Take these away from him and he loses his desire for life; the instinct for perpetuation of the species dies. Bibles have killed more Indians than have bullets; and the Great White Father at Washington has been more deadly to our aborigines than has the Great White Plague.

Now, in spite of all of these dismal considerations, it seems very improbable that *Homo sapiens* is going to die out in the near evolutionary future. Whether the dominating and surviving group is to be White with minor ingredients of other stocks, or Mongoloid with lesser strains, seems problematical and, for my purposes, unimportant. An appraisal of the present biological status of the particular great physical division to which we belong is my immediate concern.

Appraisal of Man's Present Biological Status

Homo sapiens has been a continual resident of Europe for at least 25,000 years. A comparison of the physical characteristics of the cave-dwellers who ousted the ape-like Neanderthal men with those of Europeans of today shows very little anatomical change. I suppose that if you were to look for evolutionary improvement over this short stretch of time, you would first of all examine the skull to ascertain whether the brain has increased in size, whether the teeth and jaws have improved their functional ability, and whether the nose has bettered its status as an olfactory and respiratory organ. You would then look at the spine to see whether it manifests any progressive change in its curves and anatomical minutiæ; you would inspect the pelvis to find out whether it has become a more efficient weight-transmitting and visceral-supporting limb girdle. You would inspect the bones of the legs to see whether they have become larger and stronger, and you would carefully review the foot to find out whether it has increased its structural and functional efficiency.

Now I may say at once that such an examination would not show a single improvement in man's anatomical status during the last 25,000 years, as revealed by the skeleton. The brain has not increased its size (if anything, it has become smaller); the spine has not improved its curves; the pelvis, with its weak sacro-iliac joint and its wide-open aperture, is still the same unsatisfactory mechanical compromise. The bones of the lower extremity in civilized city-dwellers have indeed become somewhat more massive and better adapted for supporting the body weight in standing and walking over level surfaces, and the feet are perhaps a little larger and stronger, but oftener broken down and misshapen.

On the other hand, our reviewer of skeletal evolution would find certain clear evidence of anatomical degeneration. The jaws have gone on shrinking until often they are too small to accommodate the permanent teeth. The latter erupt hither and yon, so that they jostle each other out of position, and the upper and lower arches meet in relations which prevent proper mastication. Frequently the lower jaw has failed to develop forward, so that the upper teeth protrude in a forlorn and rabbity fashion, while the chin retreats feebly into the neck. Sometimes the upper dental arch has shrunk so that the lower jaw is protrusive and undershot. The third molars, or wisdom teeth, last to erupt, now frequently remain imbedded in their bony crypts, where they grow perversely, crowding and killing their normally placed neighbors. A horrible process of decay has infected the teeth, beginning even in infancy. The gums recede from the dental crowns and pus pockets immerse the roots in a vicious bath teeming with micro-organisms, which infect the throat, the ears, and sometimes break loose and run riot through the entire body.

The nasal skeleton has continued to contract laterally and to arch degeneratively upward, so that the septum becomes skewed to one side, the internal nasal structures are pathologically enlarged, and the respiratory passages are cramped and obstructed with adenoidal tissue. Air must be taken through the slack jaws and open mouth, unfiltered, full of dust and noxious bacteria. The times may not be out of joint, but the nose and jaws of modern man indubitably are.

However, I would not depress you unduly by a dismal account of conditions which are not necessarily irremediable. Man will continue to win through, or at least to sneak by, however crippled by regressive changes, if only he continues to bolster his faltering organism by the activity of his cunning brain.

Relation of Cultural Status to Biological Status

A few words may be devoted here to the relation of modern man's material culture to his biological status. Peoples who live by collecting natural food products and by fishing and hunting are generally considered to exist upon the lowest cultural level. Such peoples tend to exhibit the largest number of primitive physical characters and at the same time to show fewest evidences of disease and degenerative evolutionary features, except when they have come in contact with civilization. Jaws and teeth are almost invariably well developed and free from disease. Manifestations of deficiency diseases due to inadequate nutrition are usually absent. Life is hazardous and short, but comparatively healthy.

Pastoral peoples, who live upon domesticated animals and their products, and who tend to be mainly carnivorous, usually exhibit also a stability of skeletal structure and a relative immunity from pathological conditions of the jaws, teeth, and bones. Malformations are rare. Degenerative diseases are ordinarily conspicuous by their absence. At such levels of culture, medical science is either undeveloped or probably completely ineffective.

When man shifts to an artificial, agricultural basis of subsistence, and presumably gains a more ample food supply, physical deterioration seems to set in. Its beginning is noted in the onset of dental caries, periodontal disease, malocclusions of the teeth, arthritis, increased fragility of skeletal structure, and occasional manifestation of rickets and other diseases referable to malnutrition. Physical abnormalities become more common; there are sporadic indications of chronic constitutional ailments, of acute infections, and even hints of malignant growths. As long as man has to eat everything which he can find and masticate, he seems to maintain his organic equilibrium. As soon as he begins to command enough food to be able to pick and choose, he eats too much of the same foods and suffers from malnutrition. It is to be doubted that the span of life of primitive farmers is longer than that of hunters and nomads, although the hazards of existence are less. What they have gained in security and abundance of food, they are likely to lose through unsanitary conditions in their settled abodes, communicable diseases, and unbalanced diets.

With the development of urban civilization and industry, physical deterioration becomes appallingly common. All sorts of pathologies multiply; enlarged communications bring new and virulent infections; every sort of physical abnormality is increasingly prevalent. The biological status of man seems to decline as his culture accelerates. Medical science intervenes and becomes efficacious in the reduction of suffering and the prolongation of life, but, unfortunately, also in the preservation of the malformed, the chronically diseased, and the biologically inferior. Under the hard conditions of primitive life, a ruthless natural selection eliminates the weak and the unfit. Only the strong survive to propagate their kind.

The Changing Psychological Status of Man

The survival of the organically unsound and the perpetuation of their constitutional ailments are tolerable only if the lowering of physique is unaccompanied by mental deterioration. Civilized man endeavors to persuade himself that his intelligence improves and his mental health remains unimpaired no matter how enfeebled his body has become. He has tried to believe that mental vigor and high ideals of conduct flourish in an organic environment of pathology and degeneration.

The cumulative tradition of civilization has handed down innumerable inventions and devices for facilitating existence. The individual can maintain life and perpetuate his kind with a minimum of physical effort and with little or no exercise of intelligence. We have become parasites upon the cultural achievements of the past and upon the inventive benefactions of a few creative contemporaries. The stimuli for a full utilization of the hereditary endowment of mental equipment have diminished, since the latter is no longer essential for survival. Loss of function atrophies the intelligence as surely as disuse withers muscles and shrinks bones.

The last century has witnessed in certain advanced nations the application of a system of ethics and a practice of sociology which, on the behavioristic side, may be called humanitarianism and which, in its institutional aspect, is termed democracy. Both theory and practice are the outgrowths of the highest ideals of human conduct. There is little doubt that the optimum human society is realized under this régime, provided that its members are possessed individually of high intelligence and are habituated to a reciprocity of altruistic conduct. However, excessive altruism and indiscriminate humanitarianism are impracticable because they reduce the intelligence of the population. The noblest manifestation of human science is the extension of medical care to all classes of the population. The finest exemplifications of man's unselfishness are charity toward the weak and the helpless and forbearance for the wrong-doer. Now it is impossible to disregard the fact that the preservation of the biologically unfit lowers the physical level of the population. It is not commonly known, however, that intelligence declines with organic deterioration, and it is convenient to deny this psycho-physical parallelism, since its implications are exceedingly unpleasant. I have spent ten cheerless years in studying the relation of physique to intelligence and to economic and educational status, in the inmates of American penitentiaries, jails, and insane asylums. Every jot and tittle of the vast mass of evidence which I have analyzed indicates that inferior biological status is inextricably associated with diminished intelligence, and that the combination of the two is mainly responsible for economic inadequacy and antisocial conduct. Dismiss crime, if you like, as a pathological by-product of society. Disregard the findings I have stated without submitting my proof. Deny the logic of the contention that weak minds are found in weak bodies. Nevertheless, if you will but pause to survey the state of our society, you must join in my cry, "What must we do to be saved?"

The howl of the Roman mob, "*Panem et circenses!*" (bread and the circus) is re-echoing ominously through this nation. However, neither emotion nor rhetoric will alleviate the situation, and let him who will put his trust in such sops to Cerberus as bonuses, old age pensions, and legislation for social security. We must either do some biological house-cleaning or delude ourselves with the futile hope that a government of the unfit, for the unfit, and by the unfit will not perish from the earth.

Remedies

Now it seems to me perfectly clear that what we must do, in some way or other, is to encourage a sit-down reproductive strike of the busy breeders among the morons, criminals, and social ineffectuals of our population. Probably compulsory sterilization alone would serve in the case of the insane and the mentally deficient, but it is very difficult to enforce such a measure in a democracy, unless it has been preceded by an educational campaign which has reached all of the teachable and socially-minded individuals of the electorate. Probably the only effective method of obtaining the desired result would be to establish in our secondary schools and colleges courses of applied human biology which would disseminate knowledge of the facts of heredity and of the relation of man's organism to his behavior. Of course science really knows as yet comparatively little about human genetics, and is quite incapable of enunciating directions for breeding geniuses. But it is wholly competent to suggest measures which would prevent the birth of the majority of our imbeciles and morons. The young ought to be brought to an early realization that their success in life and their value to society depend not only upon occupational skill and character, but also upon an understanding that their reproductive function must be exercised in accordance with their individual capacities and limitations. We must inculcate into the rising generation a code of biological ethics.

The only valid reason for trying to improve the biological status of man is that he be made a better animal—more honest, more unselfish, more decent and considerate in his human relations. I think that a biological purge is the essential prerequisite for a social and a spiritual salvation. Let us temper mercy with justice and dispense charity with intelligence. We must stop trying to cure malignant biological growths with patent sociological nostrums. The emergency demands a surgical operation.

GLOSSARY

ACROCEPHALIC. High-headed. In craniology a skull in which the height is 98 per cent of the breadth or more. In anthropometry a head in which the height from the ear-hole attains or exceeds 85 per cent of the maximum head breadth.

AGGLUTINOGEN. A substance in the blood cells of any blood group which causes clumping or agglutination of the cells when blood of another group is mixed with it. The two principal agglutinogens known in human and ape blood are called A and B.

ALAE, adj. ALAR. The lateral walls of the nostrils, the "wings" of the nose.

ALVEOLAR. Pertaining to the sockets of the teeth or to the tooth-bearing portions of the upper and lower jaws.

AMPHIBIANS. A class of cold-blooded vertebrate animals intermediate between reptiles and fishes. The young usually have gills and the adults breathe through lungs. The amphibians include frogs, toads, newts, and salamanders.

ARTERIO-SCLEROSIS. Hardening of the arteries, a circulatory disease of old age.

AUTOSOME, adj. AUTOSOMAL. A chromosome other than the sex chromosome.

AUTOSYNTHESIS. The formation of a combination of elements or a chemical compound by the organism itself.

BICUSPID. A tooth provided with two cusps or conical eminences on the crown. The zoological term is premolar. Man and the apes have two each side in both upper and lower jaws.

BRACHIATION. Swinging from bough to bough in the trees by the use of the arms. A method of locomotion employed by the anthropoid apes and by the spider monkey.

BRAIN-CAST. A cast of the interior of a skull which gives a rough impression of the form and size of the brain. Plaster brain-casts are made by anatomists from the skulls of fossil man. Natural brain-casts formed by the induration of material filling the skull cavity are sometimes found in fossils.

BRACHYCEPHALY, adj. BRACHYCEPHALIC. Round-headed, or more properly short-headed. In craniology a skull of which the maximum breadth is 80 per cent or more of the maximum length. In the anthropometry of the living a head which is short relative to its breadth.

BRACHYURANIC. A skull in which the external breadth of the alveolar or tooth-bearing arch is 115 per cent or more of the length of the arch.

CARIES. Decay of the teeth.

CEPHALIC. Pertaining to the head.

CEPHALIC INDEX. The maximum breadth of the head expressed as a percentage of its maximum antero-posterior length. In the case of skulls this length-breadth index is called the cranial index.

CHAMAEPROSOPIC. Low-faced. A category of the total facial index in which the height of the face from the root of the nose to the base of the chin is small when expressed as a percentage of the maximum breadth of the face across the zygomatic arches. A total facial index less than 90 in the skull and less than 88 in the living subject. In general, a short, broad face.

CHAMAERRHINE. Low-nosed. In the skull, a category of the nasal index in which the maximum breadth of the nasal aperture is 51 per cent of the height of the nasal skeleton or more. On the living subject, a category of the nasal index in which the breadth of the nose across the alae is 85 per cent or more of the height of the nose from the root to the juncture of the septum with the upper lip.

CHROMOSOME. A rod-like body in the nucleus of the cell previous to cell division. The chromosomes are the basis of segregation and other phenomena of heredity. Chromosomes occur in pairs. Each cell of a human being contains 24 pairs of chromosomes.

CORTEX, adj. CORTICAL. Literally "bark." In anatomy the outer gray covering of the brain.

DEHISCENCE. A gaping. In craniology, gaps in tympanic plate of the temporal bone due to complete ossification. Such gaps in the bony floor of the auditory meatus are very common in the skulls of immature individuals, in those of adult females, and in Mongoloid adult skulls of both sexes.

DEMENTIA PRAECOX. A type of insanity characterized by rapid, progressive, mental deterioration and by other symptoms.

DENDROCHRONOLOGY. A system of establishing an absolute count of years by utilizing the pattern combinations of tree-rings, invented by Dr. A. E. Douglass.

DIVERTICULUM. A blind tubular process.

DOLICHOCEPHALY, adj. DOLICHOCEPHALIC. Long-headedness, long-headed. A category of the cephalic index in which the maximum breadth of the head is less than 77 per cent of the maximum length. In craniology loosely used for dolichocranial, a skull in which the breadth is less than 75 per cent of the length. Cf. BRACHYCEPHALY, MESOCEPHALY.

ECOLOGICAL. Referring to the mutual relationships which exist between an organism and its environment. As pertaining to influences upon the organism—environmental.

EOLITH. "Dawn stone." Crude and almost formless stone implements supposed to have been shaped and utilized by man before he had developed easily recognizable types of stone tools.

ENDOCRINE. A ductless gland.

EPICANTHUS, adj. EPICANTHIC. A fold of skin overhanging the free edge of the upper eyelid and obscuring either the outer or the inner corner (canthus) of the eye-opening.

EURYPROSOPIC. Broad-faced. Synonymous with chamaeprosopic. A category of the total facial index. Cf. CHAMAEPROSOPIC.

FEMUR, pl. FEMORA. The upper long bone of the lower extremity, the thigh-bone.

FOLLICLE. A small sac. The hair follicle is the sheath or sac out of which an individual hair grows.

GENE. A hereditary factor which is an integral part of a chromosome. An element concerned with the development in the offspring of hereditary characters.

GENIAL TUBERCLES. The chin tubercles, otherwise the mental spines. A pair of bony spicules on the inside of the anterior portion of the mandible, giving origin to the genio-glossal muscles, which are connected with the movements of the tongue in articulate speech.

HETEROZYGOSITY. The combination of two germ cells which are unlike in a Mendelian sense. The union of a pair of unlike factors.

HOMOZYGOUS. A cell combination of like factors, opposite to heterozygous.

HORMONE. A substance formed in an organ and serving to excite some vital process. (Oxford Dictionary.)

HUMERUS. The bone of the upper arm extending from the shoulder-joint to the elbow-joint. (Oxford Dictionary.)

HYPSICEPHALIC. High-headed in relation to head length. A hypsicephalic skull is one in which the basion-bregma height attains or exceeds 75 per cent of the maximum skull length. A typsicephalic head is one in which the auricular height is 62.6 per cent or more of the head length.

INSECTIVORES. An order of small insect-eating mammals, including tree-shrews, moles, hedge-hogs, etc. Primates are supposed to have originated from primitive insectivores somewhat like the modern tree-shrews.

IRREVERSIBILITY, LAW OF. A palaeontological principle to the effect that characters which have been lost in the course of evolution cannot be regained; that an animal cannot reverse the course of its evolution.

LACERATE FORAMINA. Irregular, jagged-edged apertures in the base of the skull which admit arteries and nerves. The size of the middle lacerate foramina is held to be an index of skull and brain development, since these foramina attain their maximum size in large-brained human races.

LARYNGEAL SACS. Air-sacs communicating with the ventricles of the larynx found in all anthropoid apes except the gibbons. They are capable of inflation and when expanded give the animal a goiterous appearance. They may serve as resonating chambers. The laryngeal sacs are especially extensive and complex in the orang-utan.

LEMUR. A group of mammals belonging to the primate order. Most lemurs are arboreal and nocturnal. They are inferior in evolutionary status and in anatomical characteristics to the monkeys and to the anthropoid apes.

LEPTOPROSOPIC. Narrow-faced. In craniology a skull of which the total face height reaches or exceeds 90 per cent of the maximum facial breadth. On the living the lower limit of leptoprosopy is 88 per cent.

LEPTORRHINY, adj. LEPTORRHINE. The possession of a nose narrow relative to its height. The uppermost limits of leptorrhiny are: in the skull 46.9 per cent of nasal height, on the living 69.9 per cent.

LUNG-FISH. A fish which has lungs as well as gills and spends part of its time on dry land, breathing air. The first terrestrial, air-breathing vertebrates are thought to have developed from some progressive form of lung-fish.

MALAR. The cheekbone or zygomatic bone, which forms most of the lower and outer borders of the bony orbit of eye. The facial breadth is measured at the level of the malars, but usually farther back upon the zygomatic processes of the temporal bones.

MARMOSET. A small American monkey of the family Hapalidae, noted for the retention of clawed digits and other primitive features.

MEATUS, AUDITORY. The channel opening into the ear.

MENDELIAN INHERITANCE. The biological law discovered by the Austrian monk, Gregor Mendel. It is based upon the segregation and recombination of unit factors in inheritance, and upon the dominance of certain characters over others. Experimentation with the inheritance of characters in many plants and animals indicates that most characters are transmitted according to the Mendelian laws, By the use of these laws it is possible to calculate for the offspring of different generations the number and proportions of appearances of dominant and recessive characters.

MESOCEPHAL, adj. MESOCEPHALIC. A head or skull which has a breadth which is medium in relation to its length. A head with a length-breadth index between 77 and 82, or a skull with a length-breadth index between 75 and 80.

MESOPROSOPIC. Medium-faced. A skull in which the total facial height is between 85 and 90 per cent of the facial breadth, or in the living a facial height between 84 and 88 per cent of the facial breadth.

METABOLISM, PURINE. The breaking down by the organism of purine, a complicated crystalline substance which by its oxidation forms uric acid.

MICROCEPHALIC. Small-headed. A term applied to skulls which fall below the normal range of adult cranial capacity. Microcephalic idiots occur most frequently in families which have histories indicating physical and mental inferiority. The cause of microcephaly is unknown.

MICROTOMIC, adj. from microtome, an instrument used for cutting extremely thin sections for microscopic work. Here used figuratively in the sense of cutting up scientific research into too thin sections.

MID-TARSAL, adj. Referring to the middle of the tarsus, the bones of the instep of the foot.

MORAINE. An accumulation of debris carried down and deposited by a glacier.

MUTATION. A new character which appears abruptly in an evolving species and is transmitted by heredity. De Vries' mutation theory involves evolution by means of mutations, rather than by accumulation of minute changes.

NASAL SPINE. A small bony process which supports the cartilages of the septum and tip of the nose.

NEOLITHIC. Pertaining to the New Stone Age, generally characterized by the invention of pottery, the domestication of plants and animals, and the use of polished stone implements.

NEOPALLIUM. The "new cloak" of the brain; all of the cerebral cortex with the exception of the olfactory areas. It includes, therefore, those parts of the brain which have undergone especial expansion in primate evolution.

ODONTOLOGY. The study of the structure and development of the teeth.

ORTHOGENESIS. The theory of evolution along straight lines, in a determinate direction, as opposed to fortuitous and haphazard evolution assumed by selection theories.

ORTHOGRADE. A gait in which the body is held erect, generally bipedal.

PALPATION. Examination by touch.

PARIETAL. One of a pair of bones which in man form the larger portion of the side-walls and roof of the middle portion of the skull.

PARIETAL FORAMINA. Small apertures, usually one in each parietal bone near the middle line, which, when present, transmit blood vessels. These foramina are larger and more constantly present in the skulls of big-brained human races, than in those of smaller-brained, more primitive human types.

PECCARY. An American quadruped allied to the swine.

PENTADACTYL. Five-digited.

PERIODONTAL. "Around the teeth." Pyorrhea is a periodontal disease.

PHYLOGENY, adj. PHYLOGENETIC. The race history or evolutionary pedigree of a group of organisms.

PLACENTA. The afterbirth, the disk-shaped, vascular organ to which the foetus is attached by means of the umbilical cord and by which it is nourished in the womb of the mother. The placenta is embedded in the wall of the maternal uterus and its processes are bathed in the maternal blood-stream. It is expelled after birth. Placental nutrition is a characteristic feature of the reproductive processes of higher mammals.

PLATYRRHINY, adj. PLATYRRHINE. Literally "flat-nosed." See CHAMAER-RHINY.

POST-ORBITAL. Behind the bony orbits of the skull. Post-orbital constriction—a pinching or narrowing of the skull behind the orbits and brow-ridges, in the temporal region.

PREMOLARS. The bicuspid teeth in front of the molars and behind the canines or eye-teeth.

PROBABLE ERROR. A statistical devicent which gives an estimate of the range of error due to the sampling process, as affecting means or other constants of random samples supposed to be drawn from universes in which the distribution of variables or attributes is normal.

PROGNATHISM. Protrusion of the jaws.

PRONOGRADE. A gait in which the long axis of the body is parallel with the ground.

PYKNIC. "Thick set," a term used by Kretschmer to designate a body-build type characterized by great trunk breadth, prominent abdomen, and general fleshiness.

ROENTGENOGRAPHICALLY. By means of X-ray photographs. Roentgen was a German physicist who discovered X-rays.

SAGITTAL. Pertaining to the sagittal suture, the median suture between the parietal bones of the skull, or pertaining to the median antero-posterior plane of the body or any plane parallel with it.

SCAPHOID. Boat-shaped. Pertaining to the skull—a cranial vault with a median antero-posterior keel, a roof-shaped skull.

SCLEROSIS. A morbid hardening of any tissue or structure (Oxford Dictionary).

SEX-LINKED. Pertaining to any hereditary character which is manifested in one sex only.

SOMATOLOGY, adj. SOMATOLOGICAL. The science dealing with the human body.

SPIROCHETE. A genus of bacteria having a spiral form.

STRABISMIC. Pertaining to, or affected by, strabismus, the turning inward of the axes of the eyes; cross-eyed.

STYLOID PROCESS. A pencil-like process which projects from the base of the temporal bone.

SUPRA-CONDYLOID PROCESS. A small, hook-like process, which occasionally appears on the inner surface of the humerus in man, a little above the elbow-joint. It occurs in lemurs, many carnivores, and other lower mammals, and is a reversionary feature.

SUPRA-MASTOID CREST. An elevated ridge on the temporal bone running antero-posteriorly above the mastoid process and marking the inferior delimitation of the attachment of the temporal muscle. In apes it attains great prominence; in the skulls of primitive man it is often pronounced; in crania of modern man it is usually reduced or absent.

TARSUS. The bones of the posterior portion of the foot, including in man the heel-bone, the ankle-bone, and five small bones of the instep.

TAXONOMY. Classification, especially of plants and animals.

TAURODONTISM. An enlargement of the pulp cavities of the molar teeth found in certain fossil men and characteristic of oxen and other ruminant animals.

TEMPORAL CRESTS. Bony ridges of slight elevation which extend, one on each side of the skull, from the post-orbital region backward, at about the juncture of the side-walls and top of the skull, and downward behind the ears. These crests delimit the superior and posterior margins of the temporal muscles, which are mainly concerned in the movements of the lower jaw in chewing and biting. The tendons of these fan-shaped, temporal muscles are inserted in the coronoid process of the mandible. The higher up the temporal crests rise on the skull vault, the larger is the area of attachment of the muscles. The relative area of the skull vault occupied by the temporal muscle attachment increases as the jaws become more projecting. In the gorilla and the orang-utan the temporal musculature covers the middle portion of the skull vault, so that the temporal crests converge backward and unite to form a sagittal crest.

TEMPORAL MUSCLES. See TEMPORAL CRESTS.

TORUS. A rounded, elongated ridge or swelling. In craniology, the frontal torus is a term applied to very large and protuberant brow-ridges which extend from the area above the outer corner of one orbit across the supra-orbital region to the external angle of the other orbit. The occipital torus is a bony elevation which extends across the back of the head, delimiting the area of attachment of the neck muscles and ligaments. Both frontal and occipital tori are exaggerated in anthropoid apes and show marked development in types of fossil man which have projecting jaws.

TRITUBERCULY. A theory of the evolution of the molar teeth originated by the palaeontologists Cope and Osborn. This theory involves the supposition that, in the course of development from simple conical teeth, the crowns of the molars became tritubercular or three-cusped, the base of the cutting triangle being directed outward in the upper jaw and inward in the lower jaw.

VARVES. Laminated deposits of sand and silt left on the ocean floor, or elsewhere, by the melting of a retreating ice-sheet. Each layer or varve is the result of one summer's melting. By counting the superimposed varves, the number of years elapsed during the glacial retreat can be determined with considerable accuracy.

WOLFF's LAW. The so-called law of hypertrophy and atrophy propounded by the German anatomist and embryologist, Wolff. It is to the effect that increase of function enlarges an organ and decrease of function causes it to diminish in size.

WEISMANN. August Weismann was a famous evolutionist who propounded the theory of the "continuity of the germ plasm," which forms the frame-work of nearly all of the modern science of genetics. According to this theory, the germ plasm is passed on from generation to generation, and although it gives rise to the body cells, it is not a product of them. Consequently, Weismann maintained that bodily modifications acquired during the life time of the individual can not be transmitted by heredity, since the body cells can not produce any effect upon the germ plasm.

INDEX